HOW

NATIONS

NEGOTIATE

Written under the auspices of

THE CENTER FOR INTERNATIONAL AFFAIRS

Harvard University

HOW
NATIONS
NEGOTIATE

FRED CHARLES IKLÉ

HARPER & ROW, PUBLISHERS

New York, Evanston, and London

127059

LIBRARY OF CONGRESS CATALOG CARD NUMBER: 64–18106

TO DORIS

CONTENTS

P R E F A C E

STATES HAVE NEGOTIATED SINCE THE BEGINNING OF HISTORY—
as they have fought wars. Compared with the changes in methods
of warfare, however, the methods of negotiation have remained
much the same. Of course, negotiation and war are not mutually
exclusive. States can live in peace without negotiating at all, they
may start to fight while they are negotiating, and if their leaders are
prudent, they will continue to negotiate even though they are at
war.

Nor is negotiation intrinsically good just because war can be so
evil. In the nuclear age, when a single battle can bring total disaster, negotiation has acquired the nimbus of Salvation that will
protect the world from destruction and eventually deliver it from
the terrible engines of war. But negotiation is only an instrument:
it can be used on the side of the angels as well as by the forces
of darkness. It may settle dangerous conflicts short of war, divert
governments from the use of force, and terminate fighting before
destruction becomes complete. Yet, it may also exacerbate hostilities, strengthen an aggressor, prepare the way for his attack, and
erode the legal and moral foundations of peace.

Although negotiation has happily been more prevalent in
the relations of states than war, it has never been studied
with the same incisiveness. From antiquity on, the strategies
and tactics of the battlefield have been analyzed more systematically and with greater precision than the strategies and tactics of
diplomacy.

The same discrepancy can be found in the present period. During
the last fifteen years, while the writings both on warfare and on
diplomatic bargaining have been multiplying rapidly, a rigorous
intellectual effort has been devoted only to the problems of war
and of preventing it through deterrence and arms control. Our
understanding of these problems has been raised far above intuition and common sense. It is based on carefully developed ideas
which all hang together, such as active vs. passive deterrence, the

functions of uncertainty and credibility, the connection between
vulnerable forces and accident-proneness, the interdependence between strategic choices and the efficient allocation of resources, and
the dilemma of common interests in disarmament and incentives
for violating agreements.

A comparable intellectual development centering on the subject
of negotiation has not yet occurred. There are, to be sure, comparable categories of literature in each of these fields. Thus, diplomatic histories of particular countries might be considered
analogous to the histories of armies and navies; both are rich in
interesting illustrations but rarely deal systematically with the
process by which opponents interact. Memoirs of negotiators and
case studies of specific conferences find their counterpart in the
memoirs of soldiers and in accounts of particular battles; both are
full of exciting material essential for any further analysis. And the
treatises on diplomatic practices correspond to the field manuals of
the military. But little has been written on the strategies and tactics
of negotiation that would be equivalent in precision and coherence
to the better studies on military defense, deterrence, and arms
control. The few books instructing diplomats how to be good negotiators (written mostly a long time ago) do not meet the
standard; they compare rather with those homilies that advise
soldiers to be obedient, brave, alert, and resourceful.

I first became interested in studying international negotiation
some three years ago while working on problems of disarmament
at the RAND Corporation. Ever since, Nathan Leites has continued
to take an active role in my work. Those who know Nathan Leites'
own writings on negotiation will easily recognize part of my debt
to him. My full debt only those will understand who have similarly
benefited, in intellectual collaboration with him, from his exceptional ability to encourage clear thinking and to enliven one's own
drabness with his fresh insights.

It is to Thomas Schelling that I owe most for the theoretical
foundation. If his work on bargaining had not preceded, my study
would have been left without a larger context and been deprived
of many essential concepts and incisive details. But not only did I
have the pleasure of reading Thomas Schelling; I constantly profited

from his advice and encouragement while writing this book at the Harvard University Center for International Affairs.

Robert Bowie, Director of the Center, and Henry Kissinger, one of its Faculty Members, contributed more than they might realize. Prolonged conversations with Robert Bowie taught me a great deal about the complex realities of negotiation and inspired my attempt to capture the meaning of its diverse outcomes. Henry Kissinger, both through his writings and in numerous discussions, gave me a better perspective and deeper understanding of Western diplomacy, past and present.

To Philip Mosely I am doubly indebted. His help and encouragement were decisive in broadening my research beyond the perusal of books and documents, so that I could learn from the practitioners of negotiation. And his superb analysis of his own important negotiating experience served me as an indispensable guide.

My gratitude also goes to Paul Kecskemeti, for his careful review and important comments; and to Harold Jacobson, Roger Fisher, and Martin Shubik for many valuable suggestions.

The working environment at the Center for International Affairs was ideal. Each year a group of senior civil servants from all over the world come to the Center. Straddling two academic years, I had the opportunity to expose my ideas to the thoughtful criticism of two such groups. Among them I wish to thank in particular Risto Hyvarinen, Ernst Jung, Louis Kunzig, and David Mark for having commented extensively on my manuscript. Many of my chapters have been greatly improved by expert advice from Morton Halperin, Karl Kaiser, James Richardson, Kenneth Waltz, and Ciro Zoppo, all past or present Research Associates at the Center.

The manuscript gained immeasurably from editorial help by Max Hall and Robert Erwin. They had the skill to ferret out not only weakness in language but also weaknesses in the thoughts behind it. Joseph Tulchin ably assisted me in the historical research and, in addition, contributed many pertinent examples and expert suggestions. Most of the typing and preparation of the manuscript was done by Connie Griffith, to whom I owe a great debt for cheerfully devoting her unflagging care to this task.

The Center for International Affairs generously supported the larger part of this study, while the initial phase was financed by the RAND Corporation with additional assistance from the Rockefeller Foundation. The grant from the Rockefeller Foundation enabled me to conduct extensive interviews of European diplomats and to study the negotiating techniques in the European Communities.

To RAND I am grateful for much more than unstinting financial support. At RAND I learned that relations between modern states can be subjected to systematic analysis and calculation without at all neglecting the emotional and irrational components of human behavior. It was at RAND that I acquired a clearer understanding of the constraints and opportunities for governments in coping with uncertainty, allocating scarce resources, and interacting with friend and foe. And it was from my former RAND colleagues that I received the initial stimulation and encouragement to tackle my difficult topic. Hans Speier and Alexander George have been particularly warm supporters, and Herbert Goldhamer imparted to me unique insights from his personal experience in negotiations.

For some months in 1962 I had the pleasure of working on this study as the guest of the Council on Foreign Relations in New York. This afforded me a welcome opportunity to exchange ideas with many experienced diplomats. And the staff of the Council thoughtfully advised me on my research and writing. In particular, George Franklin, Executive Director, and W. Phillips Davison went out of their way to be helpful.

My acknowledgments must remain incomplete. Many experienced diplomats in Washington, London, Paris, and in the European Communities have most generously granted me interviews offering insights, factual information, and an understanding of the art of diplomacy that I could never have acquired by reading. I feel it best accords with their wishes if I express my gratitude to them without revealing their identity. Without this cooperation from the Negotiators, my study on negotiation would not have been possible.

F.C.I.

Cambridge, Massachusetts
March 1964

HOW

NATIONS

NEGOTIATE

CHAPTER 1

WHAT IS NEGOTIATION?

CERTAIN SUBJECTS SEEM QUITE CLEAR AS LONG AS WE LEAVE them alone. The answers look obvious until we ask questions, the concepts appear to be well understood until we wish to define them, causes and effects are easily recognized until we seek to explain them, and all the rules pass for valid until we try to prove them. The social scientist, alas, shares the honor with the philosopher of often moving in his inquiries from the obvious to the obscure. Of course, he hopes to go beyond and to emerge with a clearer view of the whole and a better knowledge of the details than he first had on the basis of folklore and common sense. But to begin with, he must challenge the old answers with new questions.

Negotiation is a subject on which much has been said and written that seems self-evident until examined more closely. To resolve conflict and avoid the use of force, it is said, one must negotiate (Is this always the best way to settle conflict?). Negotiation requires a willingness to compromise (Why?), and both sides must make concessions (According to which law?). Neither side can expect to win all it wants (Not even if its objectives are modest?). If both sides negotiate in good faith (Who judges "good faith"?), they can always find a fair solution (And what is "fair"?). If there is a conflict about many issues, the less controversial ones should be solved first because agreement will lead to further agreement (Or will the postponed issues become harder to

1

solve?). A negotiator should never make a threat he is not prepared to carry out (What is wrong with successful bluffing?). Each side has its minimum beyond which it cannot be moved (But how about moving the opponent's minimum?).

This book is concerned with the process and effects of negotiation between governments; in particular, it seeks to relate the *process* of negotiation to the *outcome*. To begin with, two elements must normally be present for negotiation to take place: there must be both common interests and issues of conflict. Without common interest there is nothing to negotiate for, without conflict nothing to negotiate about.

There are many ways in which governments—always subject to change, idiosyncrasy, and pressure from within—relate their common interests to their conflicting interests. They may be isolationist and try to stay apart to avoid all conflict, while sacrificing the pursuit of possible common interests. Or they may simply follow habits and rules that regulate their interests and conflicts automatically without bargaining. The observance of some diplomatic practices is of this character. (So is routine buying and selling at fixed prices.) But usually a government takes account of the fact that its interests and its ability to pursue national objectives are influenced by decisions of other nations. Likewise it realizes that these other nations will be affected by its own decisions. It may try to coordinate this interaction without explicitly saying so—a process of "tacit bargaining." Or it may communicate with other governments for the explicit purpose of working out a particular combination of conflicting and common interests; that is, to reach an agreement.

One should perhaps distinguish between two kinds of common interests: an *identical common interest* in a single arrangement or object, and a *complementary interest* in an exchange of different objects. In the identical common interest, the parties want to share the *same* object or benefit from the same arrangement, which, however, they can bring about only by joining together. Hence they have to agree on the object's characteristics (concerning which they may have different preferences) and on the division of the costs and gains (where their interests are likely to conflict). Examples of agreements on such identical common interests are the U.S.-Canadian treaty on the St. Lawrence Seaway, international fishery agreements to protect the supply of fish, and, in a sense, cease-fire agreements.

When parties are interested in an exchange, they want *different* things. These they cannot obtain by themselves but can only grant to each other. The clearest examples are barters and sales. Similarly, commercial aviation agreements, where each country wants to have its planes fly to the other country, have the purpose of settling an exchange. So do agreements for mutual tariff concessions.

In reality, however, most negotiations embrace a combination of identical common interests and complementary interests. When the six European countries set up the European Economic Community, they had complementary interests in the exchange of tariff concessions and common interests in a large, unified European market. The nuclear test-ban treaty between the United States and the Soviet Union can satisfy the complementary interest in slowing down the opponent's development of new weapons and the common interest in preventing an increase in radioactive fallout or in discouraging the proliferation of nuclear weapons. Whether the identical common interests or the complementary interests dominate depends on how the purposes of the agreement are defined.

The process by which two or more parties relate conflicting to common interests is the warp and woof not only of international relations but of human society; individuals, groups, and governments engage in it all the time. We become aware of it only when we call it something special—like Molière's Monsieur Jourdain when he discovered that for forty years he had been speaking "prose." There seems to be no established term for all the ways in which parties with conflicting and common interests interact—whether explicitly or tacitly—though "bargaining" is sometimes used that broadly.

"Negotiation" in a narrower sense denotes a process that is different from tacit bargaining or other behavior that regulates conflict. As used here, *negotiation is a process in which explicit proposals are put forward ostensibly for the purpose of reaching agreement on an exchange or on the realization of a common interest where conflicting interests are present.* Frequently, these proposals deal not only with the terms of agreement but also with the topics to be discussed (the agenda), with the ground rules that ought to apply, and with underlying technical and legal issues. It is the confrontation of explicit proposals that distinguishes negotiation (as here defined) from tacit bargaining and other types of conflict behavior. Beyond this confrontation appear other moves that the negotiating parties make to strengthen their own position, to weaken that of the opponent, or to influence the outcome in other ways. The subject matter of this book includes all these moves and the ways in which they relate to the outcome. That is, bargaining moves are included in the broader sense, to the extent that they serve pending or ongoing negotiations where explicit proposals are being put forward.

Only part of the frequent changes in relations between countries are the result of negotiation. Governments often revise their expectations and attitudes toward other countries as a result of unilateral actions or tacit bargains. Military and technological developments, growth or decline in economic strength, and internal political changes continually cause the rearrangement of conflicting and common interests between nations, and this happens whether or not diplomats negotiate.

There is no simple rule as to when negotiation is needed, and when tacit bargaining or even less conscious confrontations are more effective to restructure international relations. For certain arrangements negotiation clearly cannot be dispensed with; for others it is optional; and there are some issues which are better settled without it.

Negotiation is necessary for any arrangement that establishes complicated forms of collaboration, such as a joint war effort or Britain's attempted entry into the Common Market. (In contrast, the entry of, say, the Ivory Coast into the United Nations did not require significant negotiations.) Negotiation is needed for most exchanges, such as exchanges of prisoners or the granting of mutual consular facilities, and for all transactions involving monetary compensation, as in the payment of oil royalties or the leasing of air bases. Negotiation is, of course, necessary for the setting up of formal international institutions and for any arrangement where an *explicit* agreement is essential, such as a peace treaty or an alliance system.

On the other hand, certain undertakings are arrived at in such a delicate way that explicit proposals might interfere with the process. The mutually observed restrictions in the Korean War (for instance, no attacks on the supply lines leading into North and South Korea) is an example of arrangements that would not have been facilitated or might even have been upset by negotiation. The very uncertainties of a tacit understanding may have made these restrictions more stable, because both sides were unwilling to probe and push toward the limits of the "bargain," lest it all be upset. The negotiation of an explicit *quid pro quo* might have given rise to new demands and invited more haggling and tugging than the arrangement which the parties never discussed and never explicitly settled. Furthermore, while soldiers were being killed fighting the enemy, negotiations to establish rules and restraints for the battle or on the interdiction of supplies would have clashed with domestic opinion and perhaps adversely affected the morale of the troops.[1]

Likewise, if there is a deep-seated hostility between the populations of two countries, governments may be unable to negotiate because of public opposition but may work out some arrangements of mutual interest through tacit bargaining. The relationship between Jordan and Israel is an example.

In the field of arms control and disarmament, where we have become so accustomed to large and formal conferences, important understandings can at times be arrived at without negotiation. Formal talks might, in fact, make it more difficult to harmonize some arms policies insofar as they inevitably introduce political issues or questions of prestige and legal precedents.[2]

[1] A pioneering analysis of the role of tacit bargaining in limited war is given by Thomas C. Schelling, *The Strategy of Conflict* (Cambridge, Mass.: Harvard University Press, 1960), chap. iii and appendix A. The delicate interaction of tacit limitations on air-attacks in the Korean War is discussed by Morton H. Halperin, *Limited War in the Nuclear Age* (New York: John Wiley, 1963), pp. 53-55.

[2] On the importance of tacit bargaining for arms control, see Thomas C. Schelling and Morton H. Halperin, *Strategy and Arms Control* (New York: Twentieth Century Fund, 1961), pp. 77-82.

Negotiation plays an important role in formalizing turning points in international relations, in catalyzing or at least clarifying changes that were caused by tacit bargaining or other processes, and in working out those finer shades in new arrangements between nations that the brute interplay of latent strength cannot define.

Although negotiation is necessary for any new relationship that is based on explicit agreement, an explicit agreement is usually only part of the outcome of negotiation. Negotiation may change the positions of the parties and their mutual relations in many other ways. The outcome may include, for example, tacit understandings between the parties, a clarification of the points of disagreement, a reorientation of national objectives, new commitments to third parties (allies, domestic groups, or world opinion), and propaganda effects. Many of these results may outweigh in importance whatever explicit agreement is arrived at. And even agreements themselves vary widely in their degree of specificity and the amount of disagreement that they leave unsettled.

CHAPTER 2

AGREEMENT AND DISAGREEMENT

AN AGREEMENT BETWEEN GOVERNMENTS CAN BE DEFINED AS an exchange of conditional promises, by which each party declares that it will act in a certain way on condition that the other parties act in accordance with their promises. Sanctions supported by higher authority cannot be invoked in case of a violation as they can for contracts under domestic law. Nonetheless, these promises are significant, since the parties have an interest in living up to them for other reasons.

First, as long as governments find an agreement attractive *on balance,* they will want to keep their own part of the bargain if that is the condition for the other parties' fulfillment of their promises.

Second, governments have a certain interest in keeping agreements as a matter of principle, apart from preserving the advantages of a particular bargain. If they violate an agreement, they may find it more difficult to reach other agreements in the future and will reduce the good will they might have enjoyed with other governments. Among allied or friendly countries, the desire to maintain good will is an exceedingly important motive for keeping agreements. Like a businessman's credit rating, the reputation of fulfilling the treaty obligations toward one's allies is too important to be sacrificed for one-time gains except in the case of dire emergency. Among more hostile countries there may be little good will to lose, but the threat of reprisals can help to discourage the breach of agreements. This threat is reinforced by the fact that parties that suffer from a violation have an interest in increasing the penalty to discourage others from similar violations. In other words, actual or potential victims of violations have a stake in making the breach of agreements unattractive.

Third, where a breach of an agreement necessitates a clear-cut action requiring complicated decisions, democratic governments may encounter institutional obstacles to a violation. The burden of proof would lie with those government officials who advocate that the agreement should be broken; they would have to overcome tendencies to inaction, moral and legal objections, and conflicting appraisals as to the consequences.[1]

There is no simple relationship between the process of negotiation and its outcome. Usually, the outcome is not simply an agreement which settles in clear-cut terms all the issues of conflict that were dealt with. Even if one ignores side-effects of negotiation, the explicit terms of agreement tell only part of the story. Important issues may have been settled only in ambiguous terms or in general principles. Other parts of the settlement may consist in tacit understandings. Frequently, there is no explicit agreement at all, but the negotiating process may have created new attitudes toward the issues of disagreement or a new common understanding as to what the disagreement consists of.

THE ROLE OF SPECIFICITY

The West has often been warned against concluding ambiguous agreements or "agreements in principle" with the Communists, because it has been the experience, when it came to work out the details of such agreements, that the Communists would renege on the understanding the Western diplomats thought they had reached. As Philip Mosely pointed out:

One of the main pitfalls in wartime Anglo-American negotiations with the Soviet Union was the tendency to rely upon reaching an "agreement in principle." . . . At Yalta the Soviet government agreed, after

[1] For an exposition of this and other factors that make governments comply with rules, see Roger Fisher, "Constructing Rules that Affect Governments," in *Arms Control, Disarmament, and National Security,* ed. Donald G. Brennan (New York: Braziller, 1961), pp. 56–67.

very lengthy argument and stubborn resistance, to participate in a reconstruction of the Polish government which would, it appeared, permit the survival of some political freedom for the great non-Communist majority of the people. By delays and quibblings over the execution of the "agreement in principle" during the next few months, the Soviet government secured about ninety per cent of the original position with which it had come to Yalta and thus strengthened beyond challenge the small Communist minority in its dominant control of the country.[2]

We should distinguish two different risks inherent in agreements in principle. First, the parties may conclude such an agreement, unaware that their interpretations of the implicit parts of the bargain are in conflict. Second, there is the risk of deliberate violation; that is, one party violates what it *knows* the other party thought was a mutual—though tacit or unwritten—understanding as to how the general guidelines were to be carried out.

In the case of unintentional misunderstanding, one or the other side will feel cheated when it comes to carry out the agreement later on. The remedy against this is greater specificity; but to make agreements more specific is often too time-consuming and may lead to rigid agreements that will soon become obsolete. A case might be made that the Yalta agreements, in part, involved unintentional misunderstanding rather than deliberate violation. Stalin's view of the world may have led him to believe that the Western leaders expected him to exercise total political control wherever they let him maintain *de facto* military control. He may have thought that the agreed principles contradicting this were only for domestic consumption in the West and that the leading Western statesmen could not be so naïve as to expect him to tolerate Capitalist parties in areas that they left to his sole control. Therefore, when he set out to collect what (he could have thought) had been implicitly granted to him at Yalta, he may have felt that the disappointment of the Western leaders was feigned. More likely, however, Stalin knew that most Western leaders expected him to act differently.

The second risk, that of deliberate violation, is of course not confined to agreements in principle—the most explicit details may be violated, too. But as long as an agreement in principle is

[2] Philip E. Mosley, *The Kremlin and World Politics* (New York: Vintage Books, 1960), pp. 25–26.

being observed in letter though not in spirit, the government of the aggrieved country will find it more difficult to prove intentional violation, both to satisfy itself and to convince its allies or domestic opinion.

Winston Churchill may have sensed this difficulty in the spring of 1945, when he tried to convince President Harry Truman that American forces in Germany should not be withdrawn to the occupation line previously agreed to with the Soviet Union, until Soviet behavior in Eastern Europe conformed better to the Western understanding of the Yalta agreement. On May 12, Churchill cabled to the President: "I have always worked for friendship with Russia, but, like you, I feel deep anxiety because of their misinterpretation of the Yalta decisions. . . . Surely, it is vital now to come to an understanding with Russia, or see where we are with her, before we weaken our armies mortally or retire to the zones of occupation."[3]

Churchill's recommendation might have found greater support within the American government had he been able to list a number of clear-cut violations of the Yalta agreement instead of having to refer to Soviet "misinterpretation." For example, there was a White House meeting on April 23, 1945, where the Secretary of State, Edward Stettinius, said that the Russians had "receded" from the Yalta agreement on the Polish question and that their insistence on having the Communist Lublin group accepted as the Polish government was "directly contrary to the Yalta understanding." But not all those advising President Truman in this meeting agreed with Secretary Stettinius' interpretation. According to Charles Bohlen's notes of the meeting, Admiral Leahy said that "he had left Yalta with the impression that the Soviet government had no intention of permitting a free government to operate in Poland, and that he would have been surprised had the Soviet government behaved any differently than it had. He thought the agreements were susceptible to 'two interpretations'. . . and that a break would be serious, but that 'we should tell them that we stood for free and independent Poland.' "[4]

[3] Winston S. Churchill, *Triumph and Tragedy* (Boston: Houghton Mifflin, 1953), pp. 573–74.
[4] Walter Millis (ed.), *The Forrestal Diaries* (New York: Viking, 1951), pp. 49, 51.

There is further evidence that the ambiguity of the Yalta agreement inhibited the American government from opposing the Soviet take-over in Poland more forcefully along the lines suggested by Churchill. At the end of May, 1945, prior to the Potsdam Conference, President Truman sent Joseph E. Davies, former U.S. Ambassador in Moscow, on a special mission to see Churchill. Davies, according to his own report of this mission, told Churchill that the President "wanted to know exactly what the engagements and agreements with the Soviets were. If there was disagreement as to what they were, he wanted to clarify that situation definitely, if possible." After having listened to Churchill's complaints about Russian violation, Davies gave him his personal reaction, that "it was not the facts, so much as the interpretation of the facts, which might have a destructive effect upon all hope for a decent, just peace structure for humanity. . . ." Davies added that, in his opinion, "American armies would promptly be withdrawn to the occupational zones agreed upon. . . . If agreements now entered into were clearly defined between the three great Powers and if such agreements were violated in such a way as to establish clearly that any great Power was bent on world domination hostile to the American way of life, then and only then, would the American people accept the possibility of having their armed forces fighting in Europe."[5]

One should not confuse, however, the risks inherent in agreements in principle with the risks of exchanging possession for a promise. The exchange of possession for a promise played an even more important role in the Western disappointment with the wartime and early postwar agreements with the Soviet Union. Or more precisely, many of these agreements compounded the two risks: possession (or potential possession) was exchanged for a promise that had been spelled out only in general principles. Had the promise at least been specific, it would have been easier to halt the exchange (as Churchill had urged in vain).

[5] U.S. Department of State, *Foreign Relations of the United States: The Conference of Berlin (Potsdam) 1945* (Washington, 1960), I, 68, 71, 73–74.

DISPUTES ABOUT SPECIFICITY

Western diplomats, having learnt the dangers of ambiguous agreements with Communist governments, usually insist on detailed and specific language in any new agreement. Since Communist negotiators tend to resist specificity, this can lead to prolonged disputes as to how specific the text of an accord should be made.

However, such disputes are essentially a symptom of disagreement about the substance, not the form, of the settlement. This is the reason why they are so common and take up such an inordinate amount of time in East-West negotiations, whereas they are rare between Western nations. For if nations are agreed on a bargain they wish to conclude, there should, on the one hand, be little objection to spelling it out in detail and, on the other, somewhat less interest in recording the details. When the Soviet delegate in disarmament conferences protests against the Western efforts to specify control provisions, he is right in saying that there ought to be trust to make such detailed commitments unnecessary. If there was trust, however, there would be not only less interest in specificity on the Western side but also fewer objections to specificity by the Soviets. By refusing to have an agreement recorded in detail, the Soviets indicate that agreement on these points, in fact, does not exist.

The government opposed to specificity expects that it might later want to give the agreement another meaning than that which the opponent tries to read in; but during the negotiations it does not want to avow the latent disagreement. (If the latent disagreement was avowed, the dispute on how specific the treaty should be made would turn into a dispute about substance.) The government in favor of specificity expects to make a violation of its understanding of the agreement less likely, or at least less costly to itself. The very fact that the opponent explicitly subscribed to the understanding will make it somewhat harder for him not to comply. The more flagrant the violation, the easier it is for the victim to rule out misunderstanding and to enlist some support from those who believe—for moral or political reasons—that agreements should generally be kept.

In agreements between Western governments, a high degree of specificity is sometimes desired, not so much to discourage violations or to prevent misunderstandings, but to clarify the domestic consequences of the international undertaking and to enable government officials to implement the accord in full detail. In contrast to East-West negotiations, however, the details can usually be settled in drafting committees or by groups of experts, since the original lack of specificity in the preliminary accord is merely an expedient and does not cover up some fundamental disagreement. Within the European Communities, the specification of details in agreements-in-principle is an important function of the supranational institutions (such as the Commission of the Common Market). The ministers of the Six (participating countries) prepare the broad outlines of an accord and settle the essential bargains, after which the supranational executives take over to complete a draft agreement.

Although Communists are known for exploiting ambiguities in agreements, they do not always prefer less specificity than Westerners. The nuclear test-ban conference provides not only examples of issues on which the Soviet Union wanted ambiguous language but also examples where the West preferred ambiguity.

In the fall of 1958, at the very beginning of the test-ban conference, the American and British delegates fought hard (and successfully) to win Soviet consent for inclusion into the draft treaty of many articles containing specific control provisions. On other articles in the test-ban treaty, however, it was Tsarapkin, the Soviet delegate, who fought for more specific language. For example, in January, 1959, the British delegate proposed that an article be worded so that "each of the parties" to the treaty would agree to the installation of the detection system. Tsarapkin objected to the phrase "each of the parties" and asked that it be replaced with a specific listing of the three original parties. "An attempt to avoid naming in the treaty the Powers assuming the principal obligation . . . ," Tsarapkin warned, "cannot fail to raise serious doubts about the real purpose of our talks."[6]

---

[6] Conference on the Discontinuance of Nuclear Weapon Tests, Verbatim Record of the 33d Plenary Meeting, Jan. 9, 1959 (GEN/DNT/PV. 33), p. 5; 35th Plenary Meeting, Jan. 13, 1959, p. 21.

Similarly, in a later phase of this conference, agreement had been reached that the Western powers, the Soviet Union, and the non-nuclear powers should each provide exactly one-third the staff in every control post. Tsarapkin did not want to leave the selection of the last third to the discretion of the chief administrator of the detection system. He demanded more specific language according to which the last third was to be subdivided into three parts between nationals from Communist, Western, and non-aligned countries: "We cannot rely on spoken words. Of course, you speak fine words, Mr. Wadsworth, about not seeking advantages for yourselves. . . . Let us put these fine words—we agree with them—into the treaty."[7]

There is a special reason why Western and Soviet negotiators took alternating roles in the test-ban conference, in demanding specific treaty language on issues where the opponent preferred ambiguity. In the 1958–60 version of the test-ban treaty, many of the articles had the purpose of influencing the action of an arbiter.

In contracts under domestic law, specificity can predetermine the court's interpretation in case of dispute. At least, it will make the court's decision more predictable; and the more predictable the outcome in court, the less likely is litigation to begin with. The situation is similar between governments. Specificity can be used to bind an arbiter to the preferred interpretation of an agreement, while ambiguous language leaves him more freedom. Some international arbiters are reluctant to become involved in disputes between governments and often choose an easy way out by claiming that the issue is beyond their jurisdiction. If a party fears that this might happen, it will try to spell out or make mandatory those actions by the arbiter that are in its interest. In the Laos conference of 1961–62, this objective lay behind the Western insistence on a detailed description of the rules of access and reporting functions of the International Control Commission.

On the other hand, a negotiator may be basically distrustful of an arbiter, fearing that he might assume too much power in pursuit of his own ambitions or favor the opponent. In this case, specificity will be demanded in order to reduce the arbiter's freedom and to

[7] 164th Plenary Meeting, Feb. 2, 1960, p. 19. (This was before the Soviet Union withdrew its agreement to a single neutral administrator.)

curtail his discretion. This is what Tsarapkin had in mind in the above example, when he objected to leaving the selection of the last third of control personnel to a neutral administrator, albeit with the unwritten understanding that Communist, Western, and neutral nationals should be equally represented.

CONSENSUS ON AMBIGUITY

Two consequences of ambiguity have been distinguished so far: (1) the parties have an honest misunderstanding about implications that the agreement fails to spell out; or (2) one party, while knowing what its opponent expected of the bargain, may pretend that it had a different understanding of it (i.e., the ambiguities are exploited to cover up a deliberate violation). There is a third possibility: the parties to the agreement know that the ambiguous terms mean different things to each of them. It may be more appropriate to call this *equivocality* than ambiguity. Equivocal language is used to cover up disagreement on issues which must be included for some reason in a larger settlement or which must be dealt with as if there was agreement. An equivocal agreement is similar to a partial agreement that leaves certain undecided issues for future negotiation, with the difference that the equivocal terms serve to cover up differences rather than mark them for future resolution.

According to a French saying, international agreements would be impossible without conflicting mental reservations. Indeed, there is often complicity in creating the alleged misunderstanding. The parties knowingly choose equivocal terms so that they can pretend to agree even where they continue to disagree. As Lester Pearson recalled from his diplomatic experience:

I know that there have been occasions, and I have been concerned with one or two, when, as the lesser of two evils, words were used in recording the results of negotiations or discussion whose value lay precisely in the fact that they were imprecise, that they could be interpreted somewhat freely and therefore could be used not so much to record agreement as to conceal a disagreement which it was desired to play down and which, it was hoped, would disappear in time. It is a practice, however, which is only rarely justified.[8]

[8] Lester B. Pearson, *Diplomacy in the Nuclear Age* (Cambridge, Mass.: Harvard University Press, 1949), pp. 47–48.

A recent example may be the reference to a possible link between the partial test-ban treaty and a non-aggression pact, which the Western and Soviet negotiators put into their joint communiqué of July 25, 1963, when they announced that the treaty had been initialed. The Soviets had tried to link the test ban with a non-aggression pact between NATO and the Warsaw Treaty countries, but the United States and Great Britain were opposed. When Khrushchev finally realized that he could not exploit the Western desire for a test ban with such a tie-in, he must have wanted to conceal his failure. The Western powers possibly cooperated in saving him embarrassment (perhaps they thought it was the price for the test ban) by agreeing to the following equivocal language in their communiqué: ". . . the three delegations discussed the Soviet proposal relating to a pact of nonaggression. . . . [They] have agreed fully to inform their respective allies in the two organizations concerning these talks and to consult with them about continuing discussions on this question with the purpose of achieving agreement satisfactory to all participants."

Incidentally, one should not confuse this use of equivocal terms in agreements with equivocal negotiating positions. Ambiguity and equivocality in negotiating positions serve other purposes, such as to maintain flexibility during the bargaining process or to probe the opponent's position.

RESIDUAL DISAGREEMENT

Even an agreement whose terms are explicit often leaves some issues unsettled, despite the fact that they are neither extraneous to its subject matter nor trivial. However, these issues may have been clarified by the negotiations that led to such a partial agreement. The residual disagreement can be explicit in the sense that certain issues are marked "for future negotiation," implicit in the agreement's equivocal language, or latent if differences originally ignored or viewed as unimportant later turn into serious disputes.

Residual disagreement is by no means universal. With the benefit of historical hindsight we are able to identify a number of negotiations that settled in a definitive way all issues with which they were concerned. Examples can be found among the voluntary

City" in the Italian peace treaty after World War II, disturbed
Italian-Yugoslav relations until 1954. The disposition of the Saar
territory between France and Germany was left somewhat indeterminate after both world wars. After World War II, this issue
stood in the way of a French-German *rapprochement* until a final
settlement could be reached in 1955. Frequently, however, any
agreement would be impossible without the separation of refractory
conflicts. The Antarctica Treaty of 1959, which reserves this polar
region for non-military uses, states explicitly (Article IV) that the
treaty shall not affect any of the previous claims to territorial
sovereignty. Had the old territorial claims and disputes not been
exempted, Argentina, Chile, and perhaps some of the other signatories could not have been brought into accord. Similarly, the
Treaty of Rome establishing the European Economic Community
(the Common Market) could, in all likelihood, not have been
concluded without postponing agreement on a common agricultural policy until the end of the first phase in this three-phase
program for economic integration.

What negotiators often fail to realize is that they may settle an
issue inadvertently, even though they formally exempt it from an
agreement or explicitly reserve it for future negotiations. The
Yugoslav and Western occupation zones in the Free City of Trieste
closely predetermined the final partition of the city; the Antarctica
Treaty will probably weaken the territorial claims notwithstanding
the special exemption; and the Potsdam Conference of 1945, by
leaving "the final delimitation" of the German-Polish frontier to
"the peace settlement," carried the administrative boundaries of
Poland from the fluid postwar situation into an indefinite future at
which time the *de facto* borders will have become as rigid as state
frontiers agreed to in a treaty.

Churchill, for one, realized at the Potsdam Conference that the
postponement of a settlement for Poland's western frontier might,
in fact, make the existing administrative boundaries permanent.
The minutes of the session at which this issue was discussed record
that "the President said he did not see the urgency of the matter.
It would be helpful to have a preliminary discussion and the matter
would not finally be settled until the peace conference." Churchill,
however, now arguing more with Truman than with Stalin, said

(according to these minutes) "that with great respect he wished to explain the urgency of the matter. If the settlement of the question were delayed the present local situation would be consolidated. Poles would be digging themselves in and taking effective steps to make themselves the sole masters of this territory. The longer the problem waited the more difficult it would be to settle it."[12]

In other negotiations, it is more appropriate to regard a settlement with important residual disagreements as a phase in a continuing confrontation of the same powers. The residual conflict is not so much postponed as channeled into new directions, and new rules for handling it are agreed upon. For example, the 1954 agreement on Indochina left Laos' position between the Communist camp and the West uncertain. (Laos' fate was undetermined because the 1954 agreement linked it to the then unpredictable internal power-struggle between Communist and anti-Communist forces, although some of the signatories, particularly Great Britain, expected that it would be neutral.) As a result, East-West bargaining about Laos continued almost without pause for another eight years, both at the negotiating table and through the confrontation of military forces in the field.

To recapitulate the various forms of residual disagreements, we might distinguish among five different reasons why negotiators may settle for an incomplete agreement. First, the parties may want to clarify what they disagree about so as to better focus future negotiations on the unsettled dispute. Second, they may want to postpone refractory disputes for future negotiations in order not to hold up agreement on related issues that are ripe for settlement. Third, they may want to clarify their disagreement in order to contain it—to keep their broader relations, as it were, uncontaminated. Fourth, they may use their partial agreement to place the residual

[12] *Foreign Relations of the United States: The Conference of Berlin (Potsdam) 1945*, II, 249. This view was also expressed in a British aide-memoire to the American government: "If the British and the United States governments allow the permanent settlement of the frontier to be postponed indefinitely, only putting their views on record for the present, the difficulties of settlement at a later date will be aggravated. . . . In these circumstances the assurance given by M. Vyshinsky to the effect that the presence of Polish Administration does not prejudice the fate of German territory, which is for discussion at the Peace Conference, is of little practical value" (*ibid.*, I, 778–79).

dispute into a new context where it can be handled more safely or more cheaply. Fifth, they may be interested in certain symbolic or hidden implications of having a signed agreement, even though it fails to settle anything.

To clarify this last category, the formality of concluding an agreement must be distinguished from its content. The term *pseudo-agreement* will be used here to designate a pact which is all formality, which does not record any new settlement. That is to say, a pseudo-agreement contains no new exchanges of complementary interests or new combinations of common interests. Nonetheless, the parties may read certain implications into it. If all parties had the same hidden content in mind and were mutually aware of this, they would in fact have concluded a tacit bargain for which the pseudo-agreement might serve as a symbol. But in international relations such a meeting of minds is rare. Usually the parties attribute no significant bargains to a pseudo-agreement, and if they do, their attributions are likely to differ. For example, in 1933 Mussolini may have promoted the Four-Power Pact simply because he felt that he was gaining in prestige by concluding a treaty with the other leading European powers, although it was only a façade.

The conclusion of a pseudo-agreement among powers whose relations are strained is sometimes construed as though these powers had exchanged promises to be more accommodating toward each other in the future. A non-aggression pact between NATO and the Warsaw Pact countries might be an example.

Similarly, statesmen may read into a pseudo-agreement a mutual commitment to reach significant agreements in the future. According to this view, the pseudo-agreement will act as a catalyst for some real settlements. Many Westerners felt this way about negotiations with the East—in the 1950s more so than today. Agreements with the Russians were sought after, not for their content, but "to make further agreement easier." Henry Kissinger pointed out the dangers of this view:

The inevitable consequence of such a conviction is that more ingenuity is expended in finding things to agree on, no matter how trivial, than in coming to grips with the issues that have caused the tensions. In the process, a curious distortion takes place. The difficulties which are "ironed out" are often soluble only because they are inconsequential. But the mere fact that they are settled is taken as a proof of the possibility of "progress."[13]

Sometimes there is an additional factor which accounts for the interest in agreement as a formality apart from content. As will be discussed in more detail later, those who are involved in negotiations may come to feel that their efforts failed should the conference end without an agreement, particularly if the negotiations have been going on for a long time. Consequently, they become anxious to reach some kind of a formal accord because they regard this formality as a token of success, independent of the terms of the agreement.

CARRY–OVER FOR FUTURE NEGOTIATIONS

The amount of agreement reached and the residual disagreement left do not encompass the entire outcome of negotiations. In addition, there may be latent effects which impinge on the course of subsequent negotiations. Even if a conference ends without any agreement—neither an explicit nor a tacit one, neither a specific nor an ambiguous one—the issues dealt with may have been permanently altered. This effect of negotiation is latent, since it materializes only if a future conference leads to an agreement on the same issues.

Carry-over effects result from the fact that a government normally changes its position between the beginning and the end of a conference—that is, a negotiating position is rarely totally inflexible. If the conference ends without agreement and the same issue is taken up again in later negotiations (perhaps with some new participants), the government is likely to start out with a position that is closer to the one it held at the end than at the beginning of the previous conference. There are three reasons for this.

First, there is often considerable justification in viewing the prior and succeeding conferences as a single negotiation. Given such a view, a government may feel that it would be improper to

[13] Henry A. Kissinger, *The Necessity for Choice* (New York: Harper, 1961), pp. 189–90.

abandon its final position from the initial conference, in the same sense that it may be considered improper to withdraw an offer after it has been accepted or to revert to a harder position from a more conciliatory one during a single negotiation.

Second, the terminal position in the original conference may become part of a government's propaganda stance or of its public image, thus acquiring a certain rigidity, like a dogma. Officials often tend to become personally committed to certain views as to what the goals and negotiating positions of their government should be, and these commitments may survive into the next negotiation.

Third, the internal decision-making process in a government may suffer from inertia or work at cross-purposes, so that the only internally agreed position for the new conference is the one left over from the previous one. Also, broad objectives and definitions of issues have a certain inertia, because revising them would require changes in official terminology, doctrine, budget allocations, or related policies—all of which are hard to push through without the pressures of ongoing negotiations.

East-West disarmament negotiations, ever since 1946, produced a considerable carry-over effect from one conference to the next, both on specific positions and on broad objectives and definitions of issues. Although the London disarmament conference of 1957 did not result in any agreement, it predetermined important positions for the test-ban conference which began a year later.[14] And on general disarmament, the United States became increasingly committed between 1959 and 1962 to the principle of "general and complete disarmament," as a result of negotiatory pressures from the Soviet Union. By 1962, this commitment had acquired a permanence that is likely to survive from conference to conference, as if it had been an original American objective of long standing.

Some observers of the Geneva disarmament talks feel that the Russians, too, are not merely revising their proposals occasionally

[14] This carry-over has been analyzed by Ciro E. Zoppo, *The Issue of Nuclear Test Cessation at the London Disarmament Conference of 1957: A Study in East-West Negotiation* (RAND Corporation Research Memorandum 2821 [Santa Monica, Calif., 1961]).

but are gradually changing their objectives and doctrine, learning that they indeed have some common interest in the disarmament objectives advanced by the West. At the present time, it remains to be seen whether this education toward a new doctrine will permeate from the 'Soviet delegation in Geneva to the inner decision-making councils in Moscow.

The question of carrying over a position from one phase of negotiation into the next became important in connection with a Western proposal on the Berlin issue. Toward the end of the Geneva Foreign Ministers' Conference in 1959, the three Western powers advanced a proposal for a five-year interim arrangement, providing (among other things) for East German "agents" of the Soviet Union to control traffic and for curbs on propaganda and intelligence activities in Berlin. The Soviet Union rejected this. Half a year later the three Western Powers and the German Federal Republic made a declaration in Paris which abandoned the interim proposal. The Bonn government was reported to be jubilant that this position would not be carried over into the negotiations in 1960, since it considered the political curbs on West Berlin and the partial recognition of East Germany quite dangerous. In January, 1960, Adenauer stated very bluntly, not only that it would be false to resume summit negotiations at the point where the Foreign Ministers' Conference was broken off, but also that the Western proposal had been rejected and therefore "no longer existed."[15]

There are other long-term effects from negotiation, in addition to the carry-over of positions and objectives into subsequent conferences. A government may reveal its estimate of the balance of power by the way in which it negotiates, and this will affect its bargaining strength in the future. Also, the tactics that it uses will be remembered by other parties and influence their expectations when they deal with this government again. This "bargaining reputation" will be discussed later, but first we have to analyze why governments enter negotiations.

For negotiations to start on some issue, one of the parties, or a mediator, must take the initiative. There has to be an explicit

---

[15] Quoted from Hans Speier, *Divided Berlin, The Anatomy of Soviet Blackmail* (New York: Praeger, 1961), p. 80.

proposal to hold a conference, to begin diplomatic talks, or at least the new issue has to be introduced into ongoing discussions. Negotiations do not start accidentally or through forces of nature. Therefore the government taking the initiative must have an objective in mind for starting them, and the governments joining in must have their reasons for participating.

CHAPTER 3

FIVE OBJECTIVES

As the richness of diplomatic history illustrates, there is an enormous diversity in international negotiations. Governments are constantly engaged in diplomatic bargaining, ranging from casual contacts to large formal conferences. In order to bring out common traits and render this variety more manageable, one must distinguish among different purposes for which the parties negotiate. The aims or objectives of governments in international negotiations can be classified adequately into five types: (1) extension agreements, (2) normalization agreements, (3) redistribution agreements, (4) innovation agreements, and (5) effects not concerning agreements. In reality, the negotiating parties always pursue a mixture of several of these types of objectives, although one of them may predominate. Moreover, in one and the same negotiation, the dominant objective of one party is often of a different type from that of the other party.

Negotiations for the purpose of an *extension* agreement are meant to continue the "normal"; that is, to prolong existing arrangements which are acceptable to some, if not all, parties involved. Examples are the extension of tariff agreements, the renewal of rights to maintain an overseas military base, or the replacement of important officials in international organizations. Negotiations for the purpose of a *normalization* agreement are meant to terminate the abnormal or to formalize arrangements tacitly arrived at, such as to stop fighting through a cease-fire or truce, to re-establish diplomatic relations, or to end a temporary occupation in exchange for a military alliance and regularize other postwar uncertainties through a peace treaty.

Negotiations for the purpose of a *redistribution* agreement are characterized by a demand of an offensive side for a change in its favor, at the expense of a defensive side, the change consisting of a new distribution of territory, political influence, institutional powers and rights, economic and military assets, or the like. Essentially, what the offensive side gains, the defensive side loses; hence the offensive side has to couple its demand with the threat of causing worse consequences if the demand is refused. Negotiations for the purpose of an *innovation* agreement deal with the setting up of new relationships or obligations between the parties, with the founding of a new institution, or with a new arrangement for controlling objects and areas. In contrast to redistribution, the change supposedly works to the advantage of all parties concerned, though not necessarily to equal advantage.[1] Finally, parties that negotiate for the sake of other *effects not concerning agreement* are interested in such results as propaganda, intelligence, or dissuading the opponent from the use of force.

EXTENSION

The following recent negotiations are examples in which the extension type of objective predominated for both sides: the renewal of cultural exchange agreements between the United States and the Soviet Union, the extension of status-of-forces agreements between the United States and some of its allies, the renewal of the agreement for the sharing of financial burdens within NATO, and the replacement of Trygve Lie by Dag Hammarskjöld as Secretary-

---

[1] Thomas C. Schelling (*The Strategy of Conflict*, p. 21) introduces the distinction between the "efficiency" aspect of bargaining and the "distributional" aspect: the former consists of exploring for mutually profitable adjustments; in the latter the better bargain for one party means less for the other. Innovation negotiations are clearly dominated by "efficiency" bargaining, while redistribution negotiations are dominated by "distributional" bargaining. In extension and normalization negotiations, these two aspects are usually mixed. There are, of course, many gradations between a pure redistribution and innovation negotiation, ranging from exclusively "distributional" negotiation, through mixed "distributional-efficiency" bargaining, to purely "efficiency" cases.

General of the United Nations. The outcome of such negotiations may be an agreement that simply confirms the status quo or one that makes slight changes in the existing relationship. (If there are major changes, the outcome represents a redistribution or innovation.) The initiative to negotiate might be taken by any one of the parties or by an international institution.

If no agreement is reached, the result is a change from the status quo; that is, there will be an interruption of customary relations between the parties or a discontinuation of the existing arrangements that were based on earlier agreements. Sometimes this interruption is avoided by a tacit understanding to extend the status quo temporarily; or to put it differently, the negotiations result in a tacit extension. The principal incentives to agreement are the disadvantages of interrupting existing arrangements, as for example, the economic losses from an expired trade agreement, the inconvenience of an unfilled vacancy in an international organization, or the military disadvantage to one side and financial loss to the other if an agreement for a foreign base is not extended.

An important characteristic of negotiation for an extension is the strong influence exercised by the previous agreement. The old agreement limits the area of dispute, introduces weighty precedents, and may even provide specific means for settling differences regarding the renewal. For the replacement of officials in an international organization, for example, the institutional framework often circumscribes the choices and methods of negotiation quite narrowly. Sometimes there are arbitration procedures to bring in third parties if the original parties fail to reach agreement among themselves.

NORMALIZATION

Examples of negotiations where the main objective of all parties was a normalization agreement, are Litvinov's talks in Washington in 1933 leading to American recognition of the Soviet Union, the negotiations for the peace treaty with Japan in 1951, the negotiations between Egypt, Israel, and United Nations mediators on the armistice of 1949, the Panmunjom conference on the Korean armistice, and (to a large extent) the 1961–62 Geneva conference on Laos. At peace conferences, however, the principal parties frequently have other objectives, apart from normalization. The Paris Peace Conference of 1919–20 and the Potsdam Conference with its sequels from 1945 through 1946, for example, served purposes of redistribution and innovation as well as normalization. The League of Nations, an important issue at the Paris Peace Conference of 1919, is an example of an innovation.

In situations where fighting will continue or threatens to resume unless agreement is reached, public opinion and other domestic forces may exert considerable pressures on the negotiators to agree. Often, there are important asymmetries in the susceptibility to such pressures. American negotiators at Panmunjom and their superiors in Washington felt very strongly the yearning back home for an end to the fighting, but their Chinese and North Korean opponents —while sensitive to the military weakness of their side—remained relatively immune to popular sentiment in their countries.

Apart from these pressures for agreement, negotiations for the purpose of normalization are strongly influenced by the *instability* of the "abnormal" situation they are supposed to settle. If fighting continues while negotiations are prolonged, one side may gain through force what it failed to gain through bargaining. Or, at least, it may shake the opponent's confidence in his ability to defend his military position and thus make him anxious to reach an agreement. After a temporary suspension of fighting, however, the threat of a resumption of hostilities tends to become less effective for bargaining purposes, unless supported by existing military capabilities or preparations that make a new offensive both likely and dangerous to the opponent.

The Korean armistice negotiations would probably have led to an agreement much sooner, or on terms more favorable to the United Nations side, if the latter had been able to demonstrate to the Communist side that it might launch a major offensive. In the spring of 1953, when General Mark Clark as the UN Commander in Korea met President Dwight D. Eisenhower, he had prepared "a detailed estimate of the forces and plans required to obtain military victory in Korea should the new administration decide to take such a course." But according to General Clark, the newly elected President showed no interest in using the threat of such an offensive to exert pressure on the truce negotiations: "The question of how much it would take to win the war was never raised."[2]

In the event that no normalization agreement is reached, the "abnormal" situation will initially continue; but because of its instability, further changes usually ensue in short time. After the failure of cease-fire negotiations, continued fighting will change the fortunes of war; after the failure of truce negotiations, the cease-fire may erupt again into fighting. Conversely, hostilities may gradually subside despite the failure of negotiations, so that a tacit truce will in fact be established.

REDISTRIBUTION

Negotiation for the purpose of redistribution is characterized by a clear and permanent division between an offensive side and a defensive side. The demand by the offensive side is often directed against one of the weaker or more exposed allies on the defensive side. In the most acute form of this type of negotiation, the offensive side presents its central demand in the form of an ultimatum (that is, a position put forward as final), with only ancillary issues left for bargaining, and it not only makes its threat highly specific but also announces that the threat will be carried out at a definite date unless the central demand is satisfied.

If the offensive side is successful, agreement in this type of negotiation will lead to a change in the status quo, as the defensive side complies with all or part of the demand. The classic illustrations are the Munich agreement and its sequel in March, 1939, when President Hácha of Czechoslovakia was forced to surrender the rest of his country to Hitler. There are other illustrations, however, of a far less aggressive character and an entirely different political tenor. For example, Iceland's claim in 1958 to a twelve-mile zone for exclusive fishery was backed up by the threat of force against British vessels. After some resistance, Great Britain, as the defensive side, essentially complied with the Icelandic demands.

If the offensive side is unsuccessful, an agreement may still re-

[2] Mark W. Clark, *From the Danube to the Yalu* (New York: Harper, 1954), p. 233.

sult, whereby the defensive side consents to exchange some face-saving formula for a formal withdrawal of the demand. For example, the negotiations for the lifting of the Berlin blockade of 1948–49 resulted in an agreement by which the Western powers consented to a Foreign Ministers' conference with the Soviet Union, which was to start eleven days after the termination of the blockade and discuss problems regarding Germany and Berlin. (This conference reached no agreement of substance.) However, if either side is stubborn, redistribution negotiations may end without any agreement. In this case, there are two basic outcomes: either the status quo is preserved tacitly, which means that the offensive side gives in completely, or the offensive side carries out its threat or part of it. When the Soviet-Finish negotiations in the fall of 1939 failed to induce Finland to cede the territories demanded by Russia, the Russians carried out their threat and attacked Finland.

There are some distinguishing features between negotiations for a redistribution and those for an innovation. In redistribution, the conflicting interest is the principal topic of negotiation, whereas the common interest remains tacit or is shunted into peripheral bargaining. The conflicting interest simply stems from the demand by the offensive side. The common interest lies in the mutual desire to avoid violence; that is, the offensive side would rather keep its gains more modest than carry out its threat, and the defensive side would rather relinquish something than challenge the threat. Occasionally, a complementary interest in an exchange is added to this basic common interest, such as the formal withdrawal of a threat in exchange for a face-saving formula, or the preservation of long-term friendship in exchange for a modest concession. (This was the idea of the British government when Mussolini demanded a free hand in Abyssinia: to buy Italy's friendship by granting Mussolini part of what he asked for.)

In negotiations for an innovation, on the other hand, it is the common interest, or alleged common interest, which constitutes the primary topic, while the conflicting interests are relegated to the details. Threats are scarcely used for innovations. But for redistributions, the offensive side must always threaten, or at least issue strong warnings.[3]

[3] A distinction between "threats" and "warnings" is developed in chap. 5.

A demand for institutional changes in an international organization may have the objective of a redistribution of political power. In contrast to institutional innovations, such changes are clearly to the disadvantage of the defensive side. They are the issue of conflict, while the common interest, if any, is extraneous to them. An example is the Soviet demand that the United Nations Secretariat be headed by a "troika" instead of by a single, independent Secretary-General. Since this change was firmly opposed by many UN members, including all the other permanent members of the Security Council who had the power to veto it, the Soviet negotiators had no chance of success unless they could find an effective threat.

After the sudden death of Dag Hammarskjöld in 1961, it seemed as if the opportunity for such a threat had come. As expected, the Soviet negotiators tried to tie their demand for a "troika" to the threat that they would veto the replacement of the single UN Secretary-General. In other words, they tried to link a redistribution agreement on the "troika" with an extension agreement for the staffing of the UN Secretariat. In the former they were opposed by parties that could veto the redistribution; in the latter they, in turn, could veto the kind of staffing that the same parties wanted. In principle, a tie-in between an extension and a redistribution agreement can be very effective—the offensive side trades its consent to the extension in exchange for the demanded redistribution. (This is the essence of labor-management negotiations.) In this particular case, however, the tie-in could have been used for a compromise only, since the "troika" could not be traded for the replacement of a *single* Secretary-General, the two being incompatible. As it turned out, the Soviet negotiators lacked the skill to advance their cause significantly by a compromise. (They might have succeeded, for instance, in obtaining a "troika" of powerful Deputy Secretaries, in exchange for their consent to the election of a single Secretary-General.)

There is an interesting difference in the reaction of public opinion to negotiation for normalization and for redistribution. A cease-fire, armistice, or peace treaty—the ostensible goal of negotiation for normalization—is usually supported by public opinion on both sides, and the publicized dispute concerns only the terms for settlement. (An exception is the propagandistically important opposition of Egypt and other Arab countries to a peace treaty with Israel.) In negotiation for redistribution, on the other hand, the offensive side usually appears in the public eye as the disturber of peace—unless the redistribution is aimed at the liberation of occupied areas or colonies. In modern times, if liberation or decolonization can be neither the true objective nor a plausible pretext, it takes someone as bold as Hitler to admit unashamedly that he is making a demand for a change entirely to his advantage. Although Hitler still used the pretense of liberating the Sudeten Germans in the Munich conference, he felt no embarrassment that he had to do without a pretext in the subsequent negotiations with Hácha.

Characteristically, Khrushchev says that his demands for West Berlin aim not for a change of the status quo to his advantage but for a normalization of the aftermath of World War II. As part of this tactic to enlist public support, Khrushchev argues that what he is after in West Berlin is merely to clear up old business: "The need to do away with the vestiges of World War II by signing a German peace treaty."[4] On the surface, Khrushchev's demands for a "free city" of West Berlin could be viewed as a normalization. But the Western powers fear that Khrushchev's real goal is a redistribution: to detach West Berlin from the Federal Republic of Germany—the ally of the West—and gradually to incorporate the city into the Communist bloc. The history of Eastern Europe since World War II gives ample ground for this interpretation.

WHY DOES THE DEFENSIVE SIDE NEGOTIATE AT ALL?

In examining the motives of the defensive side for entering redistribution negotiations, one must distinguish two possibilities. In certain cases, the defensive side may have concluded that it is better to yield, for if it did not, the offensive side would in all likelihood carry out the threat, and this would result in greater losses than yielding would. Here negotiation has the purpose of cutting the losses—for instance, by obtaining a face-saving arrange-

[4] *Tass* statement of July 12, 1962. This is a constantly recurrent theme in the Soviet statements on Berlin.

ment or some small compensation, or by improving the prospects for friendly long-term relations with the offensive side.

A recent example is the transfer of West New Guinea in 1962 from Dutch administration to Indonesia. It appeared very likely to the Netherlands and the United States (the latter being largely responsible for the settlement) that Sukarno would carry out his threat and attempt to take West New Guinea by force. Sukarno might, in fact, have welcomed a "war of liberation" to rally his people and cover up economic mismanagement at home. Although the Dutch might have successfully defended the territory (certainly if given American naval help), the losses from doing so seemed greater to the American government than the losses from giving up the territory, because West New Guinea was an economic burden for the Netherlands, and a war with Indonesia would have been costly and might have driven Sukarno closer to the Communists. (Of course, as in all appeasements, there was the question whether it might not do greater harm by setting a bad precedent and encouraging Sukarno to make further territorial demands.)

On the other hand, in many redistribution negotiations the defensive side has concluded that it is better not to yield, either because the costs of yielding seem greater than the costs from whatever the offensive side threatens or because it seems unlikely that the threat will be carried out. In such situations, why should the defensive side want to negotiate at all?

This very question has been a source of prolonged differences between Washington and London on one side and Paris on the other in connection with Khrushchev's demands for Berlin. The French government maintained that it was unwise for the Western powers to enter into or show interest in negotiations. In a speech to the French Parliament in December, 1961, the Foreign Minister, Couve de Murville, explained some of the objections to negotiating on Berlin:

This problem, paradoxically, is whether the French, the Americans, and the British should take the initiative to propose to the Russians the setting-up of a four-power conference. I say "paradoxically" because, after all, it is the Russians who have raised the question of a change of status quo. Looking at it differently, it would mean that we should ask them to discuss their conditions for our staying in Berlin; that is, to discuss the concessions we would have to make to them so that they agree, to a certain extent and perhaps for a certain time only, that our troops can stay and that the freedom of West Berlin thus will remain more or less guaranteed.[5]

One can be more specific about the risks that the defensive side runs by negotiating on a redistribution demand. First, the negotiators of the defensive side might feel they ought to demonstrate flexibility; therefore they offer concessions that go some way toward satisfying the offensive demand. Second, they might lower their expectations and adapt their image of the status quo so as to bring it closer to the opponent's position (a process to be discussed later). Third, their view of the character of the negotiations may gradually change from a redistribution to a normalization. That is, they may come to regard a situation that has been the subject of prolonged negotiations as abnormal. Ergo, they will deem it appropriate to change the status quo so as to normalize it.

Despite these risks of negotiating, the governments of the defensive side may have countervailing reasons for meeting with their opponents, even though they conclude that they need not yield. They may be in favor of negotiation because they think that it has certain advantageous effects unrelated to any agreement. That is, they pursue side-effects. In addition, some Westerners when faced with certain offensive demands favor negotiation in order to find out what the opponent "really" wants. Thus they imply that the opponent could not be so brutish as to want what he in fact keeps demanding. They feel the opponent's true goal must be more reasonable or more realistic, and then a solution satisfactory to both sides could be found.

INNOVATION

Negotiations with the objective of innovation are meant to create a new relationship or new undertakings between parties. They are exemplified by the conferences on the Treaties of Rome to set up

---

[5] *Journal Officiel de la République Française* (Sénat), Dec. 5, 1961, p. 2297.

the Common Market and Euratom, the discussions on the treaty demilitarizing Antarctica, the conference for the statute for the International Atomic Energy Agency, and the marathon talks for a nuclear test ban. Disarmament negotiations normally pursue a mixture of objectives in which this type predominates.

As to the initiative, it is usually quite clear which party has made the first move proposing the innovation. Sometimes, this initiator continues to push for agreement; at other times, the initiative for the innovation may shift from one side to the other (in contrast to redistribution negotiations, where it is always the offensive side that wants the change). For example, in the nuclear test-ban negotiations it was at first clearly the Soviet Union that was pressing for a ban while the United States remained reluctant; but since 1960 or 1961 these roles have been reversed.

What pressures are available to the parties primarily interested in an innovation, to induce reluctant partners to agree? An important way of exerting pressure is the mobilization of domestic political support among the prospective partners. Jean Monnet's Action Committee for the United States of Europe has been instrumental in rallying the support of important political groups among the Six behind the Treaties of Rome and subsequent steps toward European integration. One of the important functions of the European Parliamentary Assembly in Strasbourg (the parliament of the Six) is the domestic support that it can generate within the member states to strengthen the hand of the European Executives on innovations advancing integration.[6] For innovations in the disarmament field, the initiators seek to exert pressures through public opinion within the countries of reluctant opponents as well as through neutral countries. (In part, these pressures may be designed to make the opponent disarm unilaterally, rather than to force an agreement on him.)

To win over those who hesitate to go along with an innovation, the warning of exclusion is often more effective than pressures

[6] These three Executives (the High Authority of the Coal and Steel Community and the Commissions of the Common Market and Euratom) use resolutions by the European Parliament to defend their position in the Council of Ministers (which represents the six governments). The ministers normally do not want to disregard the views of the European parliamentarians, who are also members of their home parliaments.

of public opinion. A party that is at first reluctant or indifferent toward an innovation may join merely because it is afraid of becoming an outsider.

When President Eisenhower first proposed the creation of an International Atomic Energy Agency in December, 1953, he said that "the United States would be more than willing—it would be proud to take up with the others 'principally involved' the development of plans [for such an agency]. Of those 'principally involved,' the Soviet Union must, of course, be one."[7] The United States government followed up this invitation in a diplomatic exchange with Moscow, but the Soviet government took a negative attitude. Nine months after his initial proposal, President Eisenhower therefore declared: "Although progress in this plan has been impeded by Soviet obstruction and delay, we intend to proceed—*with* the cooperation and participation of the Soviet Union if possible, *without* it if necessary."[8] This warning was given weight by a number of American initiatives: among them the exploratory talks with seven other friendly nations and the rapid expansion, early in 1955, of bilateral agreements between the United States and twenty-four countries for aid on peaceful uses of atomic energy. A year later, the Soviet Union joined in establishing the International Atomic Energy Agency, after it obtained certain concessions modifying the original American design.[9]

In April, 1945, when Molotov came to see President Truman a few days before the United Nations was to be launched at San Francisco, it seemed uncertain whether the Russians would cooperate in creating the new world organization, since deep differences had already arisen over the Yalta agreements. President Truman told Molotov that the United States was determined to go ahead with plans for the world organization, or as the President put it privately to his advisers, that he "intended to go on with

---

[7] Address by President Eisenhower to the United Nations, Dec. 3, 1953.

[8] The President's press release at the signing of the Atomic Energy Act, Aug. 30, 1954.

[9] In the fall of 1955 the Soviet Union entered the negotiations on the preparation of the statute for the Agency, and in October, 1956, the revised Statute was finally adopted by 81 nations. For an excellent history see Bernard G. Bechhoefer, "Negotiating the Statute of the International Atomic Energy Agency," *International Organization*, XIII (Winter, 1959), 38–59.

the plans for San Francisco and if the Russians did not wish to join us they could go to hell. . . ."[10]

The warning of exclusion, however, is ineffective against a government which thinks the innovation will not be successful (or would not succeed without its participation). A cardinal error of British foreign policy during the 1950s was the belief that European integration would not succeed. In 1950, the British turned down the Franco-German invitation to participate in the negotiations which translated the Schuman Plan into the Coal and Steel Community, and in 1955 they stayed away from the Conference of Messina which established the principles for the European Economic Community and Euratom. Subsequently they sent only an observer to the committee of experts which, on the basis of the Messina principles, prepared the report that led to the Treaties of Rome. And they soon withdrew their observer again when pressed to assume a positive attitude toward European integration.[11]

While the initiator of an innovation will want to have essential parties included, he has to be careful lest his efforts to win over reluctant participants jeopardize his basic goals. In the negotiations for the implementation of the Schuman Plan, Jean Monnet removed the principle of a supra-national authority as a topic of dispute and compromise by making its acceptance the condition for participation in the negotiations. The British refused to meet this condition.[12] It has occasionally been said that such a condition is contrary to diplomatic practice among friendly nations. With perhaps more validity, however, it might be argued that, without violating diplomatic standards, initiators of a new proposal who invite others to discuss its implementation may define the agenda so as to exclude alternatives incompatible with their proposal.

There are many situations where the initiator of an innovation

[10] Harry S Truman, *Memoirs* (Garden City, N.Y.: Doubleday, 1955), I, 80; and Walter Millis (ed.), *The Forrestal Diaries,* p. 50. Three days earlier, however, the President was less sanguine; when Harriman asked him whether America would go ahead with the United Nations plans even if the Russians dropped out, Truman replied the truth of the matter was that without Russia there would not be a world organization (*Memoirs,* I, 72).

[11] Karl Kaiser, *EWG und Freihandelszone* (Leiden: Sythoff, 1963), p. 37.

[12] According to Anthony Nutting (*Europe Will Not Wait* [London: Hollis & Carter, 1960], p. 29), this condition merely provided the British government with the excuse it wanted for staying out.

cannot use the warning of exclusion to win over reluctant parties. The participation of certain countries may be so essential that their exclusion would make negotiations meaningless. In any disarmament negotiation of a global scope, the United States and the Soviet Union, of course, play such a role. So would Communist China and several other powers, if disarmament progressed beyond the initial phase.

Other situations do allow the warning of exclusion to be used against essential parties. An interesting example is the Antarctica treaty. In spite of the fact that Soviet participation was essential for an agreement to *demilitarize* the region, the United States, as the initiator, did have a warning of exclusion available. If the Soviet government had obstructed agreement (for example, by objecting to inspection), the United States could have switched from the demilitarization project to a project for *regional security* based on the exclusion of the Soviet Union. (The only countries close to Antarctica are U.S. allies and South Africa, and all claims to Antarctic territory were made by allies, with the only unclaimed sector generally recognized as a potential U.S. claim. Given allied cooperation—an important qualification!—the Soviet Union could have been effectively excluded, for example, through a condominium.) This possibility never came into the open during the negotiations, in part because the conflict of interest was relatively mild—unlike the usual feeling in disarmament negotiations. Nonetheless, as a latent threat it may have contributed significantly to the successful conclusion of the Antarctica treaty.

The warning of exclusion can be ineffective for two reasons: either the innovation is meaningless without the participation of those who oppose it,· or it requires approval by an international organization in which the opponents have a veto. It is for the latter reason that initiatives for revising the United Nations Charter have made so little headway.

There are cases, however, when even the obstacle of the veto has been overcome. The treaty of the European Economic Community provided that a common agricultural policy be gradually established according to certain principles, but it left all the important details to future negotiations. France expected to be the chief beneficiary of the integration of agriculture, while Germany stood to lose; and without German consent, agricultural integration would have been held up.[13] Initially it seemed that the French negotiators had no leverage to win German consent. But when the transition of the Common Market from its first to its second stage came up for negotiation in 1961, the French refused to agree to it unless agricultural integration was included. This created sufficient pressure on the Germans, since they were generally interested in the transition to the second stage (as were the other members of the Common Market). This *iunctim,* as the Germans call such a tie-in, combined two innovations: one (the transition to the second stage) in the interest of all the parties, and another (agricultural integration) in the interest of only some of the essential parties.

The French government was less interested than the other members of the Common Market in the transition to the second stage as such, apart from the integration of agriculture. Or at least it gave the appearance of being less interested, which was made easy by its well-known coldness toward the majority voting provided in the second stage. This lack of interest was an essential aspect of the *iunctim,* because it made credible the French threat to veto the transition. The *iunctim* also had the advantage of offsetting the domestic strength of the German farmers, who were opposed to agricultural integration, with the strength of industrial and other groups in Germany that wanted to have the Common Market move into its second stage.

Incidentally, the history of the provision in the Common Market treaty which enabled France to veto the second stage illustrates how negotiators sometimes acquire a bargaining advantage by accident or for the wrong reason. This provision was requested by France and reluctantly accepted by the other five member-countries in 1956 in the belief that the French economy might need an escape from rapid integration. But in 1961 the French could use this escape clause for almost the opposite purpose: to prevent the Germans from escaping a more rapid integration of agriculture.

[13] After the first two stages of the Common Market, the agricultural policy could have been adopted by majority vote. From the French vantage point in 1961, not only would this have meant considerable postponement, but in view of the possible entry of Great Britain and other countries, the opposition to agricultural integration might also have become stronger.

FIVE OBJECTIVES OF NEGOTIATION

	Extension Agreement	Normalization Agreement	Redistribution Agreement	Innovation Agreement	Side-Effects
Subject of negotiation	Continuation of normal (renewals or replacements).	Termination of abnormal (cease-fire, truce, resumption of diplomatic relations).	New distribution in favor of offensive side (surrender of territory; liberation of colonies).	New institutions or other arrangements of mutual interest.	The less likely the agreement, the more important the side-effects.
Main characteristics of negotiating process	Strong influence of previous agreement: as a precedent, and in limiting area of dispute.	Strong influence of situation at time of negotiations. Domestic or third-party pressures toward normalization.	Continuous division between offensive and defensive side. Continuous open threat of offensive side.	Inducement of mutual benefits, and risk of exclusion. A specially interested party may act as initiator.	Side-effects continue to flow from negotiating process.
In case of prolonged negotiations	Both sides lose.	In case of continuing hostilities, stronger party may win by force instead of negotiation.	Defensive side postpones loss, but redistribution may begin to look like normalization.	Interest in innovation may shift from one side to the other.	
In case of *no* agreement	Interruption of customary arrangements.	*Either* continuation of fighting (or of abnormal relations) *or* subsiding of fighting (tacit truce).	*Either* status quo *or* implementation of threat by offensive side.	Continuation of status quo.	Side-effects nonetheless materialize and may be used to vindicate negotiations.

As a sidelight on the types of objectives for negotiation, it is worth noting that domestic groups opposed to an innovation always picture it as a redistribution to the detriment of their own country. This happened with the various moves in European integration, where at one time the Germans were supposed to gain at the expense of the French, at another time the French or Italians at the expense of the Germans. Similarly, the nuclear test ban has been criticized by some Americans as resulting in military gains for the Soviet Union with no offsetting advantages for the United States.

SIDE–EFFECTS

The very process of negotiation can have important effects which do not concern agreement. These "side-effects" may be one of the reasons—or sometimes the only reason—why governments engage in diplomatic talks. Indeed, side-effects may provide the motive not only for going along with negotiations started by others but even for *initiating* negotiations. Proposals and speeches at the conference table, contacts with the opponent's diplomats, and the interest aroused among third parties may all contribute to various foreign-policy aims without leading to a settlement of the issues ostensibly discussed. For example, the negotiating process (or its simulation) can launch propaganda, produce intelligence, or modify political attitudes of nonparticipants.

If Western governments are engaged in negotiations where agreement appears highly unlikely or even undesirable, they frequently stress certain benefits from such side-effects. Of course, these side-effects may not materialize, or if they do, they may not meet the expectations of the parties that pursued them. Also, it is sometimes doubtful whether these alleged benefits are the real reason for negotiating or whether a government advances them to rationalize what it is doing out of habit or to conceal the fact that it clings to unrealistic hopes for a satisfactory agreement.

Side-effects are such an essential aspect of negotiation that they must be discussed more fully. Before going on, however, it may be worthwhile to scrutinize the five types of negotiation objectives as a group in the accompanying Table.

CHAPTER 4

NEGOTIATING FOR SIDE-EFFECTS

SIDE-EFFECTS—THAT IS, EFFECTS NOT CONCERNING AGREEMENT —may be an important part of the outcome, even if all parties negotiate primarily for the purpose of reaching agreement. They may arise either by accident or by design of one party or all parties involved. When diplomacy produces agreements only rarely—as between East and West—the objective of producing side-effects, in fact, often dominates. A type of side-effect that is frequently given as the main reason for negotiating is to keep in touch with the opponent.

MAINTAINING CONTACT

Secretary of State Dean Rusk was asked in a press conference on July 12, 1962, whether negotiations on Berlin had not reached a point where there was little to talk about, since the Soviets were willing to discuss only the diminution or elimination of the basic position of the Western powers. "No," the Secretary replied, "I think both sides still believe, as they have for some time, that maintaining contact on these issues is itself important, even though there has been no clear view as to how they might lead to a satisfactory solution." One of the leading exponents of this theme, that negotiating is of value apart from any agreement, is Walter Lippmann, who wrote in one of his columns:

The best reason for continuing to talk, though no agreement is in sight, is that by remaining in close diplomatic contact, Washington and Moscow have been able to prevent the dangerous situation in Berlin from getting out of control. . . . With no lasting settlement in sight, it is enormously important that Moscow and Washington be in such close contact that they cannot be dragged into war by local accidents and local misunderstandings. That is the reason why the talks as such, why continual meeting and talking as such, are a good thing.[1]

As Lippmann values East-West negotiations on Berlin, irrespective of agreement, so he values negotiations on disarmament. "It is so easy to write off as hopeless the coming disarmament conference," he noted in March, 1962, "that one may ask why the British, the Soviets, and we are taking the trouble to attend it. The reason is that nuclear war would be mutually suicidal, and that therefore the nuclear powers must keep in contact, must keep talking. . . ."[2] The view that negotiation helps to keep in contact was also expressed by President John F. Kennedy with regard to his Vienna talks with Khrushchev in 1961: "No new aims were stated in private that have not been stated in public on either side. The gap between us was not, in such a short period, materially reduced, but at least the channels of communication were opened more fully."[3]

There are two reasons why negotiation for the purpose of maintaining contact may be found desirable. First, the talks or conference may be seen as providing a forum for the exchange of views, either continuously or sporadically, on issues other than the ostensible topic of negotiation. Second, the meetings between the negotiators may be viewed as a *potential* channel for emergency communication and crisis bargaining.

Belief in providing a forum suggests that governments need the pretext of being engaged in some specific negotiation in order to communicate on other subjects. Where ordinary diplomatic relations are inadequate or nonexistent, it might be true that it is easier occasionally to improve contacts for some pretended negotiation than for general purposes. In journalistic accounts of diplomacy,

---

[1] *New York Herald Tribune,* June 5, 1962.
[2] *Ibid.,* March 8, 1962.
[3] President Kennedy's address to the nation, June 6, 1961.

however, the importance of this subterfuge tends to be overrated because a specific negotiation makes better news than an unfocused exchange of views.

Belief in keeping a potential channel open for communicating in an emergency has been stressed primarily for East-West negotiations. This line of reasoning tends to presume that governments of great powers behave like petulant persons, whose feelings might become so antagonistic that they would break off all contact unless pledged to reach agreement on some specific issue. On the contrary, although negotiations have often been broken off for tactical reasons, great powers do not stop communicating with each other purely out of pique. There is little evidence that ongoing negotiations are the prerequisite for communication in a crisis. One pertinent illustration is the settlement of the crisis about the Soviet missiles in Cuba in October, 1962. The emergency bargaining between Kennedy and Khrushchev took place without difficulty through diplomatic channels. The heads of the two major nuclear powers did not require negotiations on general and complete disarmament, on Berlin, or on a fisheries agreement "to keep in contact." To the extent that there were difficulties of communication, they resulted not from a lack of ongoing negotiations but from inadequate *technical* communication links.

The idea that ongoing negotiations might serve as emergency channels does not seem valid. A more supportable view is that a history of past negotiations establishes a *habit* of communicating, which may induce governments to keep in touch during emergencies. Such a habit is well ingrained between Moscow and Washington but lacking between Peking and Washington.

SUBSTITUTING FOR VIOLENT ACTION

According to a view which is fairly common in the West, the process of negotiation can be so gratifying to one's opponent or can entangle him so much in an obligation not to interrupt it that he will desist from some violent action he might have otherwise taken. Negotiating becomes an alternative activity in itself, one that distracts the opponent from offensive or otherwise undesirable moves.

What remains unexplained in this view is why the mere process of negotiation should provide a substitute for mischief. Is your opponent misled to wait for gains at the conference table, although you neither intend to let him win nor expect to find a mutually rewarding solution? Is the activity of negotiating with you politically or emotionally so rewarding to your opponent that he will be soothed and will desist from pressing his claims by force? Or, would your refusal to negotiate infuriate your opponent more than your refusal to accede to his demands?

Speaking about the Berlin crisis, Senator Mansfield said in June, 1961: "In early 1959, a military showdown appeared imminent to me. . . . It was forestalled by an almost continuous round of sub-summit and summit conferences and visitings back and forth. . . ."[4] But then in the summer of 1961, according to Walter Lippmann, "General de Gaulle imposed a veto on negotiations. Not long after that veto there took place the action of August 13 to raise the wall in Berlin. In all likelihood, had the West been allowed to explore the problem of negotiating, the action of August 13 would not have taken place, at least during the explorations."[5] Similarly, Lippmann and others have suggested that owing to the Rusk-Gromyko negotiations after August 31, 1961, Khrushchev removed his December 31, 1961, deadline for signing a separate German peace treaty.

Experience does not support the attribution of such beneficial effects to the mere process of negotiation (with no agreement in sight) and of disastrous consequences to its interruption. Would the Communists have found it unnecessary to build the Berlin wall if they had been allowed continuously "to explore the problem of negotiating" with the West? Perhaps the Soviet resumption of nuclear testing in 1961, in the midst of ongoing test-ban negotiations, can be explained as an exception to the rule that negotiating tends to serve as a substitute for violent action. But the removal of the December 31, 1961, deadline for the German peace treaty does not support such a rule either, because since 1958 there has been a long succession of Soviet deadlines, some more explicit, some vague, and they have always withered away, whether

---

[4] *Congressional Record,* June 14, 1961, p. 9598.
[5] "Refusal to Negotiate Cost the West Dearly," *Los Angeles Times,* Oct. 26, 1961.

there were exploratory talks, broken-up summit meetings, or no negotiations at all. And if we go farther back in history, the exceptions to such a rule are even more glaring: the Franco-British negotiations in Moscow in the summer of 1939 did not prevent Stalin's pact with Hitler, and the interruption of the Japanese-American negotiations on December 7, 1941, is well remembered.

While these many exceptions invalidate the flat rule that negotiation provides a substitute for violent action, they do not contradict a sound core of this idea. Being engaged in negotiation may keep a government from taking some action disadvantageous to the opponent, provided two conditions are met: (1) the government so restrained must deem it likely that if it took the action, the opponent would break off the negotiations; and (2) the government must value the avoidance of a break in negotiations—even when there is no agreement in sight—more highly than the action from which it desists. Both these conditions were met for the U.S. government during the moratorium on nuclear tests from 1959 to 1961. The U.S. government expected that its resumption of testing would lead to the threatened Soviet walk-out from the test-ban conference, and it considered such a rupture of the negotiations (for which it might be held responsible) more undesirable than a continued uninspected moratorium.

Similarly, in case of negotiations on a truce or some other normalization agreement, a party may be led to give up violence by the very fact that talks are taking place, provided, again, that (1) this party thinks violence would cause the opponent to break off the talks, and (2) that it considers continued talks more important or more profitable than trying to make gains through the use of force. This is what happened at the beginning of the Korean armistice negotiations. "In June, 1951, the Communist forces were falling back steadily, suffering grievously," wrote Admiral Joy, who was chief of the UN truce delegation. "Then Jakob Malik issued his truce feeler. As soon as armistice discussions began, United Nations Command ground forces slackened their offensive operations."[6]

A related side-effect is that ongoing negotiations may serve to

[6] C. Turner Joy, *How Communists Negotiate* (New York: Macmillan, 1955), p. 166.

communicate warnings against the use of force. In redistribution negotiations, the defensive side can try to convince the opponent that his use of force would meet with grave reprisals. This is expressed by the idea that "we must tell the Russians where we stand," to prevent them from miscalculating the consequences of pushing too far. Thus, the *process* of negotiation may serve to deter the opponent, not because it provides him with a substitute for his planned offensive, but because it relays a warning against the use of force.

This side-effect should not be confused with the tactic of promoting agreement by making the consequences of no-agreement seem more disadvantageous to one's opponent. In that tactic, one side wants an agreement and predicts all sorts of dire consequences if none should be reached, including perhaps the use of force. But in the case of deterrent warnings as a side-effect, the negotiating process is used to discourage an offensive move by predicting painful reprisals, while both sides may have little interest in, or hope for, an agreement.

INTELLIGENCE

The process of negotiation may be used to gather intelligence about an opponent. Sometimes the information thus obtained can be more important than the way in which the issues under discussion are settled. A government, by the way it negotiates, may reveal its long-term aims, expose differences with its allies or domestic conflicts, and divulge the point at which an offensive by the opponent would meet with resistance.

In redistribution negotiations, the offensive side may well be more interested in discovering this point of resistance than in making gains through an agreement. It may learn, from what the defensive side says or fails to say, that certain offensive moves are safe. This possibility provides a further reason for questioning the notion that redistribution negotiations help the defensive side by providing the offensive side with a substitute for violent action. Walter Lippmann, in the passage quoted previously, thought the Berlin wall would not have been erected "had the West been allowed [by De Gaulle] to explore the problem of negotiating."

But negotiations on Berlin took place on and off for a long time before the wall was built! It was perhaps not the temporary interruption in negotiations that induced the Russians to build the wall, but rather the Western emphasis on free access to *West* Berlin only, to the neglect of the rights for free circulation within *all* of Berlin.[7]

One can easily find other examples of redistribution negotiations that did not produce any agreement but had this side-effect of informing the offensive party how far it could safely advance. In 1935, Mussolini's talks with the British and the French prior to his attack on Abyssinia may have succeeded in reassuring him that the opposition of these powers to his military adventure would be weak. The British and French negotiators, in trying to find a peaceful settlement for Mussolini's demands, offered him half a loaf: the Hoare-Laval plan for a large zone of Abyssinia to be allocated exclusively to Italian economic development and in return for an Abyssinian corridor to the sea at the expense of some British and French possessions. Even though this proposal was criticized in the League of Nations and disavowed by the British cabinet, it might have made Mussolini's grab of the whole loaf look less dangerous, and it conditioned the British Parliament, the French public, and League members to the idea that substantial gains by Mussolini over Abyssinia would be tolerated by Great Britain and France.

Looking back at this episode, the British negotiator, Sir Samuel Hoare, felt he should have made a greater effort to convince

[7] Apart from this narrow focus of the Western negotiating position, additional signals from the West might have reassured the Russians that they could safely build the wall. In this connection, a statement by Senator Fulbright has often been cited. A few weeks before the wall went up, Fulbright is reported to have said on television that the closing of West Berlin as an escape hatch "might certainly be a negotiable point. . . . I mean we are not giving up very much because I believe that next week if they chose to close their borders they could, without violating any treaty. I don't understand why the East Germans don't close their border because they have a right to close it. So why is this a great concession?" (*New York Times*, Aug. 3, 1961). It is doubtful, however, whether this statement significantly encouraged the building of the wall, especially since Senator Fulbright said a few days later in the Senate that the right to move within all sectors of Berlin was not negotiable and that his television statement was meant to apply to travel restrictions between East Germany and all of Berlin (*Congressional Record*, Aug. 4, 1961, p. 13659).

public opinion at home of the merits of his plan: "How we and the French were only making recommendations at the express request of the League . . . , how much of the territory involved in the proposed change was unadministered and unpopulated desert, and finally how formidable were the risks to Europe of a complete break with Italy."[8] But if surrender of half the loaf had been made more acceptable to Britain, Mussolini would not have been deterred from taking the whole loaf! What was needed was a firmer indication that Mussolini would meet with resistance from Britain or at least with effective League of Nations sanctions. Such a course was made difficult by the fact that the French Premier, Pierre Laval, was so anxious not to antagonize Mussolini.

DECEPTION

A side-effect of negotiation which may be viewed as the converse of intelligence is deception. One must distinguish deception as a side-effect unrelated to agreement from deception as a technique for getting good terms in an agreement. The *technique* of deception is unavoidable in certain negotiating situations. Assume, for example, that your opponent offers you terms good enough so that you would rather accept them than be without an agreement. If you want your opponent to make you a still better offer, you may have to deceive him into believing that you would prefer having no agreement to accepting his offer.

But the deception to be discussed here has nothing to do with the terms of agreement. It is a side-effect of negotiation which may serve other foreign-policy objectives or military moves.

The talks of Japanese diplomats in Washington prior to the attack on Pearl Harbor are sometimes mentioned as an example of a negotiation for deception. But this interpretation is incorrect. These talks, while obviously not alluding to the specific attack, did not lull the American government into a false sense of security and were never intended to do so. On the contrary, they clearly were redistribution negotiations and as such provided warning of Japan's aggressive intentions. Given these Japanese demands and

[8] Viscount Templewood (Sir Samuel Hoare), *Nine Troubled Years* (London: Collins, 1954), p. 192.

the implied threats of force, an attack was indeed expected by the American government—although not against Pearl Harbor.[9]

An example of negotiation for deception can be found in the history of the Hungarian Revolution in 1956. Between October 31 and November 3, the new Hungarian government under Nagy negotiated with the Soviet ambassador about the withdrawal of Soviet troops and Hungary's wish to become neutral. Through these talks, the Soviets gained the necessary time for preparing their attack to crush the revolution and for setting up the Kádár puppet government. The Soviet ambassador kept promising to Nagy that the Russian troops would soon be withdrawn, and he tried to dissuade the Hungarian government from making appeals to the United Nations.[10]

Deception—as a side-effect of negotiations—may also have the opposite aim: instead of gaining time to prepare one's own use of force, such deception may have the purpose of diverting another country from the use of force until the opportunity for it has passed. This is what Secretary of State John Foster Dulles tried to do in the fall of 1956 when Britain and France threatened to use force against Egypt to reverse Nasser's nationalization of the Suez Canal. Dulles tried to put the British and French off by a rapid succession of new schemes, such as invoking the Constantinople Convention (which guarantees the international character of the Canal), summoning an international conference, establishing a new international board for the operation of the Canal, and forming a club of the Canal users. At first, Prime Minister Eden thought the Americans would support the use of force as a last resort: "Our Ambassador in Washington," Eden recalled in his memoirs, "assured us at this time that the Administration completely accepted the impossibility of leaving the control of the Suez Canal in the hands of a man like Nasser. Though they would strain every

[9] Robert J. C. Butow, *Tojo and the Coming of the War* (Princeton, N.J.: Princeton University Press, 1961), chap. ii; and Roberta Wohlstetter, *Pearl Harbor: Warning and Decision* (Stanford, Calif.: Stanford University Press, 1962), pp. 233–46, 263–77.

[10] Ferenc A. Váli, *Rift and Revolt in Hungary: Nationalism versus Communism* (Cambridge, Mass.: Harvard University Press, 1961), pp. 364, 368–69, 373–74; and Paul E. Zinner, *Revolution in Hungary* (New York: Columbia University Press, 1962), p. 325.

nerve to bring about a settlement by negotiation, they realized that in the last resort force might have to be used and they understood the necessity for the military precautions which we and the French were taking." However, Eden soon became worried that these prolonged negotiations with the Americans and with Nasser might deprive him of his principal bargaining power—the threat of force. "There was always a danger," he said in his memoirs, "that the passage of time and the multiplication of talk would weaken the resolve of [the powers negotiating with Nasser]. . . . The question was, how long we could pursue diplomatic methods and economic sanctions, which very likely would not succeed, before the possibility of military action slipped from our grasp."[11]

With the benefit of hindsight, it can now be argued that Dulles should not have tried to divert Britain and France from the use of force through deceptive negotiations but should have made it clear that the United States would oppose military action as long as the Canal was operated satisfactorily, while supporting a common Western position to reach a new arrangement with Egypt. But then, Dulles' delaying tactics might just as well have worked, leading to a situation for the Suez Canal much like the present, and without the unhappy episode of the Anglo-French attack, which— apart from being inadequate as a military operation—could scarcely have brought a long-term political solution.

PROPAGANDA

Propaganda—like intelligence and deception—can be either a technique for getting good terms of agreement or a side-effect of negotiation which serves other foreign-policy objectives. The former, propaganda as a bargaining technique, will be discussed later. The latter, propaganda as a side-effect, has three aspects. These may be termed: negotiating to have a sounding-board, negotiating to gain prestige, and negotiating to show rectitude like the Pharisee saying his prayers.

The *sounding-board* effect of negotiation occurs mainly at high-level conferences and summit meetings. Such conferences serve to

[11] Anthony Eden, *Full Circle* (Boston: Houghton Mifflin, 1960), pp. 497–98, 509.

publicize a government's views and policy goals, since national objectives presented in the form of conference proposals receive wide publicity and elicit serious discussions and evaluations within other governments. Policy aims that are put forward as negotiating proposals make a deeper impact on other countries than if they were simply promulgated at home as a government program. For example, the Soviet disarmament proposal for the abolition of foreign bases emphasizes Soviet objections to American bases more continuously and perhaps more effectively than earlier Soviet pronouncements that made the same point outside a negotiating context. By contrast, the position of the United States and other Western powers in favor of German reunification and/or self-determination in East Germany lacks impact precisely because it is not being reiterated as a negotiating proposal.

Some governments value negotiation for a different kind of propaganda effect, which might best be characterized as *publicity* or *prestige*. Like the junior politician who wants to be photographed talking with the President, these governments feel that their name and political standing are enhanced by attending international conferences or summit meetings, even though nothing of substance is decided. (If important decisions may be reached between the principal participants at a conference, participation by additional parties is no longer a matter of mere prestige but can actually serve to influence these decisions.) It has been speculated that Khrushchev's frequent demands for summit meetings in the late 1950s were partly motivated by his desire to enhance his political prestige. It seems a little curious that the leader of the second most powerful country in the world should have wished to gain international publicity and respect in this way—but it cannot be ruled out.

The main reason why being engaged in negotiation can serve propaganda purposes is that so many beneficial effects are attributed to it. Negotiation is thought to be desirable not only because it may prevent conflict by producing an agreement but, according to the views previously discussed, because the very process of negotiating is believed to help maintain contact and provide a substitute for violent action, even if no agreement is in sight. Given the prevalence of these views, governments are reluctant to refuse negotiation, no matter how unlikely or undesirable an agreement. They fear that such refusal would impair the good will of groups important to them—their own parliament, the public in allied countries, or other governments, for example.

These audiences may judge quite superficially in praising those willing to negotiate and censuring those who refuse. Outside groups may have only a vague notion as to what negotiating means and how it relates to the merits of the issue. Governments that negotiate in order to win public approval value the act of negotiating as the Pharisee values prayer. It is not the thoughts behind the prayer that matter, or the purpose pursued, or the deeds before and after—what counts is that the ceremony be performed with the proper gestures. If this becomes the only purpose of prolonged negotiations, ridiculous and corrupting consequences follow: the prayers can be performed by the prayer wheel! Some cynics maintain that conferences on general disarmament have reached such a state.

It is paradoxical that the view according to which the act of negotiating is in itself meritorious prevails particularly in a field where prolonged negotiations have been singularly unsuccessful— the field of *general* disarmament (as distinguished from more limited and specific disarmament issues). This paradox cannot be fully explained by the great value that is attached to the ostensible objectives of disarmament conferences, because anyone interested in these objectives must harbor some doubt whether this particular style of negotiation is the best road toward them, what with the dismal record of the past. Incidentally, the propaganda advantages of participating in disarmament conferences seem to be overrated both by the Soviet government and by policymakers in Great Britain and the United States. The French government seemed to lose little, or may even have gained some, prestige in the eyes of uncommitted countries and the Western public, by abstention from the fruitless Eighteen-Nation Disarmament Conference since 1962.

It would be wrong to maintain that the *principal* aim of Western governments in general-disarmament conferences is to make propaganda in the sense of wanting to appear good by engaging in a good activity, again like the Pharisee saying his prayers. But it seems undeniable that the Pharisaic aspect receives considerable attention by Western policymakers. A symptom of this is the frequent reversal of roles between the United States and the Soviet Union in gleefully pressing the other side to resume negotiations on disarmament precisely when the opponent is unprepared or disinclined to do so.

Even persons strongly in favor of negotiations on general disarmament have come to the conclusion that the governments engaged in the comprehensive disarmament conferences neither expect nor seek agreement but are trying to put the other side in the wrong. As John Strachey wrote:

> How can we avoid the lamentable conclusion that these offers and counter-offers for treaties of general and complete disarmament are never meant to be taken seriously as schemes which might actually be implemented? It is not the mistakes, prejudices or "mistimings" of this or that negotiator or statesman which are at the root of the repeated failure. It is that the negotiators and statesmen have no belief in what they are perhaps inevitably doing. They are playing the game of political warfare, busily putting each other in the wrong before the bar of world opinion. We are not witnessing, as Mr. Noel-Baker seems to imply, a high drama in which each act has, it is true, so far ended in failure, but which might at any moment open a new era for humanity. We are not witnessing a Greek tragedy but an international farce.[12]

IMPACT ON THIRD PARTIES

In August, 1939, while Molotov directed open negotiations with the French and British on a mutual-assistance treaty against German attack, he secretly negotiated a non-aggression pact with the Germans. The Soviets may never have intended that their negotiations with the Anglo-French delegation should lead to an agreement, but they surely could use these negotiations to improve their bargaining position with Hitler. They continued the talks with the French and British up to the day Ribbentrop arrived in Moscow

[12] John Strachey, *On the Prevention of War* (London: Macmillan, 1962), p. 162. This evaluation of disarmament negotiations has been carried further by John W. Spanier and Joseph L. Nogee, *The Politics of Disarmament: A Study in Soviet-American Gamesmanship* (New York: Praeger, 1962), who maintain that these negotiations *solely* serve propaganda purposes but that this is nevertheless a recognized function worth pursuing.

to sign the pact with Stalin and Molotov. This was undoubtedly one of the most dramatic triangular situations in modern history, where contrary negotiations were carried on simultaneously, one of them resulting in an important agreement and the other one affecting the terms of this agreement, although in itself it settled nothing.

To what extent were the three parties aware of this triangle? The Germans did fear that their proposals might strengthen Stalin's hand in his negotiations with the Western powers. On May 22, 1939, the German ambassador in Moscow reported to Berlin: "We must be extremely cautious in this field as long as it is not certain that possible proposals from our side will not be used by the Kremlin only to exert pressure on England and France." And a few days later, the German Foreign Office wrote back: "We are of the opinion here that the English-Russian combination certainly will not be easy to prevent."[13] The British, on the other hand, had no knowledge of the secret Nazi-Soviet talks and were only vaguely suspicious. As late as July 20, the British negotiator in Moscow, William Strang, reported to London, that while a break in the fruitless negotiations might drive the Soviet Union into isolation or a deal with Hitler, to continue negotiations, "although producing no immediate concrete results, would still probably worry Hitler. Russia would also be less likely to remain neutral or be on the wrong side in the case of war."[14] (The Western idea that the process of negotiation will discourage unfriendly action!) Completing the third side of this triangle, Göring sent a certain Herr Wohltat to London in July, allegedly with Hitler's knowledge. However, the British did not exploit this dubious emissary to put pressure on Stalin. We can only speculate, of course, whether doing so would have raised Stalin's fears that the British might connive at a German attack against him and thus have induced Stalin to conclude the mutual-assistance treaty with the Western powers.

Ongoing negotiations between two powers that belong to op-

[13] U.S. Department of State, *Nazi-Soviet Relations, 1939–1941* (Washington, D.C., 1948), pp. 8, 9.
[14] E. L. Woodward and R. Butler (eds.), *Documents on British Foreign Policy 1919–1939* (Third Series, Vol. VI [London: H.M.S.O., 1953]), p. 426.

posing alliances can have an impact on other allies who feel left out. Even though there is no agreement, the very fact that negotiations take place may be enough to stir up fears among some allies that a "deal" might be made at their expense. After De Gaulle opposed Britain's entry into the Common Market in January, 1963, mentioning the close link between Great Britain and the United States as one of his reasons, there was some apprehension in Washington that the French government might start separate negotiations with the Russians.

These fears, at least for the time being, did not come true. In fact, critics of Washington's diplomacy suggested that the shoe might fit the other foot. For example, Governor Nelson A. Rockefeller argued that "before engaging in hints about the possibility of separate French deals with the Soviets, we should recall that it was the present administration which set the precedent." Rockefeller reminded the public that in 1961 the U.S. government "negotiated with the Soviets over Berlin against the wishes of France and against the better judgment of the Federal Republic of Germany. The administration then strongly implied that it was ready to enter into arrangements which would involve recognition of Communist Eastern Germany in some form, and thus to weaken our long-standing commitment to German unification."[15]

At about the same time, Dean Acheson spoke even more explicitly of what he considered to be the deleterious side-effects on European allies from the American-Soviet negotiations on Berlin:

Since the disastrous Camp David meeting Germans have been disturbed over our constant negotiations with the Russians under Russian threats. Fruitless as they have been, with no real concessions made, they seem to Germans to edge toward increasing recognition of the East German regime, they kept German politics continuously upset and moved German sympathy toward General de Gaulle's support of German ambitions. . . . Our flirtation with Moscow, like many which have no serious purpose, has succeeded only in embittering more legitimate relationships.[16]

[15] Nelson A. Rockefeller, in a statement released to the press in Chicago, Feb. 9, 1963.
[16] Dean Acheson, in a speech at the University of California, Berkeley, March 13, 1963.
It would transcend the scope of this study to go into other problems of al-

Negotiating for some desired side-effect may have undesirable secondary consequences. By negotiating for Pharisaic propaganda, a government may make limited agreements less likely. By negotiating so as to offer the opponent a substitute for violent action, a government may reveal to the opponent how far he can safely advance. And negotiating to maintain contact may make allies distrustful.

---

liances, such as the excluded third party, shifting two-party alliances in a power triangle, etc. See George Liska, *Nations in Alliance: The Limits of Interdependence* (Baltimore, Md.: Johns Hopkins Press, 1962), for a recent treatment of this topic.

THE CONTINUAL THREEFOLD CHOICE

THE OUTCOME OF NEGOTIATION, AS STATED PREVIOUSLY, MAY range from total disagreement to complete agreement, with varying mixtures of ambiguity and specificity in the eventual settlement. Moreover, there are many side-effects of the negotiating process that have nothing to do with an agreement between the negotiating parties but concern relations with third parties, international publicity, attitudes toward the use of force, or other matters. If one pursued all these heterogeneous effects, the process of negotiation would blend into the whole field of international relations like a seamless web. It is necessary, though, to keep some of these ramifications in mind when focusing on the central question as to how the negotiation process leads to the particular terms of an agreement.

What determines the arrangement of common and conflicting interests which emerges at the end of negotiations? How do diplomats personally affect the results, the gains and losses in the settlement? What is the effect of various tactics on the terms of the bargain that is struck?

A rudimentary system of analysis will serve to describe the effect of the negotiating process upon the terms of agreement if, step by step, certain complications and refinements are added so as to make this system conform more closely to reality. The rudimentary system subsumes all the negotiator's decisions under three basic choices: (1) to accept agreement at the terms he expects the opponent would settle for (the "available" terms), (2) to discontinue negotiations without agreement and with no intention of resuming them, and (3) to try to improve the "available" terms through further bargaining. Not only can the negotiator's decisions be subsumed under these three basic choices, but most of his actions can be understood as being designed to influence the opponent in *his* threefold choice. The threefold choice is implicitly exercised by each party throughout the negotiations, although explicitly the negotiators may face it only at certain junctures.

For brevity, the first of the three options can be summed up as *to choose the available terms.* This means to choose agreement at the terms that have been offered by, or seem to be immediately acceptable to, the other party (or parties).

In multilateral negotiations, it is true, a government often does not have the option of agreeing to the terms offered by, or acceptable to, the other parties, because the other parties disagree among themselves. Thus this government can no longer choose agreement by yielding to the terms of the opponent (as it theoretically always can in bilateral negotiations); it can only make choices that render agreement most likely (abstain, vote with the majority, buy off a recalcitrant party, etc.).

In bilateral negotiations the "available terms" can be described more simply. If a government is negotiating an agreement that is to be cast in the form of a treaty, the terms available at any particular time consist of the articles already agreed to, articles offered by the opponent, plus those terms for articles not yet discussed that the government expects its opponent would be ready to grant. Usually, the available terms are not spelled out during the early phases of negotiations. To the extent that the decision-makers consciously face the option of *choosing the available terms,* they must know— or at least believe that they can estimate—all these terms. Of course, if they decide to choose these terms, this does not mean that they will actually obtain agreement; it merely means that they expect to do so by accepting what they believe to be the terms for which the opponent is ready to settle.

The second option can be designated as *to choose no-agreement.* It means stopping negotiations and giving up the effort to settle with the other party for an explicit new arrangement. This choice still permits the government to use unilateral measures and tacit bargaining for improving the situation at issue, although it is distinct from the tactic of interrupting negotiation with the intention of inducing the opponent to soften his terms. A government which interrupts negotiation wants to put pressure on the opponent and may continue to bargain by other means, in the hope of resuming negotiation under better conditions.[1] But a government which *chooses no-agreement* discontinues all efforts to get an agreement. (However, even this move is not always final: sometimes the opponent can re-initiate negotiation by offering new incentives or by creating new pressures.)

The third option, to engage in *further bargaining,* covers not only a further confrontation of explicit proposals at the conference table but also any other moves by the government for the purpose of strengthening its own negotiating position and weakening that of the opponent. A choice to engage in *further bargaining* usually means more than just a postponement of the choice between available terms and no-agreement; it is a decision to make additional efforts for improving the available terms. If *further bargaining* is not accompanied by such efforts, it represents an interruption of negotiation with a passive attitude. That is, it becomes merely a waiting period during which the choice between available terms and no-agreement is held in abeyance, perhaps in the hope that extraneous new developments might help to change the opponent's mind.

If you are the negotiator, how do you choose among these three options? You will compare the probable gains and losses from agreement at available terms with the estimated consequences of no-agreement. Then you will estimate whether further bargaining is likely to lead to an improvement over the better of these first two options, while allowing for the risks and costs of further bargaining. Assume you have chosen to engage in further bargaining so as to improve the terms for agreement, in preference to either of the other two options of no-agreement and agreement at

---

[1] To repeat, "negotiation" in this book is defined as a process in which explicit proposals are put forward ostensibly for the purpose of reaching agreement on an exchange or on the realization of a common interest where conflicting interests are present.

presently available terms. In this case, your objective is to make your opponent choose agreement at the terms you will make available to him, which implies that *he* will have to reject no-agreement and give up further bargaining.

Before this interaction can be analyzed further, some concepts that play a central role in bargaining must be defined so as to give them a more precise meaning than their common usage.

WARNINGS, THREATS, BLUFFS, AND COMMITMENTS

Warnings, threats (whether bluffs or not), and commitments are moves made by a party for the purpose of changing the opponent's expectations and consequently influencing his choices. If you issue a warning or a threat, you try to alter your opponent's expectations about *his* gains or losses that would result from certain choices he can take; if you make a commitment, you try to alter your opponent's expectations about *your* future conduct, by changing your own incentives.

Warnings and *threats* thus belong to the same category, but they differ from one another. In both the warning and the threat, the menacing party tries to dissuade its opponent from making a certain move or from refusing to comply with a demand. To warn or to threaten means to predict to the opponent (or to those who might influence him) that he would suffer a certain loss if he did not comply. The difference between a warning and a threat lies in the role played by the warning or threatening party in the causation of the predicted loss.

On the one hand, the party that warns points out to the opponent *natural* consequences that are likely to follow from his noncompliance. These consequences flow from the laws of nature, economic or technical developments, or because other parties, as well as the warner himself, simply pursue their own interests. More precisely, to the extent that the warner's own actions contribute to the opponent's loss, these actions must be in the warner's interest for other reasons than that they cause a loss to the opponent. In fact, the actions would have been in the warner's interest even if the warning had never been made.

The party that threatens, on the other hand, asserts that it will make a special effort so as to cause the opponent to suffer the predicted loss should he fail to comply. In contrast to the warning, the threatener's course of action that results in the opponent's loss is not, by itself, in the threatener's interest. Indeed, this course of action may be costly for the threatener—perhaps even more costly than the loss is for the opponent. If the threat had not been made, or if the opponent was not to be forced to comply, it would never be worthwhile for the threatener to take this course of action. Given the fact that the threat has been made and has failed to compel the opponent, it may or may not be worthwhile for the threatening party to take this course of action.[2]

In the warning, the prediction of the opponent's loss is an act of bargaining, but the action which causes the opponent's loss after he has made the unwanted move is independent of the bargaining; the action would take place whether or not it inflicted a loss on the opponent. In a threat, however, both the prediction of the loss and the act of causing it are bargaining moves; the threatener causes the loss *only because* he has made the threat and does not want to turn out to be a bluffer, or because he wants to enforce compliance since he failed to obtain compliance by threatening.

Why are some warnings and threats ineffective? Your opponent may not heed your warning or not give in to your threat for three reasons: he may expect that it will be less costly to absorb the losses you predicted than to meet your demand; he may decide that these losses will be less harmful than the damage done to his bargaining reputation by giving in (this will be explored farther on); or, finally, he may not believe that your warning will come true or that you will carry out your threat. Disbelief in a warning is different from disbelief in a threat. The former is a question of factual belief: Is the warner's prediction correct or not? The

[2] The distinction here between threat and warning closely parallels that employed by Schelling (*The Strategy of Conflict,* pp. 123 ff.). Schelling emphasizes the extent to which carrying out a threat is undesirable to the threatener. "The distinctive character of a threat is that one asserts that he will do, in a contingency, what he would manifestly prefer not to do, if the contingency occurred, the contingency being governed by the second party's behavior." With a change of emphasis, however, a threatener is here defined as one who asserts he would, in a specified contingency, take some action which in itself is of insufficient interest to him, *perhaps* even costly, and whose only purpose was to inflict a loss on the opponent or force him to comply.

latter depends on the anticipated motivation of the threatener: Will the threatener, after his opponent fails to comply, be sufficiently motivated to inflict the predicted damage upon the opponent? If not, the threat will have turned out to be a *bluff*.

Whether or not the threat is a bluff can be decided only after it has been challenged by the opponent's noncompliance; before that, the threatener may still change his mind. What matters to the threatened party is not so much the attitude of the threatener at the time the threat is made but whether the threatener will have the capability and motivation to inflict the damage after he has been challenged. The threatened party, however, should not entirely ignore the question of whether the threatener, when he makes his threat, means it to be a bluff. Because if the threatener does not intend to carry out his threat even at the time he makes it, he will be particularly reluctant to have it challenged lest his bluff be called. The opponent who senses this reluctance can exploit it: he can pressure the threatener into buying him off to avoid an outright challenge.

In international negotiations warnings are far more frequent than threats. For example, in the test-ban negotiations, whichever side happened to be pushing for agreement (initially the Soviet Union and later the United States) issued repeated warnings about the spread of nuclear weapons to additional countries and the fallout hazard from continued testing. But these undesirable effects were presented as inevitable consequences of continued testing. Neither side ever threatened deliberately to make things worse should the opponent fail to come to an agreement. The United States did not threaten to turn over independent nuclear capabilities to its allies, nor did the Soviet Union threaten to do so for China. The President's prediction in the spring of 1962 that the United States would resume atmospheric testing unless the Soviet Union soon agreed to a treaty was perhaps intermediate between a warning and a threat.

Particularly rare are explicit threats, in distinction to hinted or implicit ones. Among the few examples of threats that can be found (conforming to the definition), most were implicit and turned out to be bluffs. For instance, when it became evident that the French Parliament would be reluctant to ratify the treaty for the European Defense Community (EDC), Secretary of State Dulles announced (December 14, 1953) that failure to bring the EDC into being "would compel an agonizing reappraisal of basic United States policy," thus hinting that American forces might be withdrawn from Europe. When the French Parliament finally rejected the EDC, no such reappraisal took place.[3] Another example of a bluff, though less publicized, was the veiled threat made by desperate British negotiators in 1958 that economic reprisals might be taken if the Common Market countries failed to agree to the enlarged free-trade area that would have joined the six Common Market members with the seven other countries that later formed their own European Free Trade Association (EFTA). Such reprisals were never taken.

It is even more difficult to find examples of explicit threats that were actually carried out than it is to find explicit threats that were not challenged or, if challenged, turned out to be bluffs. An example of an explicit threat that has been carried out is Germany's "Hallstein Doctrine," but this threat was not made for the purpose of a single negotiation. According to the "Hallstein Doctrine" the government in Bonn threatens to withdraw diplomatic recognition from any country (except the Soviet Union) that extends full recognition to East Germany. By 1963 the threat was challenged twice and carried out on both occasions. In October, 1957, Yugoslavia recognized the Pankow regime, and within three days Bonn broke diplomatic relations (though not consular contracts) with Belgrade. In January, 1963, the same happened with regard to Cuba. Breaking diplomatic relations with Yugoslavia was not in Germany's interest in itself. Bonn did so only with great reluctance and after a heated debate within the government. The move was made to preserve the credibility of the threat, and as such was entirely successful. (The break with Cuba was expected by both sides, provoked by Havana, and not regretted by Bonn.)

Warnings and threats so defined stand apart from *commitments.* A commitment is a move to convince one's opponent that one will maintain one's current position or implement one's prediction by

---

[3] It might be argued that the subsequent creation of the West European Union to some extent satisfied Dulles' condition so that his threat need not be carried out.

making it more difficult for oneself not to do so. In other words, a commitment is linked to specific intentions that have been conveyed to the opponent. By making it costly for oneself not to live up to them, the commitment suggests to the opponent that the intentions are not only true when stated but are also unlikely to change as long as the commitment cannot be annulled. If someone says that he will not retreat, he may be making a true prediction or only be boasting, but after he has burned his bridges, his intention has turned into a necessity—at least until the bridges have been rebuilt.

Commitments may serve either to make it credible that threats will be carried out when challenged or to make it unlikely that a negotiating position will be changed. That is, there are *commitments to threats* regarding a future contingency and *commitments to positions* currently held. However, commitments in international politics—unlike equivalent pledges under domestic law or in a parlor game—are both vague and fluid, their binding power is hard to determine by both parties, and they are subject to change or annulment. A commitment may make it more likely that a threat will be carried out, but it does not make it certain. Besides, something may happen tomorrow that will cancel the commitment of today.

What does the binding power of a commitment consist of? One type of commitment is based on constitutional restrictions or the power of the legislative branch, whereby a government can "force" itself to carry out a threat or stick to a certain position. To cite just one example, in 1962 Congress attached to the Foreign Assistance Act an amendment prohibiting aid to countries that expropriate American-owned property and fail to take "appropriate steps" for compensation within six months. This provided U.S. negotiators with a commitment to the threat that foreign aid would be discontinued should American-owned property be expropriated without compensation satisfactory to the U.S. government.

In other commitments the binding power stems from the fact that the executive branch of the government is subject to the influence of domestic groups or to the control of the electorate and that these domestic forces want their government to honor its promises or to carry out its threats. That is, if the executive wants to stay in power, it cannot afford an appearance of being grossly inconsistent and untrustworthy. Hence, once a pledge has been made to uphold a certain position or a threat has been issued, it would be costly for the government to act contrary to these expressed intentions.

This type of commitment is ineffective, however, for negotiations where the domestic forces deem it more important that agreement be reached than that the government remain consistent. For example, in 1959 De Gaulle repeatedly stated in public that he would not negotiate with the FLN (the representatives of the Algerian rebels) until they had agreed to a cease-fire. This commitment was too weak to prevent him from starting formal negotiations a year later without a cease-fire.

A similar type of commitment consists of a treaty or a promise to a third party that would have to be broken if the first party retreated from its negotiating position. Such a commitment is illustrated by the British pledge to the other six members of EFTA that their trading position would not be jeopardized should England join the Common Market. (The reason England gave this pledge, however, was probably not to strengthen its negotiating position in Brussels but rather to hold EFTA together in the event that it could not join the Common Market. Indeed, as long as England's prospects for joining the Common Market looked good, this EFTA pledge proved to be a hindrance.)

The commitment of tying one's negotiating position to a pledge can be strengthened if this pledge is not restricted to a single ally and a single situation, but made to represent all one's pledges to allies. This is what President Kennedy did in his speech of July 25, 1961, on the Berlin crisis: "If we do not meet our commitments to Berlin, where will we later stand? If we are not true to our word there, all that we have achieved in collective security, which relies on these words, will mean nothing."

There is another type of commitment. As will be discussed later, a party may place its bargaining reputation at stake when making a threat or advancing a negotiating position.

Commitments are so fluid because their content is often unclear and the criteria on which they are based can be eroded. What, for example, is "just" compensation for expropriated property? Or what is "adequate" international inspection, a criterion to which the U.S. government is committed in disarmament negotiations because it implanted it as a firm goal in the public mind. If a party wishes to make its commitment more forceful, it can take steps to minimize the erosion of criteria. On the other hand, the opponent can try deliberately to confuse the criteria. For instance, early in the nuclear test-ban negotiations, the Soviet delegate Tsarapkin even tried to refute the requirement for U.S. Senate ratification, in the hope of eliminating the commitment of the American delegate to reject any terms that would fail to win a two-thirds majority in the Senate.[4]

INDUCING THE OPPONENT TO WANT AGREEMENT

As long as you are negotiating but continuing to reject both no-agreement and the available terms, you are in fact trying to make your opponent choose the terms that you will make available to him (not necessarily the terms you offer, but those at which you will be willing to settle). This means that, while you are engaged in *further bargaining,* you must make your opponent prefer agreement to no-agreement and (to clinch the deal) dissuade him from further bargaining on his own behalf.

The first consideration is how to induce your opponent to prefer agreement to no-agreement. The opponent must be made to believe that the estimated consequences of no-agreement are worse for him than the terms you are willing to grant. One way of doing this is to make terms available that are more attractive to your opponent. Naturally, you will first try to do this without cutting into your own gains. That is, to sweeten the terms for your opponent, you will search for areas where his and your interests are not competitive. You may discover inducements to make agreement more valuable to your opponent without hurting yourself significantly. Formulations that help the opponent domestically fall into this category. Sometimes you may eliminate from your proposed terms aspects that are objectionable to the opponent without being of great importance to yourself.

[4] Conference on the Discontinuance of Nuclear Weapon Tests, 10th Plenary Meeting, Nov. 19, 1958.

Where there are only competitive interests, so that the terms cannot be made more interesting to your opponent without becoming correspondingly less desirable for yourself, you may promise to compensate in some other negotiation. The need for such extraneous inducements is one of the reasons for tie-ins or package deals between two negotiations. Parliamentary logrolling illustrates this process, as does its counterpart in the United Nations, where one delegate may induce another to vote for his favored resolution by promising to vote for some resolution favored by his colleague.

Instead of pulling your opponent toward agreement by making the terms more attractive to him, you can also try to push him by making no-agreement appear increasingly disadvantageous to him. It is here that threats and warnings play a key role. Warnings, as defined here, are useful where the absence of an agreement may have some inherently undesirable consequences for your opponent (without a special effort on your part). These inherent disadvantages of not having an agreement are precisely the reason why at least one of the sides wishes to begin negotiations.

Where the inherent disadvantages are not enough to make an opponent prefer a certain agreement to no-agreement, a threat will be needed. In redistribution negotiations, the defensive side is content to leave things as they are and has no incentive to satisfy the opponent's demands, unless the opponent succeeds in making a grave enough and credible enough threat. One of the particular difficulties of innovation negotiations is to make no-agreement undesirable to the opponent if the gains from agreement do not provide a sufficient pull. To last for some time, innovations usually require a certain amount of mutual accommodation. A complex and continuing cooperative undertaking cannot thrive if the parties act in a strongly antagonistic way toward each other. Therefore threats have to be used with utmost restraint—the threat of force is normally unavailable for innovations. As mentioned before, an important leverage to push reluctant parties into an innovation agreement is the prospect of exclusion.

Edward Heath, the chief British negotiator for England's entry into the European Communities, was in an unenviable position in 1962. He could not make agreement more attractive to the Six member countries without jeopardizing support at home, and he could not make no-agreement more undesirable to the Six without hurting his effort to be accepted as a loyal member. And since Britain was the excluded party, he could not use the threat of exclusion. Given the fact that France, the most powerful member of the European Communities, felt it would lose more by British membership than it would gain (in particular that it might lose its leading role in Europe), the British could not prevent France from choosing no-agreement in preference to agreement.

Both warnings and threats may be used to deter the opponent from choosing no-agreement, but both have to be supported. A variety of political, economic, or military preparations can make warnings more serious and threats, if carried out, more costly to the opponent. In addition, commitments serve to make threats credible. The opponent, in turn, can improve his prospects under no-agreement through various counteractions, so that he is less pressured to accept agreement at available terms. Such counteractions probably helped to settle the 1961–62 phase of the Berlin negotiations in favor of the West. Allied military preparations and contingency planning in the summer of 1961—in particular the strengthening of America's conventional forces in Europe—improved the means for coping with the threatened blockade. This made it less likely that the Communist threat would be carried out and less disastrous if it was. Hence the Western powers could more confidently challenge the threat and choose no-agreement instead of accepting Khrushchev's terms.

DISSUADING THE OPPONENT FROM FURTHER BARGAINING

The interaction of your threefold choice with that of your opponent must now be explored further. As has been said, it is not enough to make your opponent dislike no-agreement more than agreement at your present terms, for he is not forced to choose between these two options. He can choose to engage in further bargaining in the hope that you will soften your terms. His hope is not unreasonable, because he knows—or he thinks he knows—that you would rather have an agreement than not, even if you have to soften your terms, provided you do not have to soften them too much. But what is "too much"? If no-agreement looks sufficiently bad to you, you might be prepared to go a long way to avoid it by accommodating the wishes of your opponent. The tables can be turned; your opponent can try to influence your choice between agreement and no-agreement much as you tried to influence his. Only when he sees no gain in this attempt, while still preferring agreement at available terms to no-agreement, will he accept the terms that you make available to him. Hence to dissuade your opponent from further bargaining becomes your objective.

The most important tactic for this purpose is to demonstrate to your opponent that your terms are unlikely to become more advantageous for him. This can be done most convincingly if you can show that no-agreement will always look better to you than an agreement for which you would have to reduce your terms. If your terms are reducible only in a single big step, such as giving up a voting majority in a proposed organization, then your minimum terms (i.e., the terms below which no-agreement would seem preferable to you) may still secure you significant gains. But if your terms can be reduced in small slices (such as monetary compensation or, in fact, any complex agreement), your opponent will try to push them down to the point where you just barely gain something by having an agreement as compared with not having one. Hence you will try to make him think that your minimum lies higher than it really does.

Your opponent may realize, however, that you will still prefer agreement if you have to lower your terms. Other techniques are therefore required to demonstrate to your opponent that your terms are unlikely to soften. A useful device is a commitment not to change your terms or a commitment not to accept the opponent's demands.

Apart from trying to convince your opponent that your terms are firm, you might dissuade him from further bargaining by making procrastination seem dangerous to him. In an acute crisis, the danger of postponing a settlement is a particularly compelling reason for accepting the offered terms. Khrushchev's sudden acquiescence in October, 1962, to the demand for withdrawal of his missiles from Cuba was probably largely motivated by the fear of sudden American action—such as an air-strike against the missile sites—that would have put him in a worse position. It seemed wiser to Khrushchev completely to drop his counterdemand for a withdrawal of American missiles in Turkey than to face the risks of further bargaining.

A related technique is to make the opponent fear that one's terms, far from moving closer to his wishes, might actually harden. That is, your opponent must get the idea that he would miss an opportunity should he fail to accept your offer.

In more slowly moving negotiations, there are pressures of a different kind that can be generated to make the opponent anxious for a quick settlement. During the Korean truce talks, continued American casualties from Chinese attacks and the uncertain fate of the American prisoners induced the UN negotiators to accept the Communist terms on many issues. Often, one side suffers far more from the postponement of an agreement than the other side. Such an asymmetry is one of the most cogent factors in pushing the side that is in a hurry toward its minimum position.

Lastly, the opponent might be induced to accept the available terms by the prospect that the negotiations will end at a certain date regardless of whether or not an agreement has been reached. This prospect may arise either because a deadline has been imposed by external circumstances or because the first party deliberately created a deadline or issued a threat of rupture. After the 1946 Paris Peace Conference, the final decisions on the peace treaties were made at a Council of Foreign Ministers meeting in New York. When Molotov refused to accept most recommendations of the Peace Conference, Secretary of State Byrnes warned him: "It is with the greatest reluctance, therefore, that I have come to the conclusion we will not be able to agree upon the treaties. Having become reconciled to this, I think we should agree to disagree. . . ." Molotov was impressed by the risk of rupture when Byrnes stood by his warning, and a few days later he gave in, accepting almost all the Paris recommendations.[5]

However, threats of rupture and deliberate deadlines are double-edged swords. The opponent can turn it against you if he thinks that you are bluffing or if he is better at brinkmanship by risking more readily than you the danger of winding up with no-agreement. Your opponent can doubly tempt you not to carry out your

[5] James F. Byrnes, *Speaking Frankly* (New York: Harper, 1947), pp. 152–54.

threat to interrupt or break off negotiations: first, he can let the deadline approach closer and closer, waiting for you to make concessions; and, second, he can let the deadline pass but offer to continue negotiations. He might even consent to the fiction of "stopping the clocks" in the conference room, should this reduce the commitment of your bargaining reputation to your threat of rupture.

These drawbacks of deliberately imposed deadlines were experienced by the French Premier Pierre Mendès-France when he negotiated the Indochina settlement at the Geneva conference in 1954. On June 17, Mendès-France said he would resign as Premier unless he could produce a satisfactory cease-fire before July 20. While the Russians and the Chinese, of course, did not care about Mendès-France's resignation as such, they might have feared that a successor government would put a greater military effort into Indochina or would support the ratification of the European Defense Community that the Russians wanted to prevent. As the deadline approached, the French delegation clearly did make some last-minute concessions, and in the end the conference continued past the deadline by one day, with the "clocks stopped," so that no one expected Mendès-France to resign. It is somewhat doubtful whether Mendès-France's threat of rupture helped or hindered the French cause; but some observers feel that without the threat the conference would have ended only a few weeks later at terms slightly better for the West.

The threat of rupture can be highly effective if the negotiator is in the process of departing, in such a way that he would have no excuse at all for staying unless his opponent called him back by offering a concession. Here the negotiator is no longer saying, "I am going to leave." He is demonstrating, "I am leaving." This technique has numerous examples in diplomatic history. The ambassador of Louis XIV to Charles II, after negotiating at length over the price at which his king would buy Dunkirk from England, finally boarded a ship ready to sail for Denmark when Charles II sent for him and offered the final concession that closed the deal.[6] At the Berlin Conference in 1878, according to one account, Dis-

[6] G. Estrades, Comte de, *Lettres, Mémoires et Négociations* (London: J. Nourse, 1743), I, 377.

raeli forced Bismarck and the Russians to give in on a significant
British demand by ordering a train that would have taken him
back to London.[7]

De Gaulle reports that during his negotiations in Moscow in
December, 1944, he also used this technique successfully. Stalin
tried to obtain French recognition for the Communist Lublin Committee as the Government of Poland, before agreeing to a Franco-
Russian Security Pact in which De Gaulle was interested. But De
Gaulle did not want the pact at this price and succeeded in convincing Stalin of his determination by getting ready to leave
Moscow. The negotiations had remained deadlocked for some days,
when De Gaulle got up one evening at the end of a large dinner
party and announced to Stalin and the astonished Molotov that he
was returning home. He called for his Foreign Minister Bidault
to follow him to the French Embassy, leaving only some junior
members of the French delegation behind. These officials reported
to De Gaulle, after a long meeting with Stalin and Molotov, that
the Russians would now be ready to sign the pact in exchange for
a quite adulterated version of recognition of the Lublin Committee.
De Gaulle, however, still refused. Consequently Stalin soon
dropped all demands for recognition of Lublin, and the Franco-
Russian pact was finally signed.[8]

HEDGING AGAINST FAILURE

If a party engages in further bargaining, for the purpose of
obtaining better terms, it is taking certain risks. It runs the risk
that the outcome might deteriorate: the opponent might either
stiffen his terms or might suddenly choose no-agreement while the
first party would have preferred agreement even at the opponent's
original terms. In other situations, the improved terms resulting
from continued negotiation might not be worth the loss incurred
by delaying agreement. As said previously, it is precisely these

[7] A. N. Cummings, "The Secret History of the Treaty of Berlin," *Nineteenth
Century Review* (July, 1905), pp. 86–88. This account is disputed, however, by
W. N. Medlicott, *The Congress of Berlin and After* (London: Methuen, 1938).

[8] Charles de Gaulle, *Salvation, 1944–1946* (*War Memoirs* [London: Weiden-
feld and Nicolson, 1959]), pp. 78–81. The only concession De Gaulle made was
to announce a few days later that a French officer had been sent to Lublin.

risks that your opponent exploits when he tries to dissuade you from further bargaining and make you accept his position. Agreement occurs at that delicate point, when both you and your opponent decide to settle for the available terms rather than incur the costs and risks of trying to do better.

Other risks result from the very process of negotiation. Two of the negotiator's principal instruments—commitments and threats —have the peculiar characteristic of hurting the party which uses them if they fail to achieve their purpose. A crucial instrument for the offensive party in redistribution negotiations is the threat to hurt the opponent should he choose no-agreement (such as Khrushchev's implied threat of a Berlin blockade). If such a threat fails to make the opponent comply, the threatener is forced to choose between two evils: either he accepts the onus of being a bluffer, or he carries out the threat—an act that may do him no good at that point and may actually harm him. If a threat to break off negotiations at a certain date fails to make the opponent soften his terms, this will put before the threatener an equally undesirable choice: either he continues negotiations and thereby admits to being a bluffer, or he winds up with no-agreement where he would have preferred an agreement.

Similarly with commitments. Your commitment to carry out a threat may convince your opponent that he should take your threat seriously, but by its very nature it will make *not* carrying out the threat more costly should you prefer to do so after your opponent fails to comply. Your commitment to a negotiating position, if it fails to persuade your opponent to accept your terms, will hurt you when you want to make a concession later to avoid winding up with no-agreement. Likewise, your commitment to a deadline will aggravate your dilemma when your opponent lets the deadline pass without moving closer to your position.

These risks, in part, account for the fact that threats are usually vague and used sparingly and that commitments frequently are kept ambiguous. Where the opponent's reaction remains somewhat unpredictable, governments want to hedge against failure of their negotiating tactics. Yet, this very hedging makes threats and commitments less convincing.

CHAPTER 6

THE BARGAINING REPUTATION

THE WAY IN WHICH A GOVERNMENT NEGOTIATES AND THE CON-
ditions under which it accepts or rejects an agreement have an
important bearing on its bargaining strength in the future. In every
diplomatic confrontation, governments are trying not only to affect
the terms of agreement under negotiation but also to protect or
improve their strength in future negotiations. What they have in
mind can best be explained as a *reputation*. A government acquires
a reputation much as an individual does. On the basis of its performance in past negotiations, others will impute to it a diplomatic
style, certain motives and objectives, attitudes toward the use of
force, a degree of political will, and other attributes of power.
Bargaining strength depends not so much on what these attributes
really are as on what others believe them to be. Hence the importance of this reputation.

In Chapter 4, a number of effects from negotiation were discussed that do not concern agreement, such as propaganda,
maintenance of contact, or substitutes for violence. These side-
effects are peripheral to the bargaining process proper and may be
found in conferences where neither party seeks or expects an
agreement. A negotiator's reputation, however, *does* concern
agreement. It is shaped by the way in which he has reached
agreements in the past, and it affects his power to influence agreements in the future.

The influence of the bargaining reputation can easily be explained in the context of two opponents trying to influence each other's threefold choice between agreement at the opponent's terms, no-agreement, and further bargaining. If you are the negotiator, you know that your opponent's threefold choice will be governed in part by his anticipations of your reactions. He bases these anticipations on his image of you, concerning such attributes as your attitude toward risk-taking, your tendency to bluff, your evaluation of your own strength and his, your tendency to hold fast to a position, and so forth. Naturally, your opponent will assume a certain continuity in these attributes and base his estimates of them partly on your performance in previous negotiations. Knowing this, you will act in every negotiation not only so as to obtain a favorable outcome at that time but also so as to preserve or improve your negotiating strength in the future. The fact that these two considerations frequently conflict adds an important complication to the negotiating process.

The influence of the bargaining reputation can be paraphrased in the language of game theory: an international negotiation is never a self-contained "game" but is a phase vaguely related to a never-ending "super-game." Although each phase yields its own payoffs, the tactics used in it affect the opponent's calculations in subsequent phases and hence influence subsequent payoffs. The "super-game" comes to an end only under exceptional circumstances: a government whose existence is at stake and which expects no continuity with its successor may contemplate the losing situation (but not the winning one!) as the end of the "super-game."

However, a bargaining reputation is not permanent. It changes because governments do not behave the same way in every negotiation and memories are frequently short. Also, a particular reputation is often confined to a specific subject; what a government does in political conferences may not impress its opponents in commercial conferences.

IS HE A BLUFFER?

Whether or not your opponent imputes to you a tendency to bluff is one of the most important factors in a bargaining reputation. There are several ways of making your threats more credible. One way, as has been shown, is through commitments. Another way is to cultivate a reputation of not being a bluffer. A third way exploits the fact (to be dealt with later) that governments are organizations composed of human beings, who may carry out their threats because they tend to act in anger, impulsively, or out of feelings of revenge and spitefulness.

A reputation for not bluffing works much like a commitment: it creates a vested interest in being consistent. If your opponent takes you up on your threat, the disadvantage of carrying it out will be outweighed by the long-term damage to your reputation from not carrying it out. Your opponent, knowing this, may not challenge your threat. A reputation of carrying out one's threat can be acquired by a nation with a purely expediential orientation; it does not require feelings of honor or a moral conviction. It *pays* not to become known as a bluffer, in order to preserve one's capacity for making credible threats.

Diplomatic history records relatively few instances of clear, explicit threats that turned out to be a bluff (although explicit threats that were carried out are even rarer). Far more frequent are explicit agreements that have clearly been broken by one side. This is paradoxical, because it would seem to be as disadvantageous for a government to be known for violating agreements as for bluffing in negotiations. After all, not to carry out a threat might even be construed as a concession and used as an argument for demanding counter-concessions, but the same cannot be said about violating an agreement. And while occasional bluffs that have been called may damage the bargaining reputation, they will not ruin it. Those who are threatened next time cannot know for sure that they are facing another bluff.

This extraordinary reluctance of modern governments to have their bluffs called in an unequivocal fashion forces them to hedge by keeping threats vague. In contrast to threats for military deterrence, threats in diplomatic negotiations are usually vague whenever two conditions are met: the threatening government harbors some doubts as to whether the opponent will comply, and it anticipates that it would be reluctant to carry out the threat. Vagueness may be obtained in three ways: the threatener may not state categorically that he would inflict the reprisals on the opponent in case of noncompliance, he may not spell out what constitutes noncompliance, or he may fail to predict what the reprisals would consist of. Obviously, the vagueness will not go undetected by the opponent, who will accordingly be less impressed.

A curious example of clear-cut bluffing was Khrushchev's failure for over four years ever to carry out his repeated threats that he would sign a separate peace treaty with East Germany within a given time period unless the Western powers agreed to withdraw at least partially from West Berlin. The threat was first made in November, 1958, with a six-month time limit; then the time limit was extended by days, weeks, and months. After the Western powers had called the bluff of Khrushchev's first time limit, he put forward another one-year limit in June, 1959, and only a few days later extended it to a year and a half. A year later, in May, 1960, Khrushchev said the question would be negotiated "in six or eight months." This more veiled threat, again, proved to be a bluff. And on June 15, 1961, upon returning from the Vienna meeting with President Kennedy, he indicated again that the peace treaty would be signed within six months: "We ask everyone to understand us correctly: the conclusion of a peace treaty with Germany cannot be postponed any longer. A peaceful settlement in Europe must be attained this year."

The Berlin negotiations, like all redistribution negotiations, did require a threat by the offensive side to make no-agreement undesirable for the defensive side. Khrushchev's separate peace treaty, however, was only the first stage of such a threat. The cutting edge came with the second stage, the prediction that the East German regime would then interfere with Western access in Berlin. Having made the first stage so explicit, Khrushchev needed only to hint at the second stage and leave it to the West to fathom all its horrible implications. Initially, this tactic seemed to have several advantages. A peace treaty could be presented as normalization rather than redistribution, it was wholly in Khrushchev's power to sign it, and unlikely to provoke the West into major counteraction. Hence the first stage was credible. The second stage, for its part, was a safe threat to make. Its implementation was theoretically up to the East German Communists, and should it not be carried out—for fear of Western reprisals—Khrushchev would not be unequivocally proved a bluffer.

Soviet diplomacy, however, overplayed the two-stage threat tactic until it boomeranged. Naturally, an explicit threat with a deadline that can be carried out with impunity (hence a credible threat) must be carried out after the opponent challenges it. Otherwise the threatener becomes tinged with the reputation of being a flagrant bluffer. Since so many deadlines have passed without the East German peace treaty being signed, the Western powers and the world at large are less likely to take seriously similar threats of Khrushchev in the future. It is not so much that the credibility of Soviet threats decreased among Western decision-makers and their advisers—though this may be one effect. What counts more is the impact upon intra-allied and domestic decision-making in the West. Those who might consider it wise to heed a similar Soviet threat in the future would be hard put to justify this against those who will advise ignoring it. The proponents of a harder line might win the domestic debate, since there is little justification for giving in to threats by a proved bluffer.

When it comes to warnings or threats to break off negotiations, the Russians have been more successful in maintaining a reputation of credibility. Their past actions demonstrate that they have no inhibition against breaking up a conference. In fact, they often give the appearance of being ready to walk out any time, often without explicit advance warning. American and British diplomats, however, rarely break up an international conference. This puts them at a certain disadvantage in dealing with Soviet negotiators, since they feel under constant pressure of this latent or explicit threat of rupture. Thus during the unpoliced moratorium on nuclear testing, the U.S. government was unwilling to resume testing for fear that the Russians would discontinue the marathon talks (which could have led to criticism of the United States as having "caused" this break). Yet, after the sudden *Soviet* resumption of testing, the talks continued, and they continued also after American testing was then resumed.

The abruptness with which De Gaulle terminated the negotiations on Britain's entry into the Common Market in January, 1963, may in part have been motivated by his knowledge that it pays to be known as a man who suddenly breaks off negotiations. In 1958, he acted in a similar way when he abruptly stopped the prolonged negotiations with Great Britain and other European nations for an enlarged free-trade area. (This wider free-trade area might have dissolved the Common Market which was then just beginning to be formed.) Those who negotiate with De Gaulle know that in prolonged negotiations, rather than inching toward better terms, they may suddenly wind up with no-agreement.

Governments generally try to maintain a reputation for refusing negotiation under an explicit threat. This, of course, helps to deter threats, particularly those by the offensive side in redistribution negotiations. On this count, too, De Gaulle's bargaining reputation seems to be stronger than that, say, of the British or American government. In America and Great Britain the view that negotiation may serve as a substitute for violent action often takes precedence over the maxim that one should not negotiate under an explicit threat. Since 1961, De Gaulle has been opposed to negotiating on the Soviet demand regarding West Berlin. As his Foreign Minister Couve de Murville put it in December, 1961, at the time when the other two major Western powers were rather active in such talks: "As far as the methods [for dealing with the Berlin crisis] are concerned, we have never accepted the idea that it was possible to negotiate under a threat, even if this is the supreme threat, that of atomic destruction."[1]

DOES HE AVOID TESTS OF STRENGTH?

Between long-term antagonists, negotiation over issues of military or political importance always has a twofold effect on their balance of strength. First, the settlement reached may change attributes of power, such as the distribution of territory, the deployment of forces, or political influence. Second, the way in which the settlement has been reached may change the interplay of mutual expectations between the antagonists so as to alter their deterrents or incentives for future actions against each other. The way in which your antagonist has negotiated may lead you to revise your image of your opponent's view of the balance of forces

[1] *Journal Officiel de la République Française* (Sénat), Dec. 5, 1961, p. 2296.

and of his attitude toward the use of force. You will base your future actions against your opponent on this revised image of *his* views of your mutual power relationship.

One of the main indictments against British and French appeasement of Hitler has been that it encouraged the German dictator to increasingly bolder offensive action, because it suggested that the Western powers either felt themselves inferior in military strength or were simply unwilling to use force. On August 22, 1939, when Hitler was about to launch World War II, he reassured his commanders-in-chief: "Our enemies are little worms; I saw them at Munich."[2]

In the Cuban crisis in 1962, Khrushchev's sudden withdrawal of his missiles made it clear that he was unwilling to risk a show of strength in an area where he had local inferiority. He thereby indicated that he felt himself strategically inferior (certainly without enough superiority convincingly to threaten nuclear war) and hence did not want to initiate a local counteraction elsewhere (e.g., a blockade of Berlin) which could lead to a local war and eventual American strategic attack. Khrushchev therefore demonstrated that he doubts neither America's determination nor its superiority in strategic weapons.

The conflict concerning the Quemoy Islands also illustrates the importance of maintaining a reputation of strength. Since the mid-1950s the suggestion has been made that the United States induce the Chinese Nationalists to abandon these islands at a time when the Chinese Communists are not pressing to get them. The idea here is that, although the islands are of little value by themselves and hard to hold, their surrender under pressure would create a reputation of admitted weakness.

IS HE FIRM?

In the interplay of your threefold choice with that of your opponent, you want him to believe that he might just as well accept

---

[2] Quoted by Chester Wilmot, *The Struggle for Europe* (London: Collins, 1952), p. 21. For a recent study of the Munich conference and its after-effects see Keith Eubank, *Munich* (Norman, Okla.: University of Oklahoma Press, 1963).

your terms since they will not become more advantageous for him. His expectations as to whether or not your position will remain firm depends partly on his image of your customary behavior. If you have a reputation of asking for less and less, until a long, declining sequence of your demands has been rejected, your opponent will expect that he might gain through prolonged negotiations, and he will be reluctant to accept your terms. Your opponent's expectations, however, are affected not only by your reputation of firmness in the past but also by your interest in your future reputation. That is, you may appear unlikely to give in, not only out of habit since this is the way you have been acting in the past, but also out of calculation since giving in would spoil your reputation in future negotiations. The more you can convince your opponent that giving in would spoil your bargaining strength in the future, the more will he conclude that it is in your interest to have no-agreement rather than to soften your terms; even though for this particular instance in isolation, softened terms would still be better for you than no agreement at all. What this means is that the involvement of your bargaining reputation can serve as a commitment to your negotiation position; and the more you enjoy a reputation of always remaining firm, the more convincing is this commitment to the opponent.

This kind of commitment can be strengthened with a self-fulfilling prophecy. A party may predict that if it gave in at the present issue, it would "have to" give in over similar issues in future negotiations. The "have to" here refers to an internal organizational rigidity rather than to external pressures. By linking the present issue with certain future ones, the government tries to convince the opponent that it cannot yield, since its domestic decision-making process would then force it to yield again on those future issues. The government is in fact arguing that it is so attached to precedents that it cannot yield on the first issue without yielding on the analogous second issue.

Accusing the opponent of "salami tactics" helps the defensive side in redistribution negotiations to deny small concessions. Even the smallest diminution of the status quo becomes part and parcel of a process, a slice out of many. The defensive side commits itself to the full integrity of its position by construing the surrender of any slice as capitulation to the slicing process. Of course, this view need not be invented only for the sake of making a commitment. The offensive side might indeed want to turn the smallest victory into a series of advances. In addition, by giving in on the small issue, the defensive side might violate a guaranty to one of its allies and thereby undermine allied confidence in other guaranties and treaties.

Related here is the role of principles in the defense of a position. A government which demonstrates that it maintains a position for the sake of the principle involved indicates that it is not so much interested in the intrinsic value of that position but in the preservation of its reputation of being consistent. This interest in consistency need not be feigned, because in future negotiations the same principles might again serve to defend a position. Moreover, there is also an internal requirement for consistency in most governments, stemming from the bureaucratic need for a continuity of rules as well as from the difficulty of changing official doctrines and adapting national ideologies.

Though a reputation of firmness may discourage your opponent from trying to whittle down your position, it may also discourage him from entering negotiations at all and perhaps prompt him to create a *fait accompli* instead. Likewise, a commitment to principles may anchor your position to firm ground, but it may also keep you out of any region where the opponent would become interested in seeking agreement. This is illustrated by the Allied commitment in World War II to the principle of demanding unconditional surrender of all enemy powers. In the Italian campaign, the principle of unconditional surrender made it harder to extract Italy from German control, and in the Far East it worked against American and British interests by prolonging the war against Japan and permitting the Russians to make great gains with their last-minute intervention.[3]

The interaction of expectations is an essential feature of negotiation. The reason why your commitment to principles and your reputation of firmness help you is that they make your opponent expect that he cannot get better terms. Once he is sure that you are

[3] See Paul Kecskemeti, *Strategic Surrender* (Stanford, Calif.: Stanford University Press, 1958), especially pp. 228–30.

irrevocably committed, he will accept your terms, provided he finds them preferable to no-agreement and provided the loss to *his* bargaining reputation from accepting them does not outweigh his gains from agreement. However, your opponent need not remain passive toward these commitments and principles of yours that get in the way of his making further gains. There are techniques to loosen commitments.

In redistribution negotiations, for example, the offensive side may promise that it will not engage in "salami tactics"; it may suggest that it is making the notorious "last territorial demand," after which there will be no further conflicts. In this way Khrushchev hinted that after the solution of the Berlin crisis a general peaceful settlement of all conflicts in Europe would easily be found. Sukarno similarly reduced the resistance to his demands for West New Guinea in 1962 by declaring that he had no further territorial ambitions. Alas, after the *Anschluss* comes *Sudetenland:* less than a year after Sukarno had incorporated West New Guinea, he tried to interfere with North Borneo's merger with Malaya and so extend his dominance over this neighboring territory.

Commitments based on the attachment to principles can also be weakened by formulating the demands so that they seem to leave the principles untouched, carving out only the substance as it were. Khrushchev's promise, that West Berlin's political and economic system would be left undisturbed if his proposal for a "free city" was accepted, was designed to circumvent the commitment of the Western powers to the principle of not turning over territory to Communism. The Dutch surrender of West New Guinea to Indonesia was made easier by preserving the principle of Papuan self-determination to which the Dutch were committed. The principle was maintained because Sukarno pledged himself to hold a plebiscite in New Guinea six years later. But the Dutch must have recognized full well that elections so many years after the *Anschluss,* if held at all, would probably not be free enough to offer self-determination in substance.

As Thomas Schelling pointed out, secrecy in negotiations can be used to reduce the involvement of bargaining reputations and to eliminate those commitments whose binding power depends on public knowledge.[4] But secrecy cannot protect or suspend one's bargaining reputation entirely. For one thing, your opponent will know what happened, and *his* view of your reputation may be the most important one. In addition, the results usually become public even though the process of reacing the settlement may be kept secret.

Secrecy itself can throw negotiators under suspicion. If the public or nonparticipating governments sense an undercover bargain, a sequel unconnected with the agreement actually reached in secrecy may impair the bargaining reputation, whereas completely open negotiations could have proved the sequel to be purely coincidental. After the Cuban crisis in 1962, the American withdrawal of missiles from Turkey and Italy created such suspicions. Khrushchev's original demand for the withdrawal of American missiles in Turkey in exchange for the withdrawal of his missiles from Cuba was rejected by the United States. Accepting it would have seriously impaired the American bargaining reputation and American guaranties toward allies: it would have implied that Khrushchev could have forced an American retreat merely by canceling an advance of his own. Unfortunately, however, the United States waited only three months after the Cuban crisis to announce the withdrawal of its missiles from both Turkey and Italy for the reason that these weapons had become obsolete. Since part of the negotiations between Khrushchev and Kennedy during the Cuban crisis were kept secret, the suspicion could arise that this latter withdrawal was agreed to during these negotiations.

What happens in the reverse case, where the committed party itself wants to loosen its commitment? A party that wishes to facilitate agreement by offering its opponent a certain concession has every interest that this should not appear as a violation of its principles. It will try to make the situation appear unique and isolated, so that the concession stands all by itself and does not suggest repetition in similar contexts.

[4] *The Strategy of Conflict*, pp. 29–30.

CHAPTER 7

RULES OF ACCOMMODATION

IN NEGOTATIONS BETWEEN FRIENDLY COUNTRIES, THERE IS A SET of rules whose violation would almost invariably terminate the friendly relationship, at least temporarily. For example, unambiguous lies must be avoided, explicit promises have to be kept, invective is never to be used, explicit threats must not be issued, agreements in principle must not be blatantly violated when it comes to the execution of details, and mutual understandings must not be deliberately misconstrued later on. In addition to these hard rules, there are soft rules that cannot be violated repeatedly without eroding the friendly relationship. For instance, the opponent's domestic difficulties should not be exploited in public, debts of gratitude should be honored (e.g., a concession acknowledged as such must be returned when the opportunity arises), motives should not be impugned, and the discourse ought to be reasonable in the sense that questions are answered, arguments are to the point, facts are not grossly distorted, repetition is minimized, and technical discussions are kept on a factual level.

The parties, by adhering to these rules of conduct, may facilitate accommodation in two ways. On the one hand, they may make the negotiating process more efficient in the sense of increasing the chances for agreement on the immediate issues. On the other hand, rule-conforming conduct may reduce hostility between governments and perhaps stimulate friendly feelings between the leaders or between influential officials of each nation. These improved attitudes, in turn, will help to minimize conflict and make future agreements more likely.

Some rules of accommodation are observed even between bitter enemies whose relationship approaches a "zero-sum" conflict, as it is called in game theory. (In such a conflict, what one side gains in strength, security, or economic and political advantages, the other side loses.) Although any gain to one's deadly foe constitutes *ipso facto* a loss to oneself, in reality this loss is often outweighed by other considerations which stop the conflict short of "zero-sum." If this is the case for both sides, the prerequisite common interest for negotiation exists. And given a common interest in an agreement, both sides must also have an interest in methods that can help to bring agreement about. This explains the tacit or explicit understandings between bitter antagonists on rules to facilitate the negotiating process.

The less the hostility, however, the wider the scope of negotiating conduct that the rules can affect and the more infrequent their violation. Among friendly nations, the incentive to disregard a certain rule for the sake of a short-term gain is usually outweighed by the desire to preserve good relations.

Because of this interdependence, a change in foreign relations from hostility to friendship (or vice versa) is normally accompanied by a change in negotiating style. Often it is hard to say which is the cause and which the effect. Indeed, statesmen have tried—sometimes with success—to bring about friendlier relations by practicing an accommodating style unilaterally.

Khrushchev must have had this in mind when he maintained that the Soviet Union had been generous in recent negotiations with Iran. "It was on the Soviet government's initiative," he reported in one of his speeches, "that the Soviet-Iranian agreement was concluded, settling border issues. That agreement put an end to disputes 100 to 150 years old, and the border was redefined mostly at the expense of Soviet territory. Ours is a great country and our territory is vast. *We decided that we did not have to be closefisted, that we should rather yield some ground, but win friends.* This, as the saying goes, is better than having an extra kopek in one's pocket."[1]

The same idea, on a much grander scale, guided Franklin D. Roosevelt in his conduct of American relations with the Soviet Union. In 1942, he told William C. Bullitt, the former American ambassador in Moscow: "I have just a hunch that Stalin doesn't want anything but security for his country, and I think that if I give him everything that I possibly can and ask nothing from him in return, *noblesse oblige,* he won't try to annex anything and will work for a world of democracy and peace."[2] The failure of this approach was one of the most tragic setbacks in the history of American diplomacy.

There are less disappointing cases, however, where deep-rooted hostilities between nations did disappear when a tradition of accommodating negotiations became established. American-British relations went through such a transformation at the end of the nineteenth century, with a marked turning point in 1897 when Great Britain accepted President Grover Cleveland's request to submit her boundary dispute with Venezuela to arbitration. Although the British Foreign Secretary, Lord Salisbury, was first taken aback by the American request and its peremptory tone, he was induced to be cautious by some developments against British interests in other areas, and fifteen months later he decided to make a conciliatory move by proposing a general arbitration treaty between Great Britain and the United States, and by accepting most of the American conditions for arbitration with Venezuela. As it turned out, the British-American treaty was not ratified by the U.S. Senate, and the concessions in accepting arbitration of the dispute with Venezuela did not hurt British interests, since nearly all the contested territory was awarded to British Guiana. Nonetheless, Salisbury's concessions were followed by a lasting Anglo-American *rapprochement.*

The improvement in Franco-German relations after World

---

[1] Speech given Feb. 24, 1959. Italics added. N. S. Khrushchev, *World without Arms, World without Wars,* Book 1 (Moscow, 1959), p. 141.

[2] William C. Bullitt, "How We Won the War and Lost the Peace," *Life,* Aug. 30, 1948.

War II was facilitated by the accommodating negotiating style of both Paris and Bonn. This style was particularly important for reaching a settlement on the protracted conflict about the Saar, which had obstructed the consolidation of the new friendship between France and Germany for years.[3]

Another reason for the observance of rules of accommodation, in addition to the idea that they may lead to friendlier relations on a bilateral basis, is the expectation that other nations will reciprocate the negotiating *style*. That is, the rules establish a mutually useful form of conduct, rather than serving as an expression of good will. Each government knows that it will always be engaged in negotiation, and it may expect that its own negotiating methods will be reflected in those of its opponents. Hence governments may adopt those methods which they would like to see adopted generally. This is the equivalent in diplomacy of Kant's categorical imperative in ethics.

However, while those who observe rules of accommodation would obviously prefer the opponent to reciprocate, this is not always felt to be mandatory. Some rules are expected to produce beneficial results even if the opponent ignores them; others require reciprocation only in the long run. (As mentioned, unilateral generosity may be a means of overcoming old antagonisms.) At any rate, to some negotiators the efficacy of the rules seems secondary because they follow them as the conventionally correct behavior, in keeping with the proprieties. Breaking the rules—rather than being simply inexpedient—would appear to be unseemly, a breach of decorum, or even immoral.

Thus a negotiator may adhere to rules of accommodation for any of three reasons. First, in some situations he may think that rule-conforming behavior is expedient, either because it enhances friendly relations with another country or because it makes other countries reciprocate and thus facilitates agreement. Second, in other situations, he does not hope for such results but adheres to certain rules merely because he thinks that others feel it is proper to do so, and he is afraid to shock domestic critics or governments of third countries by breaking the rules. Third, he observes some

[3] For a thorough study see Jacques Freymond, *The Saar Conflict, 1945–1955* (New York: Praeger, 1960).

rules regardless of external circumstances because he himself would consider it unseemly or immoral to violate them. The second reason, the desire not to shock others, is particularly cogent if the negotiations can be affected by a mediator who might turn against the party that violates the rules.

Normally, negotiators do not separate these three reasons clearly. Western statesmen and diplomats, in particular, are usually motivated by a mixture of expediential calculations and moral convictions when following an accommodating negotiation style. If the adherence to certain rules is questioned at all, it is the expediential calculation which is usually stressed in private discussions within the government, while the moral justification might be emphasized in public. Very often, a rule is followed without questioning. And even if an expediential explanation is given, it may well have been invented to justify in a hard-boiled way what is obscurely but strongly felt to be the "proper" thing to do.

Some rules of accommodation can now be examined in greater detail. In many cases, incidents when these rules were *not* being observed make the better illustration, since such exceptions demarcate the customary conduct. Besides, it must be stressed that most of these rules are not universally accepted. Although some are fully shared by Communist and Western negotiators (even though there may be many breaches in their observance), a greater number are considered valid only by Westerners or by Americans alone. Discussing the rules is not equivalent to saying that all of them actually serve the purposes they are supposed to serve: they do not necessarily facilitate agreement, engender good will, or enhance any other interests of the governments adhering to them. On the contrary, some rules make negotiation more difficult; far from facilitating agreement, they create additional conflicts or lead to protracted debates.

Some of the rules of accommodation that are being observed in negotiations—or that, according to Western views, *ought* to be observed—are related to, or part of, public international law. They can be deduced from international conventions regarding diplomatic immunities and representation and from the legal doctrines about treaty-making, equality of states, and the pacific settlement of international disputes.

NEVER KILL A NEGOTIATOR

The most elementary rule of accommodation is that the opponent's representatives should not be physically harmed. In fact, the inviolability of the messenger who has been sent by a neighboring state, a rebellious province, or a feuding rival might be said to mark the beginning of international diplomacy. In spite of repeated violations during antiquity and the Middle Ages, this principle became firmly established and was gradually expanded into the modern code of diplomatic immunities.

If political authorities do not have diplomatic relations with each other—as in the case of a rebellion or war—the authorized envoy may be given a promise of safe conduct to assure him that the rule of inviolability applies despite his contestable diplomatic status. The emissary would be risking his life without such a guaranty, and, what might be worse for both parties, the negotiations might never get started. One would expect that no government would want to discredit its promises of safe conduct by imprisoning or executing negotiators to whom it gave assurances, since this could deprive it of negotiating channels at some future occasion when it might badly need them.

People have such short memories, however, when it comes to violations of international norms, that twentieth-century dictators are no more likely than ancient kings to be deterred from killing or imprisoning envoys whom they promised safety—and they have used this trick repeatedly. In March, 1945, for example, the political police of the Soviet Union invited the Polish Underground to send a delegation to Moscow to discuss the formation of a united Polish government in accordance with the Yalta agreement. The delegation had received a written guaranty of personal safety. It was made up of fifteen people headed by General Okulicki, and it included eleven leaders representing the major political parties in Poland. None of them returned from the meeting. Not until two months later did Molotov admit that these men were being held in Russia. In June, after Stalin denied that the Polish leaders had ever been invited to Moscow, they were tried and most of them sentenced to long terms of imprisonment.[4]

---

[4] See Winston S. Churchill, *Triumph and Tragedy*, pp. 497–501.

Eleven years later the same government repeated this performance. During the Hungarian Revolution, the Soviet Military Command in Hungary invited General Maléter (who had just become Minister of Defense) and other delegates of the revolutionary Hungarian government to complete certain technical details of an agreement for the withdrawal of Soviet troops. This invitation turned out to be a trap for the arrest of Maléter and his delegation by the Soviet security police.[5] Later, these Hungarian leaders were killed.

Moise Tshombe, the secessionist leader of the Congo's Katanga province, twice found out how twentieth-century diplomats—much like the ambassadors in antiquity—risk imprisonment if they displease the opponent while they are negotiating. In April, 1961, Tshombe attended a conference with officials from the central Congolese government in Coquilhatville and was arrested when he threatened to leave because of disagreement. He was not released until two months later, after having agreed to integrate his provincial army into the military organization of the central government. A year later, Tshombe again went to confer with the central government, with more explicit guaranties of safe conduct than before. When he wanted to leave for his provincial capital, after several days of fruitless negotiations, his plane was blocked by trucks of the central government. This time the United Nations, which had underwritten the guaranty to Tshombe, interceded more vigorously, and the secessionist leader was able to depart several hours later.

[5] United Nations, General Assembly, *Report of the Special Committee on the Problem of Hungary* (New York, 1957), p. 9. A similar violation of a promise of safe conduct, though not directly connected with a negotiation, was the abduction of Imre Nagy when he left the Yugoslav embassy in Budapest, where he had sought refuge. Kádár, as President of the Soviet-installed Hungarian government, had assured the Yugoslavs in writing that the Hungarian government did not desire to apply any sanctions against Nagy. As may be recalled, after this abduction Nagy was imprisoned in Rumania and later executed. The Yugoslav government condemned the Hungarian action as "a flagrant breach of the agreement reached" and as being completely contrary to the generally accepted practices of international law (*ibid.*, pp. 10–11).

AVOID DISPUTES ABOUT STATUS

Many of the long-established diplomatic customs serve to avoid
disputes about the status of negotiating parties. Examples are the
neutral meeting ground for conferences, the rotating chairmanship, and the use of alphabetic order to seat delegates in multilateral conferences or to arrange signatures on a treaty. The rule
about the neutral meeting ground, however, is often ignored: the
head of a smaller state usually travels to the capital of the larger
state; and even among big powers exceptions are sometimes made,
such as President Roosevelt's trip to Yalta to meet with Stalin, or
the selection of New York as the site of the United Nations headquarters. It remained for De Gaulle to seek out a dispute about
status, instead of avoiding it, when, after President Kennedy's
funeral, he refused to meet President Lyndon B. Johnson anywhere but on French soil.

To a large extent, rules to avoid disputes about status have
become like social conventions, whose violation would be a breach
of etiquette. But unlike some conventions that have become useless,
these rules do facilitate negotiations. This can be seen from the
prolonged quarrels which arose before the rules were established
or in cases where they failed to apply. Avoiding disputes about
status permits the parties to concentrate their negotiations on those
other issues for which the conference presumably was convened.

The negotiations at Münster and Osnabrück, which terminated
the Thirty Years War, were slowed down during the whole first
year by disputes about precedence and the admission of delegates.
Incidentally, two conference sites were chosen to avoid arguments
about status, Münster being a Catholic city and Osnabrück a
Protestant one. In 1815 the Congress of Vienna finally regulated
many aspects of diplomatic precedence. Since then, conflicts of this
sort are normally confined to conferences where one side pro-
motes a would-be participant whom the other side does not recognize as representing a legitimate government. For example, at the
1959 Foreign Ministers' Conference, the Western powers objected to the participation of an East German delegate.

A simple solution to end disputes about status, such as arise concerning the order of signatures, is often available to one of the major negotiating parties. One of the senior powers present can simply make it clear that it does not care a bit about the order of signatures and treat it as a joking matter. As a result, the order automatically loses its importance. This is what President Harry Truman and Prime Minister Clement Attlee did at the end of the Potsdam Conference. Truman recalled in his memoirs:

The draft of the communiqué was finally approved, but now the Soviet delegation raised the question of who should sign first. At the previous two conferences of the Big Three, they pointed out, the Prime Minister or the President had been first to sign the communiqué. According to the procedure of rotation, Stalin said he felt that his signature should come first on the Potsdam document. "You can sign any time you want to," I said. "I don't care who signs first." Attlee remarked that he was in favor of alphabetical preference. "That way," he said jokingly, "I would score over Marshal Zhukhov."[6]

No efficient rules have yet been developed to select a common language for international conferences. The resulting disputes are usually solved by arranging for various unnecessary translations. In the European Communities, for instance, all four languages of the member states were accepted as official ones, although informal records are mostly kept in French and German only, and in oral exchanges French predominates.

ADHERE TO AGREED AGENDA

Agreement on the agenda has two implications. First, it means that prior to, or at the beginning of, a conference the parties agree on the subjects they will discuss. (Consent to the official title for a conference can also imply an agreement to discuss a certain topic.) Second, the agreed agenda constitutes a procedural agreement as to the *sequence* in which the subjects will be negotiated. Both of these implications affect the outcome of negotiations: the subjects that are discussed obviously determine the issues that may be settled, and the particular sequence in which separable issues are negotiated may favor one side and handicap the other. At first glance, therefore, it seems obvious that negotiators should argue

[6] Harry S Truman, *Memoirs*, I, 410.

about the agenda or the title of a conference. Upon more careful examination, however, disputes about the agenda make sense only if one assumes that the parties either feel somehow bound by agreeing to an agenda or wish to exploit the fact that the opponent is thus constrained. But why, and to what extent, do parties feel bound by an agenda?

In part, negotiators may feel that they ought to adhere to an agreed agenda because this is simply a special case of the general precept that agreements ought to be kept. Western negotiators, in particular, might think it "improper" to ignore an agreed agenda or might fear that they would make a bad impression at home and among allies. In part, negotiators may have a more expediential reason in mind: that adherence to an agenda will expedite negotiation and increase the chances for agreement. Some examples ought to be inspected to see whether this expediential reason is valid.

At the beginning of the nuclear test-ban conference in 1958, East and West argued about the agenda for the first ten meetings. The Soviet Union tried to push an agenda according to which nuclear testing would first be prohibited and a control system discussed afterwards. As the Soviet delegate put it neatly in the third meeting: "The work of the Conference should start with the conclusion of an agreement." In the tenth meeting, both East and West argued that the agenda proposed by the other side was not "impartial," since it confined the discussion to the type of treaty favored by the other side. The deadlock about the agenda was finally broken in an informal meeting, when both sides agreed, at the suggestion of the American delegate, to deal with the topics proposed by each side in alternating two-day periods. In the future course of this prolonged conference, even this arrangement was quietly abandoned, and each side brought up proposals or discussed issues raised by the opponent as it pleased. Thus, while both sides quickly agreed on the expedient of a rotating chairmanship, it took them over ten meetings to decide on *rotating agenda*.

In the surprise-attack conference of the same year, East and West repeated this procedure. Considerable struggle was also reflected in the official title for this conference: "Conference of Experts for the Study of Possible Measures Which Might Be Helpful in Preventing Surprise Attack and for the Preparation of a Report Thereon to Governments." This elegant phrase was largely the accomplishment of the American delegation, which feared that a less qualified title might somehow constrain its freedom of decision in the conference, much like an agreement on an agenda.

Disagreement on the agenda has become so common in East-West disarmament conferences that the rotating agenda has lately almost acquired the quality of a diplomatic convention. The following illustration shows how meticulously the equality of two conflicting agendas may be preserved. As much importance is attached to the geometry of the competing agenda items on the page as sovereigns formerly attributed to the arrangement of their signatures on a treaty. A United Nations document of the Eighteen-Nation Disarmament Conference in 1962 records the agreement to disagree on the agenda by stating that the United States and the Soviet Union, as the two Co-chairmen of the meeting:

recommend that next priority in the Committee of the Whole should be given to concurrent consideration of proposals on:

Measures to prevent further dissemination of nuclear weapons.	Reduction of the possibility of war by accident, miscalculation, or failure of communications.

The Co-chairmen recommend that one of these two topics be presented by one of the Co-chairmen, and the other be presented by the other Co-chairman, at the first meeting of the Committee of the Whole held to discuss them. Thereafter, the two topics could be discussed at alternate meetings.[7]

Disputes about the title of a conference are not confined to East-West meetings. In the negotiations on an enlarged free-trade area that would have combined the six Common Market countries with the "Outer Seven," the Six suggested that the subject of the negotiations be defined as "European Economic Association" instead of as "European Free Trade Area," so as to support their own position in favor of a looser association between their customs union and other European states.[8]

[7] Conference of the Eighteen-Nation Committee on Disarmament, ENDC/C. 1/9, May 25, 1962, Committee of the Whole.

[8] A memorandum outlining the position of the Six on these negotiations contains the following passage: "With regard to the term 'Free Trade Area' used

Two questions must be raised about the traditional views of negotiators regarding the agenda and the title of a conference. First, we may wonder why it takes diplomats so long till they abandon their attempt to agree on an agenda (or on an official title), when it turns out that this effort merely delays substantive negotiations. In fact, if both sides are under strong time pressure, negotiations can proceed without title or agenda. Imagine that during the Cuban crisis in 1962 President Kennedy had first proposed a name for his negotiations with Khrushchev, such as "Discussions about the Removal of Offensive Soviet Missiles from Cuba," and that Khrushchev had then argued that their joint enterprise should be entitled "Conference about Possible Measures Which Might Be Helpful in Reducing Tension in the Caribbean and in Turkey," at which point Kennedy would then have made a counter-proposal for another title, and so forth.

The second question is why negotiators expect to be constrained by the agenda to which they agree. Experience shows that agreed items on the agenda are often not followed closely, and objections by a party that the opponent fails to adhere to the agenda seem of little consequence. Even if the negotiators should be concerned about public opinion, there are many ways to depart from an agenda without admitting it or without seeming to violate the agreement implied by it. For example, a negotiator might declare, after he has perfunctorily dealt with the topic favored by the opponent, that this first item on the agenda had now been sufficiently discussed, and then simply pass on to *his* favorite topic.

The rule that an agreed agenda should be observed or that there should be an agreed agenda to begin with sometimes impedes negotiations more than it facilitates them—certainly in East-West conferences. If, on the contrary, there was a rule giving each party complete freedom to ignore an agenda as soon as it felt handicapped, negotiations might move to substantive issues more ex-

hitherto to describe the Treaty under negotiation, it should be pointed out that, from the point of view of doctrine, the term 'free trade' evokes a specific economic system. In view of the content of this Treaty as now envisaged, this term does not seem to be very appropriate and should be changed. The Community suggests that the title 'European Economic Association' should be adopted" (Great Britain, *Negotiations for a European Free Trade Area*, Cmnd. 641 [London: H.M.S.O., 1959], pp. 97–98).

peditiously. There would be less need to quarrel about the agenda, since the agreed items would constitute nothing but a tentative preview of the order in which issues might be taken up. Such an optional agenda was actually adopted by the Eighteen-Nation Disarmament Conference in July, 1962. To the list of items to be discussed the following disclaimer was added: "Nothing contained herein is intended to preclude any delegation from raising and discussing any subject or proposal in any plenary session. . . ."[9]

Questioning the wisdom of the rule that an agreed agenda must be adhered to is not the same as denying that, if adhered to, an agenda can be influential. To the extent that an agenda is, in fact, being followed, its particular ordering of issues affects opportunities for tie-ins. Also, agreeing to put a topic on the agenda signifies consent that the topic is a subject of negotiation. Conversely, barring a certain issue from the agenda may help to reassure third parties that their interests will not be tampered with on this issue. (These aspects of an *observed* agenda are dealt with in Chapter 11.)

HONOR PARTIAL AGREEMENTS

Any but the most simple agreement has to be negotiated piece-meal, since all points obviously cannot be settled at once. Treaties, in particular, are negotiated article by article. (Sometimes a number of issues may be tied together, in the sense that a party makes its acceptance of an article dependent on the opponent's acceptance of another article.) While it is understood that the parties are not bound by their acceptance of individual articles in the way they are bound by the conclusion of a final agreement, each party expects that its opponent will generally preserve agreed parts as the building blocks for the over-all agreement. The very fact that the parties laboriously negotiate with each other to settle their issues point by point constitutes an implied promise that yesterday's work will not be destroyed tomorrow by reopening these partial agreements.

The rule that partial agreement should be preserved has clearly an expediential character. It facilitates negotiation. In contrast to rules regarding the precedence of parties or the agenda, reciproca-

[9] ENDC/1/Add. 3, July 24, 1962, p. 1.

tion is not essential here, because it is feasible to preserve partial agreement even if the opponent fails to do so. In the long run, however, the side which always preserved partial agreement would be handicapped, since only the opponent could exploit his hindsight or new information indicating previously accepted terms to be undesirable.

Western negotiators are generally more reluctant to reopen component parts of an agreement than their Communist adversaries. They seem to feel that it is not only inexpedient but somewhat improper to go back on agreed articles. In the first year of the nuclear test-ban conference, 1959, the United States and the United Kingdom decided they had to ask for a revision of some of the conclusions in the so-called Experts' Report (which formed the scientific basis for the original detection system) because new seismic research invalidated them. This demand for revision—strongly resisted by the Soviet Union—was presented with considerable embarrassment by the Western powers.

On the other hand, as the test-ban conference met again in the spring of 1961, after the new Administration in Washington had formulated its position, the Soviet Union withdrew its agreement to a single administrator for the detection system and later, in effect, canceled all the agreed articles by objecting to any inspection system within its territory. By wiping the slate clean of all agreed points after three years of negotiation, the Soviet Union could begin anew with a much harder position late in 1962 and offer the "concession" to accept three inspections on its territory plus a number of seismic detection stations much smaller than the one originally agreed to. By becoming known for withdrawing partial agreements, a government can improve its bargaining strength, since it acquires the reputation of easily stiffening its terms. This, as noted previously, might spur its opponent to accept its terms more quickly in the future, for fear of missing an opportunity.

Similar to the rule that partial agreement should be preserved is the notion that a completed agreement should not be annulled before it becomes effective or just before it has been signed. At the height of the Berlin crisis in 1961, the American government refused to sign an otherwise completed aviation agreement with the Soviet Union, in order to express its determination on Berlin and its general opposition to Soviet pressures.[10] A certain amount of opposition to this step within the U.S. government stemmed precisely from the feeling that it was improper to violate the rule regarding the preservation of partial or nearly completed agreements.

In the Eighteen-Nation Disarmament Conference in 1962, the Soviet Union withdrew its consent from an agreement that had reached an even more formal stage of completion. On May 29, the Soviet delegate Zorin objected to the "Declaration against War Propaganda," which he had approved the week before and which had originally been put on the agenda at his insistence. This sudden reversal might have been caused by ideological objections in Moscow or perhaps by Chinese remonstrations. Zorin's justification was curious: he referred to an article written by West German Defense Minister Strauss, a book by Edward Teller, the landing of American troops in Thailand, plus some other events of the recent week, as necessitating a complete revision of this agreement that was supposed to contribute toward general and complete disarmament. Zorin in his zeal to expunge this rather vacuous agreement went so far as to delete all references to it from the official conference records—an Orwellian move which the American delegate managed to set straight.

Similar to the reneging of partial agreements is the withdrawal of an accepted offer. In Western diplomacy, this is considered to be highly improper. It is viewed not just as a breach of promise but also as a retrogression retarding the negotiation process.

Nonetheless, in the East-West disarmament negotiations of 1955, the United States withdrew an offer after the Soviet Union appeared to accept it. This was an unimaginative reaction to the the sudden discovery that an inadequately prepared Western proposal might become the subject of detailed negotiations. Naturally, such clumsiness caused considerable public embarrassment. What happened was that the Western powers had put forward a pro-

[10] The agreement, which provided for reciprocal air services, had been initialed on August 21, 1961, and on the same day the State Department announced that this was "not an appropriate time" for going through with the agreement "in view of the international situation, for which the United States is not responsible" (*New York Times*, Aug. 22, 1961).

posal providing for the total prohibition of nuclear weapons after the constitution of an effective control organ and after major reductions in conventional forces. Then, on May 10, 1955, the Soviet Union made a proposal which accepted the general principles of this Western position but added certain provisions of its own (such as an early cessation of nuclear testing and the liquidation of foreign bases). Four months later (September 6, 1955), the U.S. delegate Harold Stassen declared that the United States was now placing a "reservation" upon all its previous substantive positions. Only after he had committed this unnecessarily cautious withdrawal did he hazard a timid move forward: "In placing this reservation," he said, "may I make it perfectly clear that we are not withdrawing any of these positions, we are not disavowing any of them. But we are indicating clearly that we do not now reaffirm them, that we turn our attention upon the central factor of the inspection and control methods. . . ." Stassen could of course have protected his position without withdrawing the American offer, by focusing on the inspection issue. The course of disarmament negotiations would probably not have been much different had the United States stood by the Western offer. The two positions would have been no closer than they were from 1961 onward, when both sides had accepted "general and complete disarmament" as their goal.

MAINTAIN FLEXIBILITY

In the West, the rule that one should be flexible in negotiations assumes a moral value. The question of whether it is expedient to be flexible is suppressed by the conviction that it would clearly be improper to be *in*flexible. Those who advocate this rule as a way of facilitating agreement would grant that in prolonged negotiations or in case of a serious conflict both sides have to evince some flexibility for negotiations to succeed. But in the short run, or to settle minor difficulties, they do not consider reciprocity as essential.

In 1961, when the Soviets were actively exerting pressure against West Berlin, Senator Mansfield said: "The responsibility which we have . . . and which the Soviet Union has, is not merely to reassert positions already assumed and which are obviously irreconcilable. The responsibility is to seek to determine whether or not there is a third way on Berlin. . . ." Similarly, a *New York Times* editorial a few months later maintained: ". . . neither Moscow nor Germany nor the Western allies can expect to win all their points. There has to be some give as well as take."[11]

The rule that there must be "give and take" has become a crippling cliché, owing to its nebulous content and because of indiscriminate claims that it is universally valid. If flexibility is deemed to be so essential, it seems appropriate to examine what it means and how it affects negotiations. A government might show flexibility by: (1) formulating its position in an indeterminate fashion, (2) offering the opponent several *specific* alternatives, (3) expressing its willingness to consider *any* alternatives proposed by the opponent, and/or (4) changing its position in response to the opponent's demands. There is yet a greater degree of flexibility. A government might not only keep its own position changeable and show openmindedness toward the opponent's proposals, but it may abandon having a position at all. Rather than being a sign of modesty, this may result from a lack of conviction or the absence of ideas on the issue under negotiation. In multilateral negotiations, smaller powers often do not care as long as their interests appear unaffected. They might even exploit their lack of a position to incur the favor of a more committed party with which they can align themselves. Similarly, in innovation negotiations, some participants may simply choose to examine what the initiating party has to propose and go along with any arrangement that does not discriminate against them.

It may be argued that negotiation is a creative process: the less attached parties are to a certain position, the more receptive they will be to the discovery of new solutions. Walter Lippmann possibly had this in mind when he wrote about the Berlin negotiations in 1961: "Someone has to begin to negotiate to begin to find out precisely what the negotiation is about. It is a mirage to expect the four Western Powers to guess correctly in advance just what Khrushchev will ask and just what he will concede, and to have an

[11] *Congressional Record,* June 14, 1961, p. 9598; *New York Times,* Oct. 18, 1961.

agreed 'position' on every guess."[12] Flexibility to the degree of not
having a position at all, however, seems a trifle too passive for the
defensive side in redistribution negotiations, especially if the offensive side clearly knows what "the negotiation is about"—which
the Russians seemed to do in their Berlin crisis in 1961.

Related to the rule of flexibility is the precept that ultimatums
should be avoided. (An ultimatum may be defined as an offer or a
demand that is presented as being unchangeable and is coupled
with the prediction that negotiations will cease if it is rejected.)
Ultimatums are, of course, the antithesis of flexibility and may lead
to the rupture of negotiations. In the West, they are often considered to be both improper and dangerous. Only in defense of
vital interests or against some extremely aggressive move are they
in keeping with the proprieties; for example, the British ultimatum
to Hitler in September, 1939. And in such situations the ultimatum
is usually not meant as a move in negotiation but as a preliminary
step to going to war. When war seems justified, the ultimatum as a
ritual preceding it seems entirely proper. In all other situations,
governments do not admit to issuing an ultimatum. Indeed, if the
opponent complains of having been given an ultimatum, most governments—even Communist ones—will ardently deny such a
charge. This shows how deeply ingrained is the view that issuing
ultimatums shows one to the world as wicked and reckless.

RECIPROCATE CONCESSIONS

A standard recommendation for facilitating agreement is that
parties should make concessions.[13] The rule that a concession by
the opponent ought to be reciprocated with a concession by oneself
combines the virtue of flexibility with the norm of reciprocity.

If one pauses to analyze the meaning of this rule, however, it is
remarkable that it enjoys such wide and unqualified support in the
West. It is often accepted as a moral precept that takes precedence

[12] *New York Herald Tribune*, Dec. 19, 1961.

[13] A "concession" may be defined as a revision of a negotiating position so
that it will come closer to the opponent's wishes; and a "compromise" may be
classed as a way of reaching agreement through concessions by *both* sides.
Frequently, the point where the two revised negotiating positions coincide,
rather than the process of reaching this point, is referred to as "the compromise."

over the question whether or not the morality of the substance of one's position would be impaired by a concession. According to this view, it is more important to negotiate "properly," by reciprocating concessions, than to maintain a "proper" negotiating position. To put it differently, not to reciprocate concessions may be regarded as unfair, without examining the fairness of either side's initial position from which the concessions would have to be subtracted.

Curiously, although concessions ought to be reciprocated, it is neither mandatory nor even proper to reciprocate the *withdrawal* of concessions. In 1961–62, when the Soviet Union canceled all its concessions of 1959 and 1960 on the nuclear test-ban treaty, the Western powers did not respond by withdrawing concessions of their own. To have done so might well have been considered objectionable by important segments of public opinion. (Also, the Western negotiators felt that they derived a propagandistic advantage from being able to blame the Soviet Union for having withdrawn its concessions.)

RETURN FAVORS

A negotiator has an incentive to grant his opponent an advantage gratuitously if he knows that he will build up a long-term credit on which he can draw later. In other words, he may find it worthwhile to let his opponent make certain gains, even without being compelled to do so in order to secure his desired terms of agreement and without getting anything in return *at that time*.

The rule that favors should be returned tends to generate feelings of friendliness in the long run. But perhaps more important, it can greatly facilitate negotiations in the short run. Under this rule each party to an agreement need not always come out with a net gain, since the balance sheet of gains and losses does not have to be closed with every single settlement. If one party should incur a net loss in order to reach agreement, it can trust that the other parties will repay it in later negotiations.

American negotiators have learned that their Communist opponents, by and large, do not observe the rule of repaying debts of gratitude. Many diplomats who have had experience with Com-

munists have even come to believe that gratuitous concessions by
the West would be taken as a sign of weakness, not as something
entitling the generous negotiator to a credit. However, this view
conflicts with the idea, discussed before, that an accommodating
negotiating style might gradually lead to friendlier relations. There
is no simple answer to this puzzle. Only cautious probing can
show whether gratuitous concessions will merely be exploited or
whether they will lead to a long-term improvement in the opponent's attitudes.

During the World War II alliance with Russia, the experience
was surely disappointing, even with negotiations on such issues
as Lend-Lease, where America was offering to help the Russian war
effort. In December, 1944, General John R. Deane, who led
Lend-Lease negotiations in Moscow, wrote a bitter letter to his
superior, General George C. Marshall. He warned Marshall that
the Russians "simply cannot understand giving without taking,
and as a result even our giving is viewed with suspicion. Gratitude
cannot be banked in the Soviet Union. Each transaction is complete in itself without regard to past favors. The party of the second
part is either a shrewd trader to be admired or a sucker to be
despised."[14]

REFRAIN FROM FLAGRANT LIES

No one would argue that a general who leads his army into
battle should eschew disguise, deception, and dissimulation. If he
succeeds in misleading his adversary, he will be called great rather
than dishonest. Diplomats, however, are expected to observe certain rules of sincerity. Like other rules of accommodation, these
are meant to facilitate negotiation or enhance good relations in the
long run. They play an important role among friendly nations,
by making communication more reliable and by engendering a relationship of trust. But their content is rather vague; what would
be condemned as a lie in one situation may be a shrewd tactic in
another.

[14] U.S. Department of State, *Foreign Relations of the United States: The
Conferences at Malta and Yalta 1945* (Washington, 1955), p. 448.

Outright lies are a serious breach of decorum, even in negotiations between hostile nations. A brazen lie may cause as strong a sense of grievance as an offensive act. This seems to have been reflected by the tenor of President Kennedy's speech on October 22, 1962, which announced the blockade against the Soviet missile buildup in Cuba. The President related how the Soviets had made two "false" statements by pretending that their armaments in Cuba were only defensive, and then he exclaimed: "Neither the United States of America nor the World Community of Nations can tolerate deliberate deception and offensive threats on the part of any nation. . . ." The lie is just as bad as the offensive missiles!

The rule that negotiators should be truthful may be interpreted more broadly, not only as prohibiting outright lies, but as requiring that no important facts be withheld. Walter Lippmann criticized the President after his speech on the Cuba crisis for not having lived up to the broader rule of truthfulness in his meeting with Gromyko a few days earlier. The President should not have "suspended diplomacy," Lippmann argued, by withholding from Gromyko the fact that he already possessed evidence as to the offensive character of the Soviet missile buildup:

> If [diplomacy] had not been suspended, the President would have shown Mr. Gromyko the pictures, and told him privately about the policy which in a few days he intended to announce publicly. This would have made it more likely that Moscow would order the ships not to push on to Cuba. But if such diplomatic action did not change the orders, if Mr. Khrushchev persisted in spite of it, the President's public speech would have been stronger.[15]

Telling the full truth—according to this argument—would have had one of two advantages: it would either (1) have induced the Soviets to retreat before the open confrontation with the blockade or (2) have made the President's speech more effective. Lippmann ignores two other possibilities: (3) that the Soviet Union might have taken the initiative politically—for instance in the United Nations—to undermine Latin American support and divide public opinion and (4) that Khrushchev might have committed himself

[15] *New York Herald Tribune,* Oct. 25, 1962.

to threats of reprisals, which would have made the crisis more dangerous.[16]

That to withhold important facts from the opponent suspends diplomacy—as Lippmann argued in the foregoing passage—may reflect a view of international negotiation which is fairly common among Americans. Harold Nicolson, in his widely read book on diplomacy, goes even further; he lays down the rule of truthfulness in its broadest possible meaning:

By [truthfulness] is meant, not merely abstention from conscious misstatements, but scrupulous care to avoid the suggestion of the false or the suppression of the true. A good diplomatist should be at pains not to leave any incorrect impressions whatsoever upon the minds of those with whom he negotiates. . . . Even if we judge negotiation by its lowest standards, it is evident that the correction of inaccurate information increases present credit and fortifies future confidence. Nor should the negotiator for one moment allow himself to agree with Machiavelli that the dishonesty of others justifies any dishonesty in oneself.[17]

Nicolson generously extends the applicability of this rule "to those who have to deal with the subtleties of the Oriental mind." He approvingly quotes the advice of a British diplomat with "long experience in the Far and Middle East" that you should not waste time "in trying to discover what is at the back of an Oriental's mind" but should make quite certain that the latter "is left in no doubt whatsoever in regard to what is at the back of *your* mind."[18]

[16] Later on, Walter Lippmann discovered this himself: "The American intention was to react sharply, but for a limited aim. . . . Had this intention become known before it was announced . . . , there was a probability that the Soviet Government would take the initiative either by proclaiming defiantly the presence of the missiles or by denouncing the proposed quarantine as an act of 'piracy.' Had that denunciation been made before the quarantine was proclaimed and enforced, both Moscow and Washington would have been committed to a collision course" (from an address delivered in Paris, *The Atlantic Community* [March, 1963], pp. 39–40).

[17] Harold Nicolson, *Diplomacy* (London: Oxford University Press, 1960), pp. 110–11.

[18] *Ibid.*, p. 111. This racial segregation of negotiators into subtle and truthful ones—a quaintly old-fashioned touch like a yellow leaf from Rudyard Kipling —was repeated as late as 1961 in an article Nicolson wrote for *Foreign Affairs* (Oct., 1961), p. 45.

Much of this has no relation to facts. A diplomat who could leave no incorrect impression whatsoever upon the mind of his opponent and had to reveal all that was back of his mind would no more be negotiating than, say, a businessman who not only posted his minimum prices but also revealed all his cost calculations and whether he expected to sell more cheaply tomorrow.

Now, among close allies it might be argued that important objectives and intentions should not be concealed from one's partner. The "special relationship" between the United States and Great Britain means, among other things, that London and Washington should keep each other fully informed about their intentions (a practice that was possibly breached by both sides in the negotiations that led up to the Suez crisis of 1956). Efforts have been made to extend this practice to other Atlantic allies. Sometimes, close allies oblige themselves explicitly to such an exchange of information: for example, France and Germany in their Treaty of Cooperation of January, 1963.

The rule against concealing one's major objectives has its counterpart in the rule that negotiators should not impugn the opponent's motives. If it is improper to harbor ulterior motives in negotiations, it is even more so to accuse your opponent of just that.

The question of motives is justifiably touchy in negotiations among friendly nations, where the assumed compatibility of major objectives provides the principal basis for agreement. However, if domestic opinion-makers attribute hidden motives to the negotiating position of their own government, the diplomats of other governments may no longer be reluctant to allude to these motives. During the negotiations for a larger European free-trade area in 1957–58 between the six Common Market countries and seven other European nations, British newspapers openly mentioned the one-sided advantages that this arrangement would have secured for the United Kingdom, and official British statements even alluded to the objective of holding up European integration.[19] As a result, however, the negotiators of the Six often impugned British

[19] Miriam Camps, *The Free Trade Area Negotiations* (Occasional Paper No. 2 [London: Political and Economic Planning, 1959]), p. 33; and Karl Kaiser, *EWG und Freihandelszone*, pp. 111–12, 115–21.

motives in private meetings. And in retrospect this was also done publicly, by De Gaulle in his press conference of January 14, 1963, when he said that Great Britain applied for membership in the Common Market:

after refusing earlier to participate in the community that was being built, and after then having created a free trade area with six other states, and finally—I can say this, the negotiations conducted for so long on this subject can be recalled—after having put some pressure on the Six in order to prevent the application of the Common Market from ever getting started.

In East-West negotiations, particularly on disarmament, the impugning of motives takes up a large amount of time and fills page after page in the verbatim records. There are protestations from the Western side of the sincerity of its objectives, accusations from the Soviets that the West harbors hidden motives, complaints from the West for having had its motives impugned, assurances from the Western delegates that they—in contrast to their opponent—would not want to question Soviet motives, new Soviet impugnations, and occasionally a cautious questioning of Soviet motives by the West.

When the nuclear test-ban conference was only in its third meeting in 1958, the U.S. delegate James Wadsworth declared: "I came to Geneva, fully convinced that the Soviet delegation would come here in good faith to negotiate, and I must say that it gives me quite a shock to find this continued misunderstanding of motives and impugnment of motives." Fifty-three meetings later, speaking about the Soviet delegate Tsarapkin, he said: "I fully believe in his sincerity, I fully believe in the wrongness of his position. He has every right, of course, to believe that our position is wrong. He has no right to question our sincerity." Another one hundred and seventy-six meetings later this protestation by the U.S. delegate continues: "But, Mr. Tsarapkin, you are now doing something which I deeply regret, particularly in view of our excellent associations during approximately two years. I beg you to refrain from impugning the motives of my country. I beg you to understand that we mean what we say. I beg you to inform your Government that we sincerely wish to see a test-ban treaty concluded on terms which are acceptable to all three of us." Mr. Tsarapkin remains undaunted. Seventy-two meetings later he accuses the West: "You do not want agreement; you know that unless there is agreement on questions of control . . . , there will be no treaty; and if there is no treaty, you will feel splendid, you will be able to continue carrying out nuclear weapon tests, alleging that you have not succeeded in reaching agreement with the Soviet Union on questions of control. That is the simple outline of what you are obviously striving to obtain from our negotiations."[20]

Evidently, such an exchange of words about each other's motives does not enlighten either side about the issues ostensibly under negotiation or about the opponent's position, even if the exchange is conducted in the conciliatory Western fashion of crediting the opponent with sincerity. The rule not to impugn motives, provided it is observed by both sides, certainly helps to expedite negotiations.

NEGOTIATE IN GOOD FAITH

To blame the opponent for not "negotiating in good faith" is a grave accusation. Most governments concede that they cannot reveal all the pertinent facts when negotiating, and some would occasionally admit—at least in domestic discussions—that they have hidden motives. But none would ever accept the charge that it was not "negotiating in good faith." Although this canon is compelling, it allows for several distinct or even conflicting interpretations. At least four different meanings might be given to this rule. "Negotiating in good faith" may mean:

1. To make it highly probable that agreement will be reached. This means concretely that a party has to lower its terms whenever the probability of reaching an agreement falls below the desired level. Evidently, if a party is "negotiating in good faith" according to this criterion, the opponent should not know it; otherwise he would have an incentive to make agreement unlikely until his terms were met.

[20] Conference on the Discontinuance of Nuclear Weapon Tests, 3d Plenary Meeting, Nov. 4, 1958, p. 17; 56th Plenary Meeting, Feb. 17, 1959, p. 31; 232d Plenary Meeting, July 21, 1960, pp. 19–20; 304th Plenary Meeting, May 10, 1961, p. 28.

Another difficulty with this criterion is that the likelihood of agreement on any given terms depends on the pressures and counter-pressures exerted. Hence a party whose terms were unlikely to be accepted could meet this criterion of "negotiating in good faith" not only by lowering its terms but, paradoxically, also by putting more pressure on the opponent so as to make agreement likely. For example, when Stalin negotiated with Finland in October, 1939, for the transfer of some Finnish territory to Russia, he came to realize that his demands precluded agreement. Then he sent the Red Army against Finland, and after some three months of fighting, the Finnish government (which had continued to negotiate with Moscow) accepted a Soviet proposal that demanded more territory than Stalin's original position. Now, according to the above criterion, Stalin was not "negotiating in good faith" in October, for he made unacceptable demands; but he was "negotiating in good faith" in March, after Red Army pressure made even greater demands acceptable.

2. Not to maintain a position which one feels sure will preclude agreement. For instance, General de Gaulle's position in 1959 that military disengagement in Europe would have to "cover a zone which is as near to the Urals as it is to the Atlantic" was certainly expected by him to preclude agreement. (This may have been a more effective way to counter Communist disengagement proposals than to refuse disengagement in principle.)[21]

According to a more stringent variant of this second criterion, a government should not make even *initial* proposals which it knows to be "unacceptable" to the opponent. This means that not only the position ultimately held but also the first proposals have to be such that there is at least a possibility of the opponent agreeing to

---

[21] De Gaulle announced this position in a press conference on March 25, 1959: "As regards turning Germany into a neutralized territory, this 'extrication' or 'disengagement' in itself says nothing to us which is of value. For if disarmament does not cover a zone which is as near to the Urals as it is to the Atlantic, how will France be protected . . . ? Certainly we are supporters of the control and limitation of all weapons of war." (Quoted in E. Hinterhoff, *Disengagement* [London: Stephens, 1959], p. 268.)

Spanier and Nogee (*The Politics of Disarmament*) maintain that in the postwar disarmament negotiations, neither side ever "negotiated in good faith" (according to this second criterion), because they always included a "joker" in their proposals to make sure they would be rejected.

them. The American government has felt curiously ambivalent toward this rule. On the one hand, it has shown great reluctance in the negotiations on Berlin to make some counter-demands regarding the Wall or self-determination for East Germany, because such demands would have been "unacceptable." On the other hand, it has maintained and vigorously defended a position on general and complete disarmament since 1961 which it clearly knows to be totally unacceptable to the Soviet Union.

3. To want an agreement of the type that is being negotiated and to be eager to have one's terms accepted. In other words, not being determined always to prevent an agreement even when terms are favorable. For example, until 1955 the Russians did not seem to want an Austrian State Treaty even if their terms on reparations and on the definition of German assets had been accepted.

4. To follow certain rules of accommodation while negotiating. Thus if a government violates the rule that concessions must be reciprocated, it may be criticized for not "negotiating in good faith."

The question is often debated whether this or that government really "wishes to negotiate" or is only pretending. Again, the meaning of this phrase "wishing to negotiate" is not clear. Usually, it seems to mean the same as "negotiating in good faith" according to the second or third criterion.

One reason why governments frequently fail to show "good faith" (according to the second or third criterion) is that they pursue Pharisaic propaganda effects. They want to appear good by being engaged in negotiation but do not wish to reach an agreement on the disputed issue.

U.S. legislation on labor-management negotiations throws an interesting sidelight on the difficulty of defining "good faith." The National Labor Relations Act of 1947 (Taft-Hartley Act) imposes on labor and management the obligation to bargain collectively. The act specifies that this obligation means that the employer and the representative of the employees must "meet at reasonable times and confer in good faith with respect to wages," etc., but that it "does not compel either party to agree to a proposal or require the making of a concession."[22] In the earlier Wagner Act, the corre-

[22] 61 Stat. 142 (1947), Sec. 8 (d).

sponding provision went further, requiring the parties to "bargain collectively in a good faith effort to reach an agreement." The question as to what the Taft-Hartley Act required as a test of "good faith" came up in a case before the U.S. Supreme Court, which decided "that the act does not encourage a party to engage in marathon discussions at the expense of frank statements and support of his position . . ." but that the National Labor Relations Board could not "compel concessions or otherwise sit in judgment upon the substantive terms of . . . agreements."[23]

AVOID EMOTIONALISM AND RUDENESS

In his enumeration of the qualities of the "ideal diplomatist," Harold Nicolson includes the quality of calm: "Not only must the negotiator avoid displaying irritation when confronted by the stupidity, dishonesty, brutality, or conceit of those with whom it is his unpleasant duty to negotiate; but he must eschew all personal animosities, or personal predilections, all enthusiasms, prejudices, vanities, exaggerations, dramatizations, and moral indignations."[24]

With this kind of advice, the exceptions are always more interesting than the rule. Sometimes, stiff upper lip notwithstanding, the negotiator should indeed display irritation, to stop his opponent from repeating the same argument or from impugning his motives. At other times he must indulge in dramatization to strengthen his commitments or to focus the discussion on the issue he prefers. And sometimes he must show moral indignation, lest his moral conviction seem doubtful to the opponent.

Although most Western diplomats would not practice Nicolson's precept of complete emotional calm, they do observe the rule that strong emotions should rarely be displayed, and they always adhere to certain conventions of politeness. According to these conventions, invective is to be avoided, the opponent is to be addressed respectfully and may not be interrupted while he has the floor in a formal session, nor should one walk out while he makes his presen-

[23] National Labor Relations Board vs. American National Insurance Co., 343 U.S. 395 (May, 1952), 72 *Supreme Court Reporter*, p. 829. See also Archibald Cox, "The Duty to Bargain in Good Faith," *Harvard Law Review*, LXXI (June, 1958), 1401–33.

[24] *Diplomacy*, p. 116.

tation, arrive deliberately late for an agreed meeting, and so forth. Between allied or friendly nations, almost any breach of these rules of etiquette provokes a deterioration of the relationship.

Yet, it is not obvious why a violation of such conventions should endanger friendly relations between countries. It cannot be explained as offending the "national honor" (except, perhaps, in case of a direct insult to the chief of state), since Western diplomats regularly expose themselves to rudeness in negotiations with the East without involving their "national honor." Nor can it be explained as an impairment of the negotiator's personal relations, since Western diplomats are quite adept at receiving expressions of hostility from the opponent's delegate without ever considering them as a sign of *personal* animosity. Indeed, in East-West negotiations, this distinction between official rudeness and good relations on the personal level is practiced all the time. The significance of rudeness in negotiations between friendly nations must result from something else. Rudeness acts as a signal, it suggests to the aggrieved government that the government of the other party is shifting to a more hostile policy. Not the invective as such, but the expectation of future unfriendly acts provokes the crisis.

In addition to the rules of politeness, friendly countries are expected to refrain from making *explicit* threats and, with certain exceptions, to abstain from intervention in the opponent's domestic affairs. It is interesting to note that these rules may take precedence over the rule of truthfulness. While it is taboo between friendly nations to make threats explicit, threats can be used provided they are disguised as warnings.

An incident between the United States and Canada early in 1963 illustrates that the rule of noninterference in domestic affairs may take precedence over the rule of truthfulness. During a debate in the Canadian Parliament on the question of whether Canada should accept nuclear weapons under U.S. control, Prime Minister Diefenbaker referred to confidential negotiations between Ottawa and Washington on this subject. The U.S. government found that these negotiations were misrepresented by the Prime Minister's statement and issued a correction (State Department release of January 30, 1963). A week later Diefenbaker's government fell. Subsequently, the American government was blamed more for its violation of the noninterference rule than the Canadian Prime Minister was criticized for his lack of truthfulness concerning confidential negotiations.

Communist negotiators do not adhere to the rule that rudeness must always be avoided. But their rudeness is not a wild outburst of emotion or coarse pugilism. No Communist diplomat has ever engaged in a fist-fight at an international conference (unlike some parliamentarians, both Communist and non-Communist, in Rome, Tokyo, and other Western-type parliaments). And Khrushchev's infamous shoe in the United Nations was used as a gavel, not as a cudgel to hit an antagonist.[25]

According to Bolshevik thought, as Nathan Leites explained in his book on the subject, "it pays to be rude." Rudeness as a technique of negotiation has its rationale as well as less conscious motivations but is not an expression of anger. It may serve as a counter-offensive to discourage the enemy, it may be a defense against inner temptations to reveal one's weaknesses (which would mean begging the enemy to desist), or it may reassure oneself that one is not succumbing to the temptation of entertaining good feelings toward the enemy or of imputing such feelings to him.[26] "If my words are disagreeable to some," Khrushchev explained in the UN General Assembly, "this means that I have achieved my aim —this is what I wanted!"[27]

Western diplomats, on the other hand, generally believe that calm, politeness, and respectfulness help to reduce feelings of hostility and hence facilitate agreement. They observe these rules not merely because they feel that rudeness is unseemly but also because they think that it is inexpedient. They remain polite, even while the opponent insults them. At the Korean armistice nego-

[25] "Diplomatic suppleness was shown," reported Adzhubei about this incident. When "Comrade N. S. Khrushchev . . . took off a shoe and began to pound with it on the desk," he "posed the shoe in such a fashion (in front of our delegation sat the delegation of Fascist Spain) that the tip of the shoe was almost set against the neck of the Fascist minister of foreign affairs, but not fully so." A subtle suppleness! (Quoted in S'ezd KPSS. Stenogr. otchet [22d Congress of the Communist Party], II, 473–74.)

[26] Nathan Leites, A Study of Bolshevism (Glencoe, Ill.: The Free Press, 1953), pp. 34–42.

[27] N. S. Khrushchev, Ovneshnei politike Sovetskogo Soiuza (Moscow, 1961), II, 474.

tiations, the Communists never referred to the Republic of Korea or the Nationalist Government of China by their official names, calling them instead "the Syngman Rhee clique" and "your puppet on Formosa." The United Nations delegates, however, faithfully used the official Communist titles, such as "Democratic People's Republic of Korea" when referring to North Korea, and "Democratic People's Republic of China" for Communist China.[28]

A related idea is that one should not push the opponent to the limit. If the last ounce is squeezed out of the opponent, he will show ill will when it comes to carrying out the agreement. A little generosity may be handsomely rewarded by friendlier relations in the long run. As Khrushchev put it (in the speech quoted at the beginning of this chapter), this "is better than having an extra kopek in one's pocket." For Communist negotiators, however, such an attitude is rather exceptional (or modern?).

EXPEDITE AND RATIONALIZE NEGOTIATION PROCESS

Part of the negotiating process consists of an exchange of words at a conference table. As discussed, there are rules of accommodation that can make this exchange more efficient and encourage friendlier attitudes. Thus, rules against invective or against the impugnation of motives serve to eliminate hostile talk (and such talk rarely helps a party to obtain better terms or to reach agreement more quickly). However, other aspects of diplomatic rhetoric that are just as inefficient usually remain strangely exempt from any rules.

This discrepancy is particularly stark in East-West negotiations. On the one hand, elementary rules of politeness may well be observed, and a pretense; at least, is being made of maintaining flexibility, adhering to the agreed agenda, and reciprocating concessions. But on the other hand, there are no rules against repetition, illogical reasoning, unanswered questions, irrelevant arguments, and pointless speeches. While Western diplomats indulge in such activity less than their Communist colleagues, neither side condemns this behavior as improper or inexpedient. Indeed, not only the participating diplomats, but the public at large have become so

[28] William H. Vatcher, *Panmunjom* (New York: Praeger, 1958), p. 209.

used to the inefficiency and pointlessness of the exchange of words in East-West conferences that this wasted motion is no longer questioned. On the contrary, instead of promoting rules against it —as rules have been promoted against, say, inflexibility or invective—diplomats perform these verbal rituals out of habit. If there are any conventions concerning the verbal exchange, they tend to promote these purposeless rituals rather than curb them.

The lack of rules to expedite and rationalize the verbal exchange is all the more bizarre in that these lengthy speeches and unresponsive arguments have little impact on the central purposes of negotiation. They affect the outcome only marginally, if at all. Their main effect is to prolong the process of negotiation. In most cases, they also fail to have a propaganda effect outside of the conference. For the repetitious speeches are heard and read by nobody but the delegates of the other side, and sometimes not even by them.

It is easy enough to imagine the existence of rules to rationalize the talk at the conference table. Much as negotiators are not supposed to out-lie each other, there could be a rule that they should not try to out-argue each other. (After all, a display of rhetorical arguments is not an efficient way of changing the opponent's position.) Much as diplomats are supposed to refrain from invective, there might be a rule that they ought to refrain from repetition. And much as the delegates are expected to show some flexibility, one could conceive of a rule that they should be responsive to questions.

There is a method, however, which sometimes helps to avoid the more irrational and inefficient aspects of the verbal exchange at the conference table. This is the *informal meeting,* where speeches are ordinarily dispensed with, questions are more likely to be answered, and repetition is reduced. Thus, as far as the conduct of the debate is concerned, "informal" negotiations paradoxically are governed by more sensible rules than "formal" ones.

THE COMMUNITY SPIRIT

Nations closely linked in a common effort sometimes develop a highly accommodating negotiating style, which resembles the decision-making process within an intra-governmental committee rather than the usual mode of bargaining between governments. The cooperation between the United States and Great Britain during World War II was conducted in this fashion, particularly on the highest level between Roosevelt and Churchill. More recently, the advocates of closer integration in the European Communities have been promoting such an accommodating style. In the negotiations among the six member states and within the Community organs, the participants are reminded regularly to act in accordance with the "community spirit," *l'esprit communautaire* as it is called in Brussels.

Back in 1950, when Jean Monnet chaired the negotiations for the formation of the Coal and Steel Community, he first taught his co-negotiators to see their task in the "community spirit." He wanted them to focus on the common interest, rather than on trades between conflicting interests, and to maximize the advantages of their joint undertaking, rather than to exchange separate gains and losses with each other. He discouraged compromises in which a party would barter a concession on one issue against some advantage on an entirely different issue. He felt logrolling or heterogeneous package deals would not be conducive to a constructive, joint effort in behalf of the common objectives. Monnet conducted the initial meetings, where the principles of the Coal and Steel Community were first discussed, without any verbatim records. The negotiators were not allowed to hold anyone else to his opinions or statements from earlier meetings. This facilitated the formation of a common view, based on a single conception of the joint undertaking, rather than on bartered compromises. Thus, in this setting a procedure proved fruitful which was the exact opposite of the rule that partial agreements should be adhered to.[29]

Of course, not all negotiations in the history of European integration were conducted in this harmonious fashion. One of the most jarring departures from the *esprit communautaire* was De Gaulle's sudden and unilateral decision to veto Britain's application

[29] Robert Schuman called these negotiations "a new type of a conference," not the usual form of negotiation in which opposing national interests were being defended. "On allait construire une oeuvre commune, à six" (Robert Schuman, "Origines et Élaboration du 'Plan Schuman,'" *Les Cahiers de Bruges* [Dec., 1953], pp. 266–84).

for membership in the Common Market. Walter Hallstein, the president of the Common Market Commission, criticized this decision in his report to the European Parliament, not so much for its substance (although he seemed to disagree with that, too), but for the way in which it was imposed upon the other five member states:

> The manner in which one member Government took and communicated its decision to interrupt the negotiations [with Great Britain] is not in harmony with the duties imposed by the Community. The results of an interruption affect the Community as a whole, not just one Member State. . . . The opening of the negotiations was decided unanimously. . . . In these circumstances one might at the very least have expected that the question of the future of the negotiations, if it had to be raised, would have been discussed fully and frankly amongst the members of the Community. . . . The life of our Community depends on everyone looking upon and treating Community matters as matters of real joint responsibility.[30]

A negotiating style in the "community spirit" is a necessary, but not a sufficient, condition for a successful integration of independent nations. Other conditions must, of course, be met, such as the formation of interest groups that cut across national boundaries, the absence of strongly conflicting objectives, and the existence of specific functions that are important to the member states and can be delegated to a supra-national level. A common external enemy also encourages integration.

What helps to preserve the "community spirit" is the interest of each partner in reciprocation. When nations are engaged in a long-term common effort, each government needs the future collaboration of its partners and remains dependent on their good will. This makes it possible to regard an act of generosity today as establishing a credit for tomorrow. And it makes it safe for negotiators to accept an agreement in principle—provided all partners have the same understanding of it—and to leave the details to the experts or technicians. The "community spirit" permits the negotiators to dispense with some of the more rigid

---

[30] European Economic Community, Commission, "Statement on the Negotiations Concerning Great Britain's Accession . . . by Walter Hallstein," Strasbourg, Feb. 5, 1963.

rules of accommodation that may seem necessary between less friendly nations, such as the pettifogging concern about agendas, the objections to a revision of partial agreements, the one-to-one reciprocation of concessions, and the stickling equality of negotiating languages. Instead, there is a strong emphasis on the common objectives, there are no important hidden motives, and the discourse is free from the wasted verbiage to which the world has become so accustomed in East-West conferences or in the United Nations General Assembly.

CHAPTER 8

DOMESTIC AFFAIRS

IT WOULD BE A MISTAKE TO VIEW THE PARTIES IN INTERNATIONAL negotiations as if they were unitary decision-makers. Domestic politics, bureaucratic idiosyncrasies, and personal motivations all influence their objectives and negotiating tactics. Governments are complex organizations, staffed by officials who compete and disagree and who must in fact negotiate among themselves to formulate the national interest in any conflict with external opponents. Indeed, individual officials as well as whole branches within the government may pursue private interests unrelated to, or sometimes even opposed to, the national interest. Each party will seek to exploit these domestic constraints of the other side and try to take advantage of any dissensions it may detect within the other party's government. However, the fact that governments are not unitary decision-makers does not necessarily benefit the opponent. The diversity of forces at work within a country can lead to greater initial demands and more rigid commitments than if a party were all of one mind.

The interplay of personalities and parochial interests is more apparent in Western governments than in Communist regimes. It is particularly significant in the United States government, whose large size and federal structure permit many forces to impinge on the conduct of foreign affairs. The government's approach to negotiation is the product of diverse personal motives, bureaucratic preferences of different departments, and various public pressures.

This interaction can be traced through debates among government officials, inter-office memoranda, committee meetings, cabinet sessions, and discussions with congressional leaders. It is a process in which news media and the wider public participate in various degrees.

MESSENGERS, DELEGATES, AND SUMMITRY

The diplomat who faces his opponent over the green baize sometimes acts only as a messenger. His powers may be so restricted that he can merely deliver prepared statements, outline positions as prescribed by his government, and receive communications from the opponent. At the other extreme is the negotiator who can take all decisions by himself; that is, while in face-to-face contact with the opponent, he can accept new proposals from the other side, develop counter-proposals on the spot, and conclude agreements or break off negotiations at his own discretion. Negotiators with such wide powers appear only at summit meetings (except for conferences on issues so minor that delegates may be given full freedom). And even "at the summit" the chiefs of government from democratic countries are usually limited in the decisions they can take by themselves.

Soviet diplomats are often constrained to act as mere messengers. This was especially true under Stalin. The narrow instructions of Soviet negotiators handicap Western delegates. Such limitations render the assessment of hard and soft spots in Soviet positions difficult, since all aspects are defended with equal vehemence until new instructions from Moscow permit a sudden concession. This difficulty is compounded by the fact that in Moscow, foreign policy is made in almost complete secrecy.

However, in the Stalin era Soviet diplomats themselves were handicapped by their narrowly limited powers of decision. Since they were unable to explore new developments at their own discretion and were not expected to contribute suggestions for new departures, they were less interested than Western diplomats in exploring the tactical weaknesses of the opponent. Also, they were less capable of engaging in debate and fencing with arguments, since they felt constrained to keep repeating the same line prepared for them in Moscow. Partly because of their narrow instructions and partly for other reasons, Soviet diplomats were unable to develop the more intimate, personal relations with the delegate from the other side that would have given them a deeper understanding of the opponent's position. Nonetheless, Soviet diplomats may have preferred to receive such rigid instructions. Knowing what their government wanted of them may have given them a feeling of safety. They were not expected to explore that treacherous border area where the opponent must be both contradicted and catered to, both attacked and seduced.

In recent years, some Soviet diplomats have acted less like messengers, and occasionally they have even developed personal relations with a Western opponent. But on the whole they still show less initiative and independence than Western diplomats of comparable rank.

Although the messenger-type diplomat may be designated "chief negotiator," he plays only a minor role in negotiation. He acts as the end of a transmission belt for communications that have been determined in his foreign office or by his chief of government, and he may collect some intelligence about the opponent which he will simply send back home. But his risk calculations, changing expectations, and personal feelings scarcely enter into the decision-making process.

More interesting is the role of the delegate who does have some powers of decision and who is given a wider latitude in influencing his home government. Traditionally, such a diplomat is still subject to guidance from his foreign minister or chief of government. But he is one of the important independent actors in international negotiation; he is not just performing a predetermined service-function like a translator or a coding clerk.

The limited authority of a delegate serves to some extent as a commitment. It is not a definitive commitment, of course, since new instructions can break it. Nonetheless, if you are negotiating with a delegate with limited authority, you realize that his instructions represent a certain barrier whose penetration would cost you time and require that you exert additional pressure. Hence your realization that you have pushed your opponent's delegate to the limit of his instructions may dissuade you from further bargaining and cause you to accept the available terms. It is precisely for this reason that your opponent's delegate may want you to be aware of his instructions and may try to convince you that it would be very cumbersome to change them. But you will seek your own information to ferret out what chances there are within your opponent's government for a change in instructions. If you are knowledgeable about the internal forces within your opponent's government, you will seek to encourage those forces that favor a revised position more advantageous to you.

To be negotiating with a delegate whose authority is narrowly limited can be a frustrating experience. When you realize that the opponent's delegate is allowed only to hold to his initial position, you may feel as if you were talking to a phonograph. It will seem futile to argue with such a delegate, the only hope is that he will properly communicate your message to his government. But in the absence of any response, you might be tempted to start experimenting with your own position, particularly if you have a strong preference for agreement. A revised version of your own position might at least produce a new response from the opponent's government and perhaps lead to new instructions to its delegate. The danger here is that you might increasingly adapt your position to that of the opponent, so as to entice a response, but fail to obtain compensating changes in his rigid instructions. To avoid both this danger and the frustration of talking to the messenger instead of to the master, diplomats often first try to ascertain whether the opponent's delegate has any authority to change his position. If not, they may refuse to become drawn into negotiations.

Yet, there are also disadvantages and pitfalls in the other extreme, where the representatives on both sides are of such senior rank that they have full authority. This raises the question of *summit diplomacy*. In the 1950s, summit meetings between East and West were a lively issue. An East-West summit meeting was first advocated by Winston Churchill in 1950, when he was still leader of the opposition. After Stalin's death, in May, 1953, Prime Minister Churchill renewed his call for a conference "on the highest level . . . not overhung by a ponderous or rigid agenda, or led into mazes or jungles of technical details, zealously contested by hordes of experts and officials drawn up in vast, cumbrous array. The Conference should be confined to the smallest number of powers . . . [and] meet with a measure of informality and still greater measure of privacy and seclusion."[1] Later in the decade, it was Khrushchev who seized the initiative in pressing for summit meetings, with the British government generally willing to go along, but the United States showing considerable reluctance.[2]

The main consideration in summit meetings (as sometimes in other types of conferences) may be the side-effects of negotiation. One reason for the American coolness toward top-level meetings was the feeling that Khrushchev wanted them primarily for propaganda purposes. The propaganda effect can be twofold. First, summits are particularly suited as "sounding boards": any policies that the participants advocate will be endowed with world-wide prominence because the news media devote such central attention to a summit conference. The summit serves like a huge megaphone for national programs on foreign policy. Second, as mentioned before, some leaders may wish to attend summits to enhance their prestige. This, too, may have been an objective for Khrushchev during the 1950s, since he was still in the process of gathering all the reins of power in his own hands.

Another important side-effect of summit negotiation is to establish or to maintain contact between the chiefs of government. According to President Kennedy, this was the primary purpose of his Vienna talks with Khrushchev in 1961. The idea here is that a face-to-face meeting will give statesmen a better understanding of each other's intentions and will strengthen the habit of communicating with one another whenever matters of conflict arise.

Less controversial and less dramatic are summit meetings between friendly powers. They fit more easily into the larger context of intimate diplomatic relations, and the broader basis of common interests facilitates the conduct of negotiations at the summit. Indeed, if friendly powers wish to collaborate extensively and in diverse fields, summit diplomacy plays a key role. Negotiation on a lower level will often reach an impasse finally, because each delegate is in charge of only a narrow sector of the over-all national in-

---

[1] *Hansard,* 515 H.C. Debate 5 s, col. 897 (May 11, 1953).
[2] For an account of this debate about summitry, see Coral Bell, *Negotiating from Strength: A Study in Politics* (New York: Knopf, 1963).

terest and cannot make trades or package deals encompassing several sectors. Who but the Prime Minister or the President can trade a tariff concession against a military advantage or a clause in a political agreement against a clause in a financial compact?

Summit meetings, in a way, are characterized by the coalescence of several processes that remain separate in other types of negotiation. The chiefs of government formulate their own proposals, put forward supporting arguments, receive information from the opponent, weigh the opponent's proposals, develop their counter-arguments, and decide whether to modify or to maintain their position. The exchange of proposals and counter-proposals and the modification of positions all take place within a few hours— or a few days at the most. Normally, different people are in charge of different phases of this process and considerable time may lapse between one move and the next. Because of this coalescence, summit diplocacy can be more efficient, in terms of the ground covered at a conference, than lower-level negotiation. But for the same reason, summit meetings are also moments of crisis, where great opportunities might be exploited or missed, and where a wrong step can cause a national disaster. As Dean Rusk put it: "The direct confrontation of the chiefs of government of the great powers involves an extra tension because the court of last resort is in session."[3]

Americans have their own historical reasons for distrusting summit diplomacy. There is the memory of President Wilson's fatal experience at the Paris Peace Conference, which dramatizes the fact that in the United States foreign policy cannot be made by the executive alone. There are other Constitutional reasons why the President finds it particularly difficult to attend international conferences. In Dean Rusk's words, negotiation at the summit "diverts time and energy from exactly the point at which we can spare it least."[4] The President can ill afford the time for the extensive preparations that negotiation usually requires, and the vast machinery of the United State government is not centralized enough fully to serve the President at a distant conference site and in situations changing by the hour. As a result, the most fatal

[3] Dean Rusk, "The President," *Foreign Affairs* (April, 1960), p. 365.
[4] *Ibid.*, p. 361.

decisions are not only taken at the spur of the moment—which is inevitable in fast-moving negotiation—but often with the advice of people who had to master the detailed issues in as hurried a fashion as the President himself.

It is true that with modern communications it may now be easier than in the days of Yalta and Potsdam to draw on the skills and expertise of the State Department and Defense Department— if the President wishes to do so. In the past the President had to rely on a few men who traveled with him and who may have had a quite limited knowledge of the issues at stake or took a rather special point of view. Thus the summit added to the influence of the special Presidential adviser who was neither elected nor appointed by Congress. It offered the occasion when a Colonel House, a Harry Hopkins, a Presidential speechwriter, or the President's press secretary were called upon to make history. Nonetheless, today any summit conference in which the American President participates is accompanied by enormous publicity so that momentary propaganda effects will inevitably be of major concern. This may not only divert attention from the more important issues, but it may put the Russians at an advantage since they know how to be more callous about public opinion.

PAROCHIAL BUREAUCRATS

Negotiators are sometimes diverted from serving the interest of their government by loyalties to a department or a service, as distinct from the government as a whole. Most international negotiations affect several government departments. In the American government, for example, tariff negotiations are the concern of the Commerce, Treasury, and State Departments, and at times the Department of Agriculture; disarmament negotiations involve the Disarmament Agency, the Defense Department, and the AEC; and in the Berlin negotiations, the State and Defense Departments are drawn in.

Usually the various government departments derive different practical implications from agreed national objectives and have conflicting domestic interests to defend. In fact, in democratic countries, the continuous bargaining that normally takes place between different parts of the government is the principal way in which the national interest becomes formulated.[5] For officials involved in negotiations, the national interest is therefore not a given constant but is something that has to be discussed in each case and frequently revised as the situation evolves.

But there is more to this than different conceptions of national objectives or different syntheses of conflicting domestic interests. Sometimes, government departments favor a certain course in negotiations in order to increase their own power or to get a larger share of the budget.

In the American government, owing to its federal structure and large size, the interests of departments and various offices intrude into the conduct of international negotiations more strongly than, say, in the French or the British government. How a parochial concern with bureaucratic power disabled the U.S. government in the pursuit of its foreign policy objectives is illustrated by Philip Mosely's account of the wartime negotiations on the zonal boundaries for Germany. During 1943–44, representatives of the United States, Great Britain, and the Soviet Union met in the European Advisory Committee in London to settle a number of postwar arrangements for Europe, in particular the zonal boundaries in Germany. The American delegation to the Committee was to receive instructions from an interdepartmental group in Washington. However, the State Department representatives in this group were unable to convince their colleagues from the War Department of the importance of settling with the Soviet Union and Great Britain the postwar arrangements for Germany. Owing to the War Department's opposition—which perhaps stemmed from the desire to reserve complete freedom of action for its occupation troops—there was no American position on how the zonal boundaries with the Soviet occupation forces in Germany should be drawn, and no specific provisions for access to Berlin were prepared. In the end, the agreed upon zones for Germany were based entirely upon a British proposal (which had originated with recommendations

[5] Charles E. Lindblom, "The Science of 'Muddling Through,'" *Public Administration Review*, XIX (Spring, 1959), 74–88. For a comparison of the British, American, and Soviet systems for coordinating the conduct of foreign policy among different departments, see Joseph Frankel, *The Making of Foreign Policy* (London: Oxford University Press, 1963), pp. 33–35.

from the British Chiefs of Staff). The only concern of the War Department was that detailed arrangements be made with the British, so that the American forces would have free access to their zone through the British zone.[6]

The interdepartmental coordination of a negotiating position can be rather cumbersome. It may bring forth a prolonged exchange of memoranda and require repeated conferences and consultations. Points that cannot be reconciled will have to be sumbitted to the President for a decision. The fact that an appeal to higher authority is possible marks the difference between bargaining *within* a government and international negotiation. Sometimes the chief negotiator and his team may spend more energy and time arguing with government officials back home, in order to have the positions of other departments changed or overruled, than in trying to change the opponent's position. Occasionally though, the sluggishness of interdepartmental coordination may serve the negotiator like a commitment: the fact that it is so difficult to change an agreed position within his government provides the negotiator with an extra incentive to resist the opponent's pressures for concessions.

The difficulty of intra-governmental coordination also helps to explain why a minimum position (distinct from the terms offered to the opponent) can be rarely maintained by a government whose departments enjoy a certain independence—as in Washington. For if such a minimum existed, the negotiator would soon be urged to fall back on it by those branches within the government that are anxious to conclude an agreement but consider the particular terms less important. Precisely for this reason, other branches within the government, for which the particular terms *are* important, will not agree to a minimum position to begin with.

[6] Philip E. Mosely, "The Occupation of Germany: New Light on How the Zones Were Drawn," *Foreign Affairs* (July, 1950), pp. 580–604. According to Mosely's account, the War Department held that the determination of the future zones of occupation "was a 'military matter' which would be decided 'at the proper time' and 'at the military level' " (pp. 587–88). Llewellyn Woodward, in the official British history of World War II, reports that Eden complained to Stettinius, that the Americans were not keeping to the directives given to the European Advisory Commission at the Moscow Conference. "Mr. Stettinius agreed that the War Department was largely responsible for the American attitude" (*British Foreign Policy in the Second World War* [London: H.M.S.O., 1962], p. 477).

DOMESTIC PRESSURE GROUPS AND SECRET DIPLOMACY

Domestic forces may desire to influence international negotiations for either of two reasons: a concern about foreign policy, or private interests. Domestic groups that are concerned about foreign policy hold their own views regarding the national welfare or regarding international issues and have their own convictions as to how principles like freedom and justice ought to be pursued in practice. This is exemplified by the groups worried about disarmament negotiations, both those in favor of reaching agreements by conceding more to the Russians and those favoring greater caution and firmness—the "peace groups" and the advocates of military strength. Other examples are the involvement of the German population in the Berlin negotiations and the interest in European integration shown by the younger generation in Western Europe.

Then there are the private-interest groups whose members are concerned with the effects of an agreement on their *personal* welfare, as distinct from holding a certain view of the *national* interest. Tariff negotiations and commercial agreements make characteristic battlegrounds for such private interests. The negotiations for the American-Japanese peace treaty mobilized both foreign-policy interests (particularly on the question of Communist China's relation to Japan) and the private interests of the West Coast fishing industry.[7]

Occasionally, the opponent can encourage these private interests to fight for his cause. Proposing to swap duty reductions in tariff negotiations has this effect. Exporting industries in the United States, for example, may become the advocates of American tariff reductions requested by European countries, if such American reductions have been made the condition for lower tariffs in Europe. In a sense, there is an alliance in tariff negotiations between private interest groups in each of the countries involved. However, these groups rarely go so far as to join forces to oppose an agreement that their governments wish to negotiate. Before World

[7] For an account of how the fishing industry influenced the course and outcome of these negotiations, see Bernard C. Cohen, *The Political Process in Foreign Policy: The Making of the Japanese Peace Settlement* (Princeton, N.J.: Princeton University Press, 1957), pp. 253–77.

War I and in the 1920s, some writers speculated about a conspiracy of the "munition makers" in sabotaging disarmament conferences. A parallel would be if industries threatened by imports conspired to prevent agreements for tariff reductions; say, the French farmer ganging up with the American textile and bicycle manufacturers to wreck a GATT conference! Such stories, of course, are usually apocryphal.

Ethnic, historical, and ideological sympathies sometimes lead domestic groups to try to influence international negotiations, as illustrated by the concern of Americans of Polish descent for the impact of the Yalta and Potsdam Conferences on Poland and the involvement of American Zionists in U.S. policies toward Israel and the Middle East.[8] Such groups represent neither private interest nor a particular view of the national interest. They express an attachment to the cause of a foreign country or a foreign population.

Governments often feel handicapped in the pursuit of national objectives if domestic interest groups become involved in their negotiations. Citizens in favor of a "hard position" will criticize any concessions to the opponent, those who want an agreement will criticize the government's "inflexibility," but neither group may take an over-all view of the prospects of getting an agreement at various terms and of the value of these terms to the nation as a whole as compared with no-agreement. For this reason, many writers and statesmen have favored *secret diplomacy*. Woodrow Wilson's phrase has been revised; nowadays it is said that governments should seek "open agreements secretly arrived at."

In the spring of 1963, U.S. Senator J. William Fulbright listened with some exasperation to Congressional hearings on the seemingly endless test-ban negotiations and offered this counsel to the Secretary of State: ". . . I rather disagree with the whole procedure you are following—that you try to get agreements of this kind in the open. I think they do not lend themselves to fruitful discussions, if everything the negotiators say has to be addressed

[8] See H. Bradford Westerfield, *Foreign Policy and Party Politics* (New Haven: Yale University Press, 1958), for a discussion of the Zionist role in the American policy regarding the Palestine question, as well as for an excellent general account of the impact of domestic forces on American diplomacy from 1939 to 1950.

to the local constituency back home, rather than to the people participating in the meeting. . . . It seems to me you ought to be able to arrange for negotiations to be private, of course making whatever you conclude public."[9] Four months after Senator Fulbright had made this comment, the test-ban talks were indeed conducted in secrecy, when Averell Harriman and Viscount Hailsham concluded a treaty with Andrei Gromyko to ban all but underground tests.

Much has been written about the merits of secret versus open negotiation since the Wilsonian injunction against secret diplomacy. Although Harold Nicolson and other writers have done a service in debunking the strictures against secret bargaining,[10] both the advocates of secrecy and those of openness have gone too far in making such a clear-cut distinction between these two forms of diplomacy—one of them being the right way and the other one being wicked. Secrecy is a matter of degree.

Negotiations are often kept partly secret. The discussions between the diplomats may not be revealed, but enough about the basic demands and offers may become known to stimulate domestic pressures for changes in the government's position. At times, the mere fact that negotiations take place about a certain issue may be sufficient to lead to uneasiness and protests among certain groups and arouse impatient demands by others that an agreement be concluded. This kind of public reaction all depends on the way in which the news media report the semi-secret negotiations.

Some of the reporting on certain phases in the Berlin negotiations in 1962, for example, maintained a feeling of crisis and urgency among the public, although there was no apparent danger of a Soviet intervention at that time. Important newspapers, particularly the *New York Times,* tended to give prominence to every encounter between the Soviet ambassador and the Secretary of

[9] U.S. Senate, Committee on Foreign Relations, *Hearing: Test Ban Negotiations and Disarmament,* March 11, 1963 (Washington, 1963), pp. 23–24.

[10] Nicolson points out that President Wilson himself negotiated one of the most important agreements in utmost secrecy, less than a half year after promulgating in the first of his Fourteen Points that in the future there should be "open convenants of peace openly arrived at." At the end of the Versailles Conference, he shut himself up in his own study with Lloyd George and Clemenceau, excluding not only the press but all other powers from the crucial deliberations (*Diplomacy,* pp. 83–84).

State and to any similar secret discussions on which Berlin may
have been a topic, portraying each of these meetings as another
fruitless round in the Berlin negotiations. This stimulated the
public feeling that the situation was abnormal and ought to be
resolved by a new agreement; that is, the crisis atmosphere fed the
expectation that a satisfactory outcome would have to be different
from the status quo. To appreciate this influence of the news media,
one must recall that every time an ambassador meets with the
Secretary of State, issues are discussed which often remain un-
resolved. The public will remain unaware of all these "negotiations" that continue day after day without a "solution," unless the
news media convey the impression that a critical situation exists.

The distinction between open and secret negotiation should not
be confused with the distinction between *formal* and *informal*
negotiation. In informal negotiations, the deliberations are usually
secret, whereas a formal conference can be either open or secret.
What distinguishes informal negotiation is that the talking done
by the diplomats is more conversational, more an exchange of
questions and answers than a confrontation of prepared statements.
In informal negotiation, the diplomats normally have a tacit understanding that all positions taken are tentative; that is, they feel
they need not adhere to the rules that partial agreements ought to
be preserved and that concessions must not be withdrawn. But
sometimes a party does not share this understanding (or breaks
it) and may complain openly that the other party reversed a position put forward in an informal meeting. Another aspect of
informal negotiation is the importance of personal relations between the diplomats. In informal contacts, negotiators are more
likely to be influenced by feelings towards each other than in
formal conferences.

Secrecy (as distinguished from informality) has two major
effects in diplomacy. First, it keeps domestic groups ignorant of the
process of negotiation, thereby preventing them from exerting
pressures during successive phases of bargaining. Second, it leaves
third parties in the dark and thus reduces their influence.

The exclusion of the public may help to overcome domestic
opposition to concessions or threats before negotiations are completed. Once the agreement is signed, it tends to act as a *fait*

accompli, weakening dissent and mobilizing interest groups in support of it. Thus the requisite domestic consent (such as Senate ratification for the United States) may be obtained in the end, whereas the individual concessions would have been opposed. At other times, open negotiations get stuck in a rut where the parties feel compelled to follow a certain formal routine, although they all realize its inefficiency. This seems to have happened with most disarmament conferences. (Actually, many secret talks on disarmament have been just as unsuccessful as the open ones!) However, if all participating governments desire agreement and feel that open negotiation would not succeed, they are likely to collaborate in maintaining secrecy. Their collaboration will usually end as soon as one side thinks that it can gain by appealing to the public. This may be done by means of a "leak" to news media. Indeed, a leak about a secret conference often gets more attention than the daily reports from open meetings. No matter what preferences one might have regarding secret versus open diplomacy, one must realize that each party will try to move toward or press for that form of negotiation from which it expects the best results.

The second important effect of conducting negotiations in secret—provided secrecy can be maintained—is to keep governments of third parties in the dark. This is essential in triangular situations, when two parties want to make a deal at the expense of a third one. On other occasions, two parties may have a common interest in keeping their negotiations secret to prevent a third party from exploiting their differences. The parties will then have to maintain a precarious balance between their common interest in excluding the third party and their conflicting interest in using leaks and publicity in order to put pressure on the opponent. This is illustrated by the Sino-Soviet conflict, about which more and more is being revealed in both Moscow and Peking.

A sub-group *within* an alliance may negotiate in secret in order to confront the other partners with a finished agreement which it will be difficult to oppose. In international organizations such coalitions are constantly formed under various degrees of secrecy. For example, there are regular caucuses among members of the United Nations General Assembly. If an alliance is to maintain its cohesion, however, partners who negotiate secretly must be careful not to give the impression of "ganging up" on the others. In January, 1963, both Paris and Bonn had to reassure the other four partners in the Common Market that the Franco-German Treaty would not be used to form secret coalitions on issues relating to the Common Market.

Prior to the wartime conference at Teheran between Roosevelt, Churchill, and Stalin, there was to be an Anglo-American meeting at Cairo. President Roosevelt was anxious that the discussions between the American and British staffs in Cairo should not give Stalin the feeling that he was being excluded from important secret negotiations. He wrote to the Prime Minister: "In regard to Cairo, I have held all along, as I know you have, that it would be a terrible mistake if Uncle J. thought we had ganged up on him on military action. . . . It will not hurt you or me if Molotov and a Russian military representative are in Cairo too. They will not feel that they are being given the 'run around.' . . . Let us take them in on the high spots." Churchill did not care for this reference to "ganging up." He cabled back: "His Majesty's Government cannot abandon their rights to full and frank discussions with you and your officers about the vital business of our intermingled armies. A Soviet observer cannot possibly be admitted to the intimate conversations which our own Chiefs of Staff must have. . . ."[11]

THE EXECUTIVE, THE LEGISLATURE, AND THE PUBLIC

In all international conferences, negotiators are prone to argue that their government has made more concessions and bigger ones than the opponent. In part, they may do so out of habit, as one of the routine forms of speech-making at the conference table.

In part, negotiators emphasize their concessions in order to induce the opponent to make concessions of his own. This may be effective, on the one hand, when your opponent feels constrained by the rule that concessions ought to be reciprocated. On the other hand, if you are negotiating with a more hard-headed opponent, you magnify your own concessions for a different reason. Such an opponent will not think that he ought to make a concession in

[11] *Closing the Ring* (Boston: Houghton Mifflin, 1951), p. 319.

return, merely to follow the rule of reciprocation. But he might be convinced that you cannot give another inch before he concedes something, since you could not afford to create the impression back home (or with other powers) that you were constantly receding while he stood firm. That is, you magnify your concessions in order to create a commitment. This commitment stems from the fact that your domestic public or your legislators believe concessions ought to be reciprocated.

However, like most negotiating tactics, this method has to be used with moderation. The negotiator must be cautious not to magnify his concessions so much that his legislators and the domestic press will turn against him. Of course, the same domestic opposition groups may favor hard bargaining on one issue and soft bargaining on another, depending on their foreign-policy preferences. For example, the British Labour Party criticized the Macmillan government for having made too many concessions when it tried in 1962 to gain entry into the Common Market. But on the nuclear test ban, Labour often criticized the Conservative government for not conceding enough to obtain a treaty with the Soviet Union.

While the inspection system for underground tests was an issue (that is, before the partial ban of August, 1963), the American negotiators at the test-ban conference were criticized for the opposite reason. From 1958 through 1962, the United States revised its demands for underground detection several times, in ways that brought its position closer to Russia's. This helped the American delegation to maintain a common stand with the British (who were under domestic pressure to concede more), and it also won support for the Western position among the neutral participants at the disarmament conference. But this series of revisions—which appeared to be unilateral concessions—was less well received by some members of Congress. Senator Thomas J. Dodd, for example, made a critical speech in which he listed a large number of American concessions and argued: ". . . we have repeatedly shown ourselves willing to compromise and to go the 'extra mile.' By this time we have gone the 'extra mile' so many times over that we have virtually lost sight of our point of departure. We have made these concessions piecemeal, so that our position at any given moment has never been too different from our position 3 months previously. It is only by going back to the beginning and laying our concessions end to end that the terrifying scope of our retreat becomes apparent."[12] Similar criticism had been voiced earlier. In August, 1962, for instance, Governor Rockefeller and other Republican leaders complained that the United States was moving "steadily toward the Soviet position."

In response to these charges, the State Department Press Officer found it necessary to justify the U.S. negotiating tactics by arguing that the new proposals were based "not on concessions but on scientific findings."[13] And Senator Hubert Humphrey defended the revisions in the American position similarly:

. . . every time I pick up a paper . . . I read about the "concessions" that we are making, which has the effect with the public of saying, "What's the matter with the administration, this Government, this country of ours—conceding to the Russians?"

It would be like this. If you found that it required 100,000 units of penicillin to check pneumonia, and you had been giving 1 million units of penicillin . . . , I suppose then we should say the doctors are making a concession to pneumonia.[14]

The drawback of such explanations on the domestic scene is that the opponent can turn them to his advantage. If Washington says that the revised Western positions are based not on concessions but on new scientific findings, the Russians can use this to argue that they, on the contrary, *did* make concessions—not just adaptions to scientific requirements—and that it is time for the West finally to make sacrifices.

Yet, even the Russians sometimes have to steer between the Scylla of failing to magnify concessions while talking to the opponent and the Charybdis of appearing to concede too much while explaining a new position to domestic critics or allies. No doubt when Khrushchev withdrew his missiles from Cuba in 1962, he would have liked to press for "counter-concessions" in exchange. But back in Moscow, it was felt necessary to let the

[12] Speech on the Senate floor, Feb. 21, 1963, *Congressional Record*, pp. 5–6.
[13] *New York Times*, Aug. 10, 1962.
[14] U.S. Senate, Subcommittee of the Committee on Foreign Relations, *Hearings: Renewed Geneva Disarmament Negotiations*, July 25 and Aug. 2, 1962 (Washington, 1963), p. 47.

First Deputy Premier, A. N. Kosygin, describe the resolution of the Cuba crisis as follows: "Who gave in to whom in this situation? We consider that it was a concession from both sides, a concession to reason and peace. . . . On the basis of compromise and mutual concessions, the acuteness of the conflict has been eliminated. . . ."[15]

Different attitudes toward concessions of course constitute only one of the reasons why the executive branch of the government may come in conflict with the legislature or with other domestic forces. More important than this question of negotiating tactics, quite different views may prevail on the objectives of agreement and on whether agreement is to be preferred to no-agreement. In fact, these more basic preferences often determine the attitudes toward concessions. If the domestic public views no-agreement as a serious failure, so that it worries only about a breakdown of a conference while showing little interest in the possible terms, it will not object to concessions. In response to the public mood, therefore, the negotiator may feel forced to accept what he considers to be unsatisfactory terms.

Secretary of State James Byrnes found himself in this quandary at the first meeting of the Council of Foreign Ministers in September, 1945, where important peace settlements for Europe and the Far East were discussed. After a number of meetings, Molotov made it clear that the Soviets would not proceed with the conference unless France and China were excluded. "We were determined to yield no further," reported Byrnes of this impasse. "Yet we were reluctant to let the first test of the peace-making machinery result in complete breakdown. . . . The public at home did not have the clear view of Soviet ambitions that the President and I got at Potsdam. . . . The first meeting of the council would be a complete failure and I realized that the failure would be attributed to me." After Byrnes had refused to yield to Molotov's demands and the conference broke up, he was still worried about what he thought was a strong preference for an agreement among the American public. "With the break-up of

---

[15] Kosygin's speech at the Kremlin Palace in Moscow, Nov. 6, 1962 (Daily Report, Foreign Radio Broadcasts, *Foreign Broadcast Information Service* [Nov. 7, 1962], p. BB15).

the council I headed for the United States knowing I had to face criticism."[16]

John Foster Dulles, who accompanied Byrnes as a Republican adviser, takes credit for having encouraged Byrnes to maintain what he thought was such an unpopular stand. "Without my presence," Dulles wrote, "Secretary Byrnes could not have known that he could come home with what, superficially, was a total failure without being subject to criticism by the opposition."[17]

After this experience, Secretary Byrnes concluded "that hereafter people would have to be more fully informed if we were to maintain a firm position in international affairs with full public support."[18] During this early postwar period, other American officials felt themselves to be under similar pressure because they thought American public opinion forced them to avoid a conflict with Russia at all costs. In March, 1946, the American ambassador in Warsaw, Arthur Bliss Lane, recommended that the United States take a firmer stand against the suppression of non-Communist parties in Poland. He wrote to the State Department: ". . . it is essential for the Congress and for the American public to be informed regarding conditions in Poland, Yugoslavia, etc. Education of the public cannot take place overnight. . . . There will be attacks on us from the left-wing press and from some of the more radical labor elements to the effect that we are endeavoring to bring about hostilities with the Soviet Union."[19]

A chief of government who feels secure about public opinion can fortify his representatives against the temptation to please the public with quick agreements. When General de Gaulle sent his foreign minister to the San Francisco conference in 1945, his instructions included a specific warning against yielding to criticism in the press:

You will have to defend yourself not only against the pressure of those Powers who are in a hurry to consolidate a balance of power which is at the moment to their advantage *vis-à-vis* us, but also against the natural desire of our own negotiators—a desire to agree with their partners, and finish the job, so to speak. But I must insist that any such

[16] James F. Byrnes, *Speaking Frankly,* pp. 104, 107.
[17] John Foster Dulles, *War or Peace* (New York: Macmillan, 1950), p. 127.
[18] *Op. cit.,* p. 107.
[19] Arthur Bliss Lane, *I Saw Poland Betrayed* (New York: Bobbs-Merrill, 1948), p. 195.

action would prove to our detriment in the present period. This means you must on no account yield even if an outcry is raised in the press and in foreign broadcasts, or even French, which may try to force you to a decision. Since we have been reduced to our present situation our most successful moves have been those that have raised the most violent storms.[20]

Sometimes the senior negotiator himself may make a special effort to gain public support and to protect himself against domestic pressure that could adversely affect his conduct of negotiations. John Foster Dulles did this rather successfully when he was the chief American negotiator for the Japanese Peace Treaty.[21] At that time, Dulles had a specific objective in mind: he knew what kind of peace treaty he wanted, and he made sure—by paying considerable attention to Congressional and public opinion—that he would obtain the requisite consent from the Senate.

However, if the negotiators (or the decision-makers instructing them) fail to develop their own objectives and strategy, their attempt to marshal public support will be vitiated: it will become a way of seeking guidance *from the public*. The mass media, editorial writers, columnists, commentators, and spokesmen for interest groups will take the lead in determining what the country should want to bargain for and how it should go about doing it. So-called public opinion—that is, mainly the current views of the news media—will become the primary concern of the government's policy, and the objectives of gaining the support of "public opinion" will be used to conceal the lack of any more substantial foreign-policy objectives.

In intra-governmental discussions, officials may rationalize their personal preferences in favor of a certain negotiating position with arguments such as "public opinion wants us to . . ." or "public opinion would not permit us to. . . ." Perhaps these officials could not get away with their facile claims if their colleagues pressed them for the following three explanations: First, how they define "public opinion" (whether it is the view of a couple of newspaper editors, a Gallup poll on a particularly phrased question, or the verdict of a popular referendum). Second, how they

---

[20] General de Gaulle, *Salvation, 1944–1946*, Vol. II, *Documents*, p. 237 (from a letter to Georges Bidault, April 17, 1945).

[21] Bernard C. Cohen, *The Political Process in Foreign Policy*, pp. 133–42.

know that public opinion, thus defined, would react in the indicated way to the issue under discussion. And third, how they came to the conclusion that public opinion should take precedence over the judgment of officials whom the electorate put in charge of foreign affairs and who ought to be better informed than the public at large.[22]

There is another risk in trying to conduct negotiations so as to please public opinion. The mood of the public may be genuinely misjudged. As a result, a negotiator may be afraid to make concessions that not only would have benefited his country but also would have been quite acceptable to the public. Conversely, he may fail to pursue his objectives more aggressively, even though his country would have supported him. Such an underestimate of public support may have handicapped the American government at the end of World War II and during the first few postwar years. The editorial opinion of a few leading newspapers and some prominent columnists may have misled the American decision-makers into believing that the country would not support a firmer stand against the Soviet take-over of Eastern Europe. A series of opinion polls from that period show that the American public, as distinct from the editorial opinion in the news media, would have gone along with a slower demobilization after World War II, thus providing the basis for a firmer foreign policy, and that Congress was influenced by a vocal minority which wanted "to bring the boys back home."[23]

All this is not to say that the views and attitudes of the electorate are not important for the conduct of foreign relations. The electorate ought to support and participate in the basic value judgments that have to be rendered, both explicity and implicitly, in foreign-policy decisions. And the people must approve of the sacrifices they may have to make in support of a foreign policy.

[22] The difficulties of defining and measuring "public opinion" are of course well known to experts. See, for example, Leonard S. Cottrell, Jr., and Sylvia Eberhart, *American Opinion on World Affairs: In the Atomic Age* (Princeton, N.J.: Princeton University Press, 1948), chap. i, for a brief and judicious discussion of these problems.

[23] Nancy Boardman Eddy, "Public Opinion and U.S. Foreign Policy 1937–1956," unpublished paper of the Center for International Studies, M.I.T. (Cambridge, Mass., 1958).

CHAPTER 9

PERSONALITIES

LIKE ANY HUMAN BEINGS, OFFICIALS WHO PLAY A ROLE IN negotiations have their emotions, personal frailties, and quirks, whether they work in the lower echelons of the government or in its highest decision-making councils, whether they stay in the home capital or participate in a conference abroad. They are all influenced by their own sympathies or hostilities; they all respond to anger, impatience, and feelings of gratitude. They have personal ambitions which are rarely, if ever, identical with the interests of their country.

NEGOTIATOR OR MEDIATOR?

Agreement in itself, regardless of the terms, may become a measure of success for a diplomat. Although it is sometimes best for the national interest to terminate negotiations with no agreement, for the negotiator himself such an outcome is often tinged with failure. He will consider an agreement as his target unless he has been specifically instructed to avoid reaching one. It is the goal toward which his efforts and labors are dedicated. In the end, especially in protracted conferences, the reaching of a formal accord will assume importance for him independent of the terms of settlement.

This view of agreement as a measure of success affects not only the chief negotiator but also the members of his delegation. In many international conferences, junior officials and supporting staff members will have to work long into the night and over weekends to evaluate some new proposal from the other side, to revise a position, or to prepare a speech for the next session. If there is no agreement when the conference ends, all this work—the carefully calculated positions and the shrewdly drafted proposals— might seem to have been in vain. As for the chief negotiator himself, it takes a detached view to remain confident that the "failure" of his conference need not at all imply that *he* has failed, much as his reaching an agreement per se does not mean he has succeeded. Indeed, if the negotiator asks himself how history will come to judge his work—and which senior diplomat does not do so?—he must realize that diplomats are generally praised for the good agreements they concluded, not for the bad ones they avoided, since historians find it hard to reconstruct what the terms and consequences of such unborn accords might have been.

This attachment to agreement per se is not new to the nuclear era. From the days of Munich in 1938, Sir Samuel Hoare recalled that he had been "caught up in the toils of a critical negotiation," like Prime Minister Neville Chamberlain and Hoare's cabinet colleagues. "The longer it went on and the more serious the issue became, the more anxious I grew to see it succeed. This is almost always the course of negotiations. As they proceed, the parties concerned in them become increasingly obsessed with the need to prevent their final failure."[1]

It seems paradoxical that the *defensive* party in redistribution negotiations (as at Munich) should be "obsessed with the need to prevent their final failure." For what do "failure" and "success" mean? The defensive side may be successful even if such negotiations "fail," since it may have deterred the offensive side from carrying out its threat and thus preserved the status quo in peace. This has been the success of the "failure" of the Berlin negotiations between 1958 and 1963. If the negotiator is attached to agreement, he may believe that there will be a "solution" for almost any negotiation, meaning that a formal accord can be found to satisfy the basic objectives of both sides. However, as long as he is engaged in redistribution negotiations, such an accord is not possible (the

[1] *Nine Troubled Years,* p. 311.

opponent's objectives being incompatible with his own). Therefore, if he remains nonetheless dedicated to finding a "solution,"
this means one of two things: either he expects that the opponent
will change to more benign objectives (such as normalization), or
he will modify his own objectives and himself furnish the "solution" by accepting a deterioration of the status quo.

As a consequence of this bias in favor of agreement, the chief
negotiator (and his team) may prefer agreement to no-agreement
more than the interests of his government would indicate. Unless
he is a disciplined public servant, he may even act as a *mediator*
between his government and that of the opponent instead of as an
advocate of his own side. Should this go so far that the reaching of
an agreement becomes his dominant measure of success, he will
resemble a broker who obtains his commission only if the transaction is concluded, while the price at which his client buys is a
secondary matter.

A tendency to mediate impinges upon the course of negotiations
in various ways. One effect is that the negotiator will seek to obtain agreement by leaving out all the hard-core residual issues of
disagreement. Carried to the extreme, this leads to the pseudo-
agreements discussed before. Another effect is that the negotiator
will be strongly devoted to the rule of flexibility. He may from the
start present his government's position in a way suggesting that
he expects to split the difference. Or, the negotiator may tempt his
own government into making concessions by predicting that they
would bring about a desired counter-concession. Occasionally, he
may even use a *fait accompli* to force his government to agree; he
might, for instance, report that the opponent has already consented
to a certain compromise at an informal meeting. And if there is a
dispute within the government over a softer position and a harder
one, the mediating negotiator will invariably take advantage of it
by pushing the soft position.

Communist diplomats hardly permit themselves to slide into
such a mediating role. Unlike their Western opponents, they do not
reveal the slightest difference between their own position and that
of their government. In fact, they probably scarcely think of having
a position of their own but see their role only as that of an advocate.
In Western democracies, on the other hand, the politically active

citizen is accustomed to look critically at the policies of his government. Even after entering government service, therefore, he is able to maintain his own views on foreign affairs. In countries like the United States, this is encouraged by the fact that senior diplomats often move back and forth between government service, private life, and political activity in behalf of the domestic opposition. Such part-time diplomats may find it more natural occasionally to act as a mediator than to maintain an unwavering advocacy of all the positions that happened to have been formulated by the administration in power.

While a tendency to mediate may be stimulated by the broker's interest in his commission (i.e., the felt satisfaction and expected advantages of having one's negotiations "succeed"), it can usually be explained by less egotistical motives. More often than not, the efforts of Western diplomats to mediate between their own government and the opponent stem from the desire to further the common good. Westerners may seek to transcend their national interests by using their insight and wisdom in behalf of a larger unity, and in the knowledge that their own government has no monopoly of the truth. Indeed, West European unity and Western alliances could never have been forged had the diplomats on all sides not been able to identify themselves with these larger interests. And which larger interest is more noble and more important than that of world peace?

Yet there is a dilemma here. If the negotiator of the first party conscientiously tries to find merit on both sides of the dispute, while his opponent does not, who will fully bring out the merits of the first party's position? Can a negotiator switch back and forth, being an advocate on Monday and a mediator on Tuesday, or will the cause of his own side fail to get a fair hearing if he "transcends" his client so often?

In 1961, when the Soviet-provoked Berlin crisis was acute, Senator Mansfield viewed the Western position with a certain detachment, probably because he had a larger common good in mind: "The responsibility which we have," he said on the Senate floor, "and which the Soviet Union has, is not merely to reassert positions already assumed and which are obviously irreconcilable. The responsibility is to seek to determine whether or not there is a third way on Berlin which corresponds more accurately to the needs of Germany today, Europe today, and the world today—indeed, a third way which meets more fully the contemporary needs of both the Soviet Union and ourselves."[2] At a later occasion in the same year, Senator Mansfield further elaborated this picture of East-West symmetry as concerned the Berlin crisis: "There are German fears of the East. There are Polish, Czech and other fears of Germany. There are NATO fears of the Warsaw Pact forces and similar fears in reverse. There are capitalist fears of Communism and Communist fears of capitalism. . . ."[3] To the extent that Mansfield, as the Senate Majority Leader, spoke for the American government, or at least for the majority in Congress, the United States mediated against its own position. While the fears between East and West may be symmetrical, this kind of mediation surely is not. There is no comparable spokesman in the Soviet government who defends "a third way" on Berlin or who speaks sympathetically of West European fears of the East.

The verbatim records of East-West disarmament conferences provide many examples of the contrast between Communist and Western negotiators in the tendency to mediate between one's own position and that of the opponent. When the nuclear test-ban conference resumed in 1961, the American delegate Arthur Dean suggested, "We must all be willing to consider new approaches which differ . . . both from our previous positions and from our . . . desires. Obviously, adjustments will be necessary on each side in the future as they have been in the past." Tsarapkin, however, expressed the "hope that our partners will . . . accept the . . . proposals submitted by the Soviet Union on the points still at issue."[4]

Discussing the impasse on the inspection issue in disarmament negotiations, UN Ambassador Adlai Stevenson wrote: "With a modicum of common sense and the desire for progress it ought to be possible to break this impasse. . . . We in the West will have to scale our demands for inspection rights in accordance with the

[2] *Congressional Record,* June 14, 1961, p. 9598.
[3] Speech at the Virginia Education Association, Richmond, Va., Nov. 3, 1961.
[4] Conference on the Discontinuance of Nuclear Weapon Tests, 274th Plenary Meeting, March 21, 1961, pp. 32, 5 (provisional).

degree of disarmament we are seeking. The Communists will have to recognize that they must live on their own territory with inspectors. . . . If East and West come into the Geneva Conference determined to break out of the vicious circle of the spiraling technological arms race they have an unusual opportunity. . . ."[5] East and West appear here almost as if they were equally far apart from a reasonable middle.

At the Eighteen-Nation Disarmament Conference in 1962, it was the British Foreign Secretary—not one of the *neutral* delegates —who said: "We begin to see much in common between the American and Soviet plans. If we can work on this common ground, we should be able to produce a master plan. . . ." And the American delegate later took the same view: "What we must try to do, is devise a single over-all agreement which draws upon the best from each proposal." But Gromyko would never show such detachment toward the proposal of his own government and abandon it at the outset in favor of some common ground. He instead expressed the hope that the Disarmament Committee, "after impartially and carefully studying the draft treaty submitted today by the Soviet Government, will recognize the need to make it the basis of the Committee's work."[6]

Early in 1963, disagreement in the nuclear test-ban conference focused on the number of inspections, the Soviet Union offering two to three inspections to detect underground tests, while the United States and the United Kingdom asked for eight to ten— later seven. (This was before the conclusion of the partial treaty.) At that time, Dr. Jerome Wiesner, the President's Science Adviser, was reported to have said in a broadcast for the Voice of America: "I am sure that this is a gap which can be closed by continued negotiations and we hope that in the next few months we will see the gap closed."[7] At the same time at a reception in Moscow, however, the Soviet Foreign Minister Gromyko, in private conversation with diplomats, "appeared to define the Soviet offer of three on-site inspections as a final figure rather than as a negotiating

[5] *New York Times*, March 11; 1962, Magazine section.
[6] Eighteen-Nation Disarmament Conference, March 27, April 4, and March 15, 1962.
[7] As quoted by Senator Dodd, *Congressional Record*, Feb. 21, 1963, p. 2661. Cf. *New York Times*, Jan. 23, 1963.

position."[8] If American officials mediate between the United States and the Soviet position, while Russian officials defend the position of their government as final, who is left to defend the U.S. position?

PERSONAL FEARS AND AMBITIONS

Instead of this tendency to play mediator, the negotiator's personal ambition may lie in the opposite direction. He may want to prove himself a hard bargainer by clinging to his position more stubbornly than is either required by his instructions or warranted by any prospects that the opponent might yield first. If a junior diplomat does this, the delegate from the other side may see through it and hold fast until the stubborn official is overruled from above. But in the case of senior negotiators, the desire to prove oneself a hard bargainer contributes to the bargaining reputation of the government as a whole. This is particularly true for the head of a government. De Gaulle's reluctance to revise any position he has taken (with the exception of his positions on Algeria), endows French diplomacy in the early 1960s with a reputation of firmness —or rigidity.

From the point of view of the national interest, however, it is undesirable that negotiators become unwilling to make concessions for fear that this might damage their *personal* reputation. One drawback, in some situations, is that this personal stubbornness may prevent an agreement that would have been in the country's interest (although in other situations stubbornness may pay off). Another drawback, more subtle but often more important, is that government officials who are very reluctant to make any kind of concession will become overly cautious in preparing their initial negotiating positions. They will insist on entering each conference with very modest demands, or with no clear position at all, so that they will not have to give the appearance of conceding points to the enemy. Such officials will ardently defend the rule that one should not make "unacceptable demands." The tendency to make modest initial demands will be aggravated if the officials have no

[8] *New York Times* (according to a report by the Moscow correspondent), Jan. 22, 1963.

reason to fear criticism for their initial modesty but will be censored only for later concessions.

Reinforcing this fear of external criticism, negotiators sometimes have another motive for making only modest initial demands. This is the fairly common human predilection for "prophylactic pessimism": to avoid later disappointment, a person may start out with deliberately lowered expectations. But in negotiation, one's expectations have a potent effect on the outcome, even while the national objectives remain firm; and in the long run stunted expectations lead to stunted objectives. By indulging in "prophylactic pessimism," diplomats become less effective bargainers. John Foster Dulles' pessimism about obtaining self-determination for the Soviet zone of Germany may have been a case in point, particularly after Stalin's death, when the uprisings in the Soviet zone and the attitudes of the new leaders in the Kremlin would have warranted a less resigned diplomatic approach.

There are other fears which may cause negotiators to pursue objectives that do not coincide with those of their government. Some diplomats worry how their actions will look in the eyes of history. They compose their inter-office memoranda, position papers, and telegrams always with a view toward a future historian who might read these documents at the distant date when the government's archives will be opened. If they expect the judgment of history to condemn the current position of their government, they will support it only cautiously and with restraint. Of course, to serve the long-term interest of their country, diplomats *should* use their historical perspective and foresight in the formulation and conduct of foreign policy. Would that some of the officials in the German foreign office under Hitler had anticipated how their actions would be evaluated by the next generation! On the other hand, the ambition to appear wise to future historians may encourage throwing good capital after bad, in an obstinate effort to prove oneself right. Diplomats with such an attitude tend to cling to their predictions and objectives long after they should have abandoned them, as if the vindication of their personal judgment was part of the national interest.

MOODS AND MANNERS OF THINKING

There are many factors that determine at what point a government decides to accept the available terms instead of engaging in further bargaining. To begin with, the terms of agreement have to create a situation that seems preferable to no-agreement. Second, the expected gains from further bargaining must seem small or uncertain compared to its costs and risks. However, the final decision to accept certain terms often results not from gain-and-loss calculations but from purely personal moods and impulses of the negotiator.

Frequently, negotiators stop bargaining at a certain point and settle for the available terms simply because they feel *impatient*.

At the Potsdam Conference, Stalin and Churchill debated at length about the western frontier of Poland and the German territory that the Russians wanted to put under Polish administration. President Truman, although he took essentially the same position as Prime Minister Churchill, entered the debate only a few times. He was in favor of passing over the disputed issue to move ahead with the conference, which meant the outcome would be that the Poles kept all the East German territory that the Russians had turned over to their administration. "I was getting tired," he writes in his memoirs, "of sitting and listening to endless debate on matters that could not be settled at this conference yet took up precious time. I was anxious also to avoid any sharpening of the verbal clashes in view of the more immediate and urgent questions that needed to be settled. I was becoming very impatient, and on a number of occasions I felt like blowing the roof off the palace." Again, toward the end of the Potsdam Conference, Truman recalls in his memoirs, "prolonged and petty bickering continued on the final wording of the protocol. I was getting very impatient, as I had many times before in these sessions, with all the repetition and beating around the bush, but I restrained myself because I saw that we were very slowly making progress in the right direction."[9]

There are a variety of other personal feelings that can affect the outcome of negotiations. For example, a negotiator who has

[9] *Memoirs*, I, 369, 410.

struggled through a long conference to settle issues of great importance to him may experience a sudden feeling of *gratitude* when the opponent turns out to be more amenable than he expected. This may spur him to throw in a concession of his own, with the idea of handing out a reward for good behavior rather than as a tactic calculated as being necessary to reach agreement.

At the Yalta Conference, Roosevelt and Churchill objected to Stalin's claim for huge reparations from Germany. Since this issue had reached a deadlock, it was decided to refer it to a Reparations Commission in Moscow, but it seemed impossible to agree on directives to this commission. At the final meeting at Yalta, when these directives were being debated, Harry Hopkins wrote the following note to Roosevelt: "The Russians have given in so much at this conference that I don't think we should let them down. Let the British disagree if they want to—and continue their disagreement at Moscow. Simply say it is all referred to the Reparations Commission with the minutes to show the British disagree about any mention of the 10 billion." Roosevelt took that advice.[10]

As a negotiator acts out of personal gratitude, so he may make a concession to another diplomat because he feels sorry for him or wants to protect him against his superiors. Philip Mosely reports that in negotiations with Soviet representatives on Bulgaria's armistice (after World War II) he once argued successfully that he might be punished unless a particular provision, desired by the American government, was inserted into the treaty. "At the word 'punished,' a sympathetic gleam of understanding came into the eyes of my Soviet colleagues, and on the following day they agreed to insert the provision. . . ."[11]

Standards of equity, as we shall see, are usually quite indeterminate. To the extent that decision-makers wish to base a negotiating position on such standards, their personal views as to what is "fair" will determine the government's position. This is illustrated by an incident which took place early in the Eisenhower administration.

In April, 1953, when the Korean armistice negotiations were

---

[10] Robert E. Sherwood, *Roosevelt and Hopkins, An Intimate History* (New York: Harper, 1948), pp. 861–62.
[11] *The Kremlin and World Politics*, pp. 24–25.

still dragging on, Emmet John Hughes, the President's speech-writer, prepared a basic speech for the President. As he worked on it with other advisers, Secretary of State Dulles urged him to make it plain that American signature of a Korean armistice would be contingent on restoration of peace in Indochina. At the last editing session for this speech, Hughes later recorded, "We 'forgot' this suggestion, for it seemed outrageously illogical to insist upon such a condition while, simultaneously, excluding as irrelevant the matter of Nationalist China and Formosa."[12] It is a curious logic which permits a flat statement that a package deal between an armistice in Korea and the restoration of peace in Indochina would be "outrageously illogical," merely because the original proposal for the package deal leaves out some other disputed issue. Why was it more "logical" to negotiate the Korean armistice separately, only —as it turned out—to have to negotiate the peace in Indochina one year later, without, incidentally, including "the matter of Nationalist China" at that time?

This incident also illustrates another point: the haphazard influence that the Washington speechwriting process may have on the conduct of negotiations. When the President's speechwriters "forgot" to include a suggestion of the Secretary of State, because it seemed "illogical" to them, did they know whether or not the Secretary—who is responsible for the conduct of foreign policy—had some larger plan in mind? To let the President say in a speech that the conclusion of the Korean armistice would be contingent on the restoration of peace in Indochina could have served a number of different purposes. It might have expedited the Korean armistice negotiations, since the demand could have been dropped later to provide a face-saving formula for the Communists in exchange for their final and crucial concession on the prisoners-of-war issue. Or, this proposed package deal could have been the opening move for a larger arrangement in the Far East, which in the end need not necessarily have excluded "the matter of Nationalist China."

[12] Emmet John Hughes, *The Ordeal of Power: A Political Memoir of the Eisenhower Years* (New York: Atheneum, 1963), p. 112. Hughes writes that he did, however, report Dulles' view to Eisenhower, who indicated support for Hughes' decision.

It is part of the job of Presidential speechwriters to make the President's statements sound eloquent and to create a favorable impact on public opinion. However, this may give the experts on rhetoric considerable say in the conduct of diplomacy, since Presidential speeches usually affect ongoing negotiations. In addition, the chief negotiator himself may take a strong interest in his effect on public opinion. This leads to what might be called the "rhetorical way of thinking": how he sounds is of greater concern to the negotiator than how he bargains.

Particularly in formal conferences, a delegate may actually adapt his day-to-day tactics to suit his taste for rhetorical effects. He will pay a great deal of attention to the speeches he reads at the conference table, which he views not so much as communications designed to influence the opponent but as a means to obtain public support. He may not realize how little attention the public pays to the verbiage in a conference and how quickly his speeches are forgotten. Indeed, the preoccupation with the exchange of words may divert the negotiator from more important moves for influencing the opponent. If a conference is protracted, he may be forced to devote so much time to the debate that rhetorical achievements become more important to him than improvements in his negotiating position. Telegrams can be found in which a delegation asks its home government that it be permitted to offer a certain concession because "this would make the position of the delegation easier"—meaning that the concession would win a debating point.

The "rhetorical way of thinking" diverts negotiators from the essence of bargaining. Preoccupation with diplomatic routines or minor details will do the same. The negotiator may become engrossed in the phrasing of a press release, the wording of a preamble, or in other aspects of an agreement that will be outdated shortly after the ink is dry. Even senior decision-makers, when reviewing the conduct of negotiations, frequently focus on ephemeral details rather than on major policy choices. In reading the minutes of intra-governmental meetings, one is sometimes reminded of Parkinson's "Law of Triviality": The time spent on any one item is of inverse proportion to its importance. Parkinson illustrates this with his finance committee which spends two and a half minutes to decide the purchase of a ten-million-dollar reactor but deliberates for forty-five minutes on how to save three hundred dollars on a bicycle shed.[13]

In the Korean armistice, for example, the only important condition, apart from the exchange of prisoners, was the location of the cease-fire line. Yet, this line received far less attention than, say, the composition of the "neutral" inspection teams. These teams have never been of any significance and are now almost forgotten, whereas the armistice line still divides the Communist from the Western world.

Perhaps it is reassuring for a diplomat to become absorbed in small details and preoccupied with routines of procedure. He can comfortably take the larger context for granted, feel less responsible for the over-all outcome, and occupy himself with the rounding out and polishing of smaller points. He can ignore the unsettling questions of whether the opponent even wants an agreement and whether his own government ought not to prefer no-agreement. During the prolonged test-ban negotiations (with the exception of the initial phase and the 1963 negotiations leading to the partial treaty), the American side was frequently immersed in small details which often became obsolete soon after they were settled.

As able a negotiator as John Foster Dulles may have succumbed to excessive concentration on details in those ill-fated episodes of his career: the Suez and Hungarian crises. He kept proposing varied schemes and legal artifices to put off England and France from using force against Egypt; but in spite of what the CIA or other intelligence sources must have told him about the impending explosion, he failed to press Nasser into specific concessions that could have been used to extract a firm commitment from Britain and France not to use force. At the same time, being so preoccupied with legal details and United Nations schemes regarding Suez, he did not try to negotiate with the Soviet Union a compromise settlement for Hungary's freedom (for example, a neutral position similar to that of Finland or a position like Yugoslavia's). Although we cannot know how good the chances were for such a compromise, the Hungarian Revolution opened the way as almost

[13] Northcote Parkinson, *Parkinson's Law and Other Studies in Administration* (Boston: Houghton Mifflin, 1957), chap. iii.

no other development could have. Dulles' failure is not excused by the fact that he suddenly became ill the very day the Soviet military intervention turned into the open attack against Budapest. American bargaining with the Soviet Union would have had to begin several days or weeks before that date, that is, while Dulles was working out details of his innumerable schemes for Suez.

A negotiator may become diverted from the essential objectives and stint too much in his ends and means for still different reasons. He may be concerned with good workmanship and success only within the narrow limits of his career to the neglect of wider national interests. Because he sticks too much to his last, he may represent his country inadequately and cause a fragmentation of the national capabilities.

For example, a negotiator who is afraid to stray from the diplomatic profession may fail to ask his government to strengthen his bargaining position through military or economic measures. W. W. Rostow concluded that one of the reasons why the United States did not move more forcefully to maintain the independence of Eastern Europe in 1945–46 was that Secretary of State Byrnes viewed foreign affairs as an area for high-level personal negotiations and was reluctant to turn to the President to change the framework within which he operated. "Only the President could have altered the pace of demobilization or the basic attitude toward Moscow. And Byrnes was not in a mood to seek the President's help."[14]

The converse case is the *military* negotiator who fails to see merit in "political" objectives. Whereas the diplomat may ignore military strength as a means to bargain for his political ends, the negotiating soldier often refuses to consider political ends in his pursuit of military objectives.

In the decisive months in the spring of 1945, when Churchill was urging that Western military power be used in behalf of a more advantageous political bargain with the Russians, General Eisenhower cabled to President Truman: ". . . I do not quite understand why the Prime Minister has been so determined to intermingle political and military considerations in attempting to establish a

---

[14] W. W. Rostow, *The United States in the World Arena* (New York: Harper, 1960), p. 180.

procedure for the conduct of our own and Russian troops when a meeting takes place."[15]

Today, of course, it is widely recognized that it was a grave mistake for the United States at the end of World War II to be preoccupied with military objectives to the neglect of political aims. Nonetheless, the American military officer, when he finds himself in negotiations with the opponent, may still fail to see that military power must serve the over-all aims of foreign policy and that the distinction between military and political objectives is only a question of emphasis between means and ends, not a choice between two divergent goals. An illustration is provided by Admiral Joy, who served as chief of the United Nations delegation during the first phase of the Korean armistice conference. This illustration is all the more remarkable because Admiral Joy's book about this conference shows a keen understanding of the weaknesses of certain Western negotiating techniques in confrontation with a Communist opponent. But after one hundred and fifty pages of penetrating insight and useful advice, Joy's book lapses into the following error: "A military armistice agreement should be no more than an agreement between opposing commanders to stop the fighting. It should never be concerned with political questions."[16]

Another personality trait that can affect the course of negotiations is the reliance of some diplomats on their personal experience from the past, instead of on an analysis of the current situation. This trait is more common among older negotiators. With diplomats of senior rank it can, in fact, dominate the conduct of foreign policy. Rather than digging into day-by-day details, the gray-haired diplomat may make excessive use of analogies, of both the historical and the personal kind. This can be infuriating to junior officials, who may work long and hard to collect and interpret the relevant facts on an issue only to have them swept off the desk with a fifteen-

---

[15] Quoted in Truman's *Memoirs*, I, 215.

[16] *How Communists Negotiate*, p. 151. Joy made this assertion to support his argument that the UN insistence on the voluntary repatriation of prisoners was a mistake. Yet, even if it should have been a mistake, the reason would have been not that an armistice ought never to be concerned with political objectives, but that this particular political objective had overriding disadvantages.

year-old anecdote: "In 1946, when I dealt with Stalin, I faced the
same situation . . . ," or "I know how Orientals negotiate; this
is just like the situation I faced in Chungking when I was stationed
there during the war. . . ." A defense against anecdotage which
sometimes works wonders is to identify the reasoning involved—
or the lack of reasoning: "That's a delightful anecdote, sir!"

More far-reaching in its implications than this anecdotage is the
penchant for *historical* analogies, especially since the addiction to
a specific analogy may be shared by many government officials. It
is a difficult question where to draw the line between useful lessons from history and the making of inappropriate analogies.

Anthony Eden's policy against Egypt after Nasser's seizure of
the Suez Canal was strongly influenced by analogies from the Hitler
era. In Eden's widening disagreements with the United States,
these analogies make a constant theme. For example, Eden records
in his memoirs that, after receipt of "a disquieting message from
Mr. Eisenhower" which took exception to the use of force against
Egypt, he replied to the President in a message on which he "had
spent much care":

> . . . I think that the divergence [between us] springs from a dif-
> ference in our assessment of Nasser's plans and intentions. May I set out
> our view of the position. In the nineteen-thirties Hitler established his
> position by a series of carefully planned movements. These began with
> occupation of the Rhineland and were followed by successive acts of
> aggression against Austria, Czechoslovakia. . . . Similarly the seizure
> of the Suez Canal is, we are convinced, the opening gambit in a planned
> campaign designed by Nasser to expel all Western influence and interests
> from Arab countries. . . . You may feel that even if we are right it
> would be better to wait until Nasser has unmistakably unveiled his
> intentions. But this was the argument which prevailed in 1936 and
> which we both rejected in 1948 [at the time of the Berlin blockade].

Again, a few weeks later, Eden sent a telegram to President Eisenhower which contained the following passage:

> There is no doubt in our minds that Nasser, whether he likes it or
> not, is now effectively in Russian hands, just as Mussolini was in
> Hitler's. It would be as ineffective to show weakness to Nasser now in
> order to placate him as it was to show weakness to Mussolini. The only
> result was and would be to bring the two together.[17]

[17] *Full Circle*, pp. 517–21, 556.

Two years earlier, at the Geneva Conference on Indochina, the attitudes of Dulles and Eden regarding the use of force were almost exactly reversed as compared to the Suez crisis. The same analogies were used, but at this time it was Dulles who substituted the "Rhineland argument" in lieu of a military analysis as to how the use of force would turn out. Eden recalls from a discussion with Dulles: "I was not convinced by the assertion which Mr. Dulles then made, that the situation in Indochina was analogous to the Japanese invasion of Manchuria in 1931 and to Hitler's reoccupation of the Rhineland. I explained that the British Chiefs of Staff did not believe that allied intervention could be limited to the air and the sea."[18]

INTERNATIONAL AFFAIRS AS PERSONAL RELATIONS

The delegates who confront each other across the conference table may be subject to personal sympathies or dislikes. They respond not only to the relationship that exists between their countries but also to the *personal* relationship between each other. Their ideas and feelings about each other affect their conduct of negotiation in many small ways—and sometimes in major ways.

According to an optimistic view of the effect of personal relations in international affairs, friendly feelings between chief negotiators will enhance friendly relations between the states they represent. For instance, when Marshal Zhukov became Soviet Defense Minister in 1955, it was said that this might have a beneficial effect on American-Soviet relations, because Zhukov and Eisenhower had been on friendly terms at the end of World War II. Similarly the close collaboration between the American and the German governments in the 1950s has often been attributed to the special trust and liking that Chancellor Adenauer was said to have had for Secretary Dulles. There are many other examples, such as President Roosevelt's close relationship during World War II with Prime Minister Churchill, or—to cite a less successful case— Roosevelt's hope to establish some personal contact with Stalin.

It is worth exploring why and under what conditions good personal relations between negotiators might facilitate agreements

[18] *Ibid.*, p. 108.

between states. One explanation is that friendly interpersonal relations may strengthen the tendency to observe rules of accommodation and may make a larger set of these rules feasible. If you, as a diplomat, are personally acquainted with the opponent's representative, you have not only the bargaining reputation of your government to protect but also your personal reputation. You will expect that the other delegate will form certain ideas about your personality and accordingly estimate how you will act. He may have the corresponding expectation about you, thus establishing a pattern of reciprocal *personal* evaluations and expectations. The rules of personal behavior appropriate for close associates or friends therefore may be transferred to some extent to the affairs of state. This will give added strength and greater scope to the rules of accommodation observed between governments. In particular, debts of gratitude acquire the character of a personal obligation if the negotiators know each other well. Between Western negotiators, who may permit themselves to see a difference between the official position of their government and the national interest, this may encourage a spirit of camaraderie and almost turn negotiation into a joint mediation effort.

Yet, there are limits as to how useful a personal friendship can be in enhancing an accommodating style of negotiation. At one extreme, the delegate will sacrifice the interest of his government to satisfy his friend; at the other, he will be forced to abuse the friendship to advance the cause of his country.

Intimate acquaintance with a diplomat helps to assess his thoughts and motives. To put it crudely: friendship is a source of intelligence. In public as in private affairs, there is that intuitive understanding of a man which may reveal how strongly he means what he says and what his basic intentions are. Whereas a close personal relation between diplomats need not lead to greater frankness, it makes dissimulation more difficult. Between diplomats of friendly countries, it may strengthen reciprocal trust; and between hostile nations, it may at least make communication more meaningful for both sides. As Anthony Eden wrote, when recalling the ten-day visit of Marshal Bulganin and Khrushchev to England in 1956: "I have found it an advantage to know the man to whom I was addressing a communication through Ambassadors. . . . As a result of ten days spent together in almost constant contact, I felt that I knew these Russians as no volumes of despatches could have revealed them to me."[19]

But in making this connection between one's assessment of a negotiator as a person and as a government official, one is implicitly assuming that there is a close harmony between the two— that the person is all of a piece, so to speak. This assumption can bring disappointment. Western diplomats often seem to be surprised about the contrast between the human attractiveness of Communist delegates and their aggressive and frequently rude official behavior. If Westerners are optimistically inclined, they will put greater weight on the personal affability of the Communist diplomat than on his official acts, and they interpret his bellicose tactics as a show that he puts on for the benefit of some diehard forces in his government. It is the bad men behind the negotiator who have to be blamed.

When Khrushchev broke up the 1960 summit conference with his cantankerous performance, it was the "Stalinists" who made him do this, wasn't it? When the test-ban negotiations that had been going on almost four years were jolted in the summer of 1961 by the sudden Soviet resumption of testing, perhaps the Chinese had forced this move in Soviet policy? And when Stalin was still alive and Communist China did not yet exist, any discrepancy between the reasonable "Uncle Joe" and less reasonable Soviet policies could be explained by blaming some unidentified "bad men" behind Stalin. As Harry Hopkins told Robert E. Sherwood, about his own reaction to the Yalta Conference, where he was President Roosevelt's closest adviser:

We really believed in our hearts that this was the dawn of the new day. . . . The Russians had proved that they could be reasonable and farseeing and there wasn't any doubt in the minds of the President or any of us that we could live with them and get along with them peacefully. . . . But I have to make one amendment to that—I think we all had in our minds the reservation that we could not foretell what the results would be if anything should happen to Stalin. We felt sure that we could count on him to be reasonable and sensible and under-

[19] *Ibid.*, pp. 404–5.

standing—but we never could be sure who or what might be in back of him there in the Kremlin.[20]

Sometimes, the Western tendency to personalize international relations leads to a paradoxical attitude: On the one hand, the negotiator may deny that he has any hard feelings against his adversary as a person, despite the latter's pugnacious behavior at the conference table; on the other hand, he often attributes the foreign policy of the opponent's government to highly personal emotions. When the opponent's government is under the sway of a dictator, this explanation may, in part, be correct. But even then, it is often dangerous to design one's diplomacy as a palliative for the psychic eccentricities of a hostile leader.

When the British statesman Halifax went to see Hitler and Goebbels in Berchtesgaden in November, 1937, he was concerned about such "questions arising out of the Versailles settlement" as Danzig, Austria, and Czechoslovakia. "On all these matters," Halifax wrote in his diary, "we were not necessarily concerned to stand for the *status quo* as of to-day, but we were very much concerned to secure the avoidance of such treatment of them as would be likely to cause trouble." And why should there be trouble? Goebbels had the answer: in contrast to Great Britain with her centuries of history, Nazi Germany was only five years old and very sensitive. Halifax was satisfied with this explanation: "This confirmed," he wrote, "what I had always been inclined to think about part of the Nazi attitude arising from an inferiority complex."[21]

If it is not an inferiority complex, perhaps there are certain moods which require satisfaction at the expense of the nation's foreign policies. A few months before Halifax's visit to Berchtesgaden, Prime Minister Neville Chamberlain wrote him a letter about Britain's relations with Fascist Italy. Eden, who received a copy, felt that Chamberlain "expressed a surprising opinion of the men we had to deal with. It was very necessary to remember, he [Chamberlain] wrote, that the dictators were men of moods. If we caught them in the right mood they would give us anything we

---

[20] *Roosevelt and Hopkins,* p. 870.
[21] Earl of Halifax, *Fulness of Days* (London: Collins, 1957), pp. 186–87, 191.

asked for. But if the mood changed they might shut up 'like an oyster.' The moral of this was, in the Prime Minister's opinion, that we must make Mussolini feel that things were moving all the time."[22]

But on other occasions, Eden himself felt he had to conduct British foreign policy so as to satisfy what he thought were the moods and idiosyncrasies of the men in power. When he visited Moscow in December, 1941, Stalin pressed him to agree to the re-establishment of the boundaries that Russia had gained in the pact with Hitler, that is, to consent to the incorporation of the Baltic states and part of Finland and Poland into the Soviet Union. Eden felt he had to give in to this demand and urged the British ambassador in Washington to obtain the concurrence of the American government. "It is our belief," he cabled, that Stalin's demand "is put to us as a test of the sincerity of our avowed desire to work with him during and after the war. It is the fruit of a long period of suspicion and misunderstanding. . . . He [Stalin] pointed to 'plebiscites' in Baltic states. Our exchanges of views on this aspect of the subject would have been even less profitable than they were if I had suggested that those 'plebiscites' were faked. . . . I'm advised by Sir Stafford Cripps (and our experience of 1939 as you will remember will tend to confirm this) that any class of haggling may only increase his [Stalin's] suspicions."[23] As one dictator may have to be humored because he suffers from feelings of inferiority, so another one because he happens to have a suspicious personality.

One is tempted from the foregoing examples of diplomatic reasoning in the 1930s and early 40s (similar quotations could be found in diplomatic telegrams and official minutes of the present time) to conclude that the most successful negotiator would be someone who managed to give the impression of wanting to see things moving all the time, of suffering from an acute inferiority complex, being prone suddenly to shut up like an oyster, and having vast suspicions.

[22] Anthony Eden, *Facing the Dictators* (Boston: Houghton Mifflin, 1962), p. 514.

[23] U.S. Department of State, *Foreign Relations of the United States, 1942*, III, 514–15. Eden's failure to point out that the Baltic plebiscites were faked illustrates the tendency of Western diplomats not to confront the opponent with unpleasant facts.

CHAPTER 10

SHIFTING EVALUATIONS

There is nothing either good or bad,
but thinking makes it so.
Hamlet, II, 2

To EXERCISE THEIR THREEFOLD CHOICE, NEGOTIATORS HAVE TO
aggregate many diverse estimates into three over-all values for each
of the three options: they must decide whether agreement on balance, with all the available terms taken together, is preferable to all
the likely consequences of no-agreement, as well as to all the prospects and risks of further bargaining. Normally, they will not tally
up these three aggregates consciously as if they were dealing with
three sums on an elaborate balance sheet. But intuitively they
must continue to size them up as they keep deciding which option
to choose. This means they must combine things that are nearly
incommensurable. Somehow they have to add up good terms and
bad ones, gains in territory and losses in lives, immediate opportunities and distant risks.

Historical hindsight sometimes reveals that both parties were
mistaken in the way they aggregated different aspects of an agreement. For instance, in the 1954 Geneva negotiations on Indochina,
the French negotiators were anxious that the agreed date for elections in North and South Vietnam be postponed as long as pos-

sible, whereas the Chinese and the North Vietnamese Communists wanted·an early election date to take advantage of disorganization and unrest. In the final bargaining sessions in this conference, the election date was traded off against the location of the demarcation line between North and South Vietnam: the sooner the date for elections, the further north would the Communists allow the line to be drawn. As it turned out, however, the elections were never held, whereas the demarcation line still divides the country. Evidently the French should not have considered an opportunity to push the Communists a hundred miles north as being outweighed by having to set the election date, say, half a year earlier (nor should the Communists—from their point of view—have surrendered territory in exchange for an earlier election date).

In addition to the difficulty of aggregating diverse aspects of an agreement, each party must weigh how its negotiating tactics affect its bargaining reputation. And at various junctures, the negotiator may also have to estimate whether it is worthwhile or not to observe some rule of accommodation. Naturally, there are no firm criteria for evaluating how one's bargaining reputation might be affected by the acceptance or rejection of certain terms. Likewise, the costs of violating rules of accommodation, or the gains from observing them, are hard to assess. In these evaluations the negotiators and those advising them are easily swayed by personal moods. At one time, a diplomat may feel angry at "world opinion" and be quite prepared to ignore rules of accommodation; at another time he may be impressed by public criticism alleging that his tactics are "unfair" and therefore become particularly accommodating toward his opponent.

UNCERTAIN CRITERIA

The distinction between *criteria* of evaluation and *objects* of evaluation is often blurred. Naturally, the objects of evaluation keep changing during negotiation: offered terms may be improved, threats may be withdrawn, new inducements may be added, commitments may be strengthened, and the balance of forces may shift. Also, the negotiator may learn of new facts concerning the opponent's strengths and weaknesses, he may see fresh alternatives, and he may discover new technical implications of the proposed terms.

Moreover, the negotiator's knowledge of his objects of evaluation is severely limited, particularly since his most important evaluations concern future events. If one judges diplomatic history from hindsight, one must be careful not to misinterpret as faulty negotiating tactics what were actually errors in prediction. Although the two types of errors are not clearly separable, one can usefully make a distinction.

When Roosevelt urged Churchill and Stalin, during World War II, to treat China as a great power and give her a permanent seat in the Security Council, his prediction about China's postwar contribution to world order was wrong; but there was nothing particularly amiss with his tactics in negotiating a Security Council seat for Chiang Kai-shek.[1] By contrast, when Roosevelt and Truman tried to secure Poland's independence at the Teheran, Yalta, and Potsdam conferences, their anticipation that Stalin might want to dominate and sovietize Poland was correct, but their negotiating tactics ineffective (mainly for failure to take advantage of the Soviet need to reach agreement with the Western powers).

Given the uncertainty of the negotiator's predictions and the changing content of his options, it is easy to recognize why he rarely holds to firm opinions in evaluating this threefold choice. What is less apparent is that he is adrift, too, in the *way* in which he evaluates his options. That is, at different moments he attaches different values to the same object.

The instability of evaluation criteria is harder to recognize, because we all depend on them in our everyday way of looking at negotiation, almost as we depend on the dimensions of time and space for looking at the world around us. The criteria provide the yardstick to measure how much the parties would gain or lose by

---

[1] Churchill's foresight on this point proved to be better. In August, 1944, he wrote in a minute to his Foreign Secretary: "That China is one of the world's four Great Powers is an absolute farce. I have told the President I would be reasonably polite about this American obsession, but I cannot agree that we should take a positive attitude on the matter. The latest information from inside China points to the rise already of a rival Government to supplant Chiang Kai-shek, and now there is always a Communist civil war impending there" (*Triumph and Tragedy*, p. 701).

accepting proposed terms; they indicate what kinds of trades are "equitable"; and they establish the bench mark by which we judge whether or not a demand is "reasonable," a concession "adequate," and a compromise "fair."

It is a common and cardinal fallacy to assume that these criteria exist independently of the negotiating process. Far from it, they are nothing but beliefs held by diplomats, their government colleagues, and various bystanders, and they are continually modified by the bargaining process. Hence these criteria cannot form a firm basis for evaluating negotiations. Quite to the contrary, it is negotiation that develops and changes them. Diplomats not only fight about terms that they evaluate in a given way; they also fight about the way of evaluation in order to fit it to their preferred terms. Even evaluations of mediators and outsiders are affected by the negotiation process. International diplomacy, in contrast to parlor games, has no score sheets or poker chips that record the gains and losses for each side. This is one of the most essential facts in understanding how nations negotiate.

Only some time after an agreement has been concluded can evaluations be made that are less dependent on the negotiating process. Historical hindsight may permit us to assess how an agreement worked out, as compared to the expectations the parties held when they reached it. It may be possible to say whether one party gained more than the other party meant to give, which aspects worked out better or worse than either party had thought, and which gambles paid off. But even with hindsight, the options that were not taken up can only be speculated on, and for many of the gains and losses the evaluation criteria will remain uncertain.

WHERE DOES A GAIN OR LOSS BEGIN?

Whenever a negotiator examines his options to see whether they would be advantageous or disadvantageous for his country, he must have some bench mark in the back of his mind that divides the plus side from the minus side. In other words, he cannot evaluate whether his country would be better off or worse by his accepting a certain term in an agreement, unless he has some notion as to what kind of terms would mean neither a gain nor a loss—something like a break-even point.

Negotiators often shift their break-even points in mid-course. This is one of the main reasons why their evaluations are so unstable. Yet, they are usually unaware that they change this basic criterion and think, instead, that their options have changed.

The Status Quo. A frequently used break-even point is the status quo. That is, any arrangement which does not change the existing situation will be evaluated as resulting in neither a gain nor a loss. However, since the world is always changing, maintaining the status quo on some isolated issue may seem like a gain or a loss from another vantage point. To the extent that a negotiator counts on things as they are at the moment, the ground is constantly shifting beneath him. Soon after a development for the worse (or better), governments and the public tend to view the new situation no longer as a departure from an earlier status quo but as a new status quo from which any improvement is evaluated as a gain and any deterioration as a loss. Here lies one reason why *faits accomplis* are feared; they can rapidly become the new break-even point.

This has happened, for example, with the Berlin wall. Immediately after the Communists had cut the city in two, the Western powers would still have considered it as a loss if, in a new agreement on Berlin, the wall had been allowed to remain. And if the Communists had agreed at that time to remove the wall, this would have been evaluated as nothing more than the restoration of the status quo—neither a plus nor a minus in a larger bargain. But two or three years later, many people in the West would consider the removal of the wall a big gain worth Western sacrifices in exchange; and it would be evaluated as neither a loss nor a gain if the wall was allowed to remain as part of a Berlin agreement.

Historical Trends. In some situations, negotiators do not use the status quo as the break-even point but regard a certain long-term development as natural or fixed in conformity with a fundamental historical trend. Although this trend may actually lead to a deterioration (or improvement) compared with the status quo, for purposes of negotiation such change is being evaluated as neither a loss nor a gain. What looks like a falling or rising curve to the historian is the break-even line for the diplomat.

Decolonization has become accepted as such a trend (but only in areas colonized by Western countries). If a native representative of an Asian or African colony travels to the metropolitan capital to negotiate on the future status of his country, he will evaluate any agreement which simply continues the status quo as a loss. In fact, both the metropolitan government and the colonial representatives will usually agree that the outcome must provide for some decolonization if it is to result in neither a gain nor a loss for either party, though they may disagree on the speed of decolonization which corresponds to such an outcome.

After the riots in the Panama Canal Zone in January, 1964, when the question of a renegotiation of the Panama Canal Treaty came up, most editorial commentators in the United States simply took it for granted that the historical trend was in the direction of increased Panamanian and decreased U.S. control. In other words, Panama had to *gain* more control in order not to *lose* in a new agreement with the United States. Or as a *New York Times* editorial put it (Jan. 19, 1964): "The big problem is who is going to control the Canal and how. Panama cannot run it alone. The United States cannot indefinitely run it, in the treaty's words, 'as if it were sovereign of the territory.' A genuinely joint United States-Panama control should be possible, and would probably be the best solution. . . . What is not possible is a continuation of the present situation without any change at all. . . ."

Initial Expectation. Quite a different break-even point, which offers an even less certain criterion of evaluation, is the negotiator's initial expectation as to how a particular term or the agreement as a whole will turn out. It is used in normalization and extension negotiations. This initial expectation, of course, is based on a number of other estimates and evaluations. It depends on precedents, on conceptions of the "normal" situation, on the estimated balance of forces (how bad the consequences would be from no-agreement), and perhaps on some ideas about a "fair" division of gains and losses.

A similar break-even point is the *opponent's* initial expectation. This point has to be estimated, of course, since the opponent may ask for more than he expects to get. The passive party in innovation negotiations frequently uses this bench mark by estimating what the initiating party expects to obtain and then measuring its gains and losses as departures from that point.

A similar approach may be used by the defensive party in re-distribution negotiations. Acting for the defensive side, the nego-tiator may base his evaluations on a break-even point that splits the difference between the status quo and the outcome that the opponent initially seemed to expect. Needless to say, the status quo cannot be defended with this criterion. Yet, negotiators who like to play the mediator tend to select this approach.

In the Berlin negotiations there were periods when American news media and commentators used this criterion as a break-even point. For example, in 1961, when many Westerners felt less hope-ful about Western presence and unimpaired freedom in West Ber-lin, an editorial in the *New York Times* (Sept. 8, 1961) suggested that agreement should be sought somewhere *between* the status quo (which the West was trying to defend!) and Khrushchev's initial demands: "The impasse will continue until and unless Khrushchev shows sincere interest in negotiation, in which both sides—not we alone—would make some concessions to the other." The same view was expressed in an editorial in *Newsweek* (Oct. 9, 1961): "Through the light and shadow of all these maneuvers had now emerged the visible trend of future negotiations. The Russians would try to obtain maximum Western recognition of East Ger-many with minimum recognition of the rights of West Berlin. The Western position would be exactly the opposite. Somewhere between the *two extremes* lay the *hopeful area* of agreement" (italics added). During the same period (Nov. 24, 1961) *The Times* (London) measured gains and losses as follows: "The essentials [of a new arrangement on Berlin] are freedom for the West Berliners, unrestricted access, economic (and hence politi-cal) links with West Germany, and the presence of Western troops. . . . To gain [*sic*] all this it would be no great sacrifice to give up espionage and provocative broadcasts, quietly to drop overt politi-cal activities such as the meeting of the West German Bundestag [in Berlin], and to accept some East German inspection of travel documents on the land and water routes."

HOW LARGE ARE THE GAINS AND LOSSES?

The negotiator, in addition to selecting a break-even point to separate the plus from the minus side, must evaluate how large his gains and losses are. In a sense, he will apply a scale or index to measure the magnitude of the advantages and disadvantages that his country would derive from the various options. He will not consciously pick a numerical scale, of course, but merely estimate these magnitudes intuitively—or feel them almost subconsciously. Various factors make these estimates subject to change as negotiations progress.

We have seen how a negotiator's infatuation with details may cause him to attach great importance to some minor issues, while neglecting issues that are of fundamental significance for his country. Also, if a great effort is required to obtain certain terms, these terms may seem more valuable than if they can be obtained easily. This is a common psychological reaction, as widespread in international relations as in everyday human affairs. Had the Russians agreed to a *partial* test-ban treaty in April, 1959—when the Western powers first proposed this solution to overcome the impasse on inspection arrangements—this would undoubtedly have seemed a less significant gain to the American government than the same treaty that was finally signed in August, 1963, after four and a half years of almost continuous negotiation.

A similar distortion occurs if a negotiator believes that an agreement is particularly valuable just because the available terms are the best he could conceivably have gotten. Such a negotiator makes the mistake of attributing to an outcome a higher value if he thinks he has pushed his opponent to the limit than if he does not think so. Even though he may be justified in deriving some personal satisfaction from having obtained the best possible terms, he should not conclude that these terms are preferable to no-agreement just because they are so close to the opponent's minimum. Getting a "good bargain" is not the same as getting a "good buy."

The converse reaction may occur if a party begins to feel that it cannot obtain what it has long tried to reach through negotiation. The disappointed party may console itself by placing a low value on the terms that now seem out of reach, although it had coveted them before. This has happened to some extent with the Western evaluation of German reunification. The reaction is illustrated by a report of a group of U.S. Senators to the Committee on

Foreign Relations. The group, concluding that the prospects for peaceful reunification of Germany through elections were remote, offered this consolation: "Obviously, the Russians do not desire it, and they are not necessarily alone in Europe in holding this position. Germany and Europe have managed to live with the division for many years."[2] (What about these grapes we tried so hard to get, but failed? Well, they are sour anyhow!)

Another source of distortion for the negotiator's evaluations is the emphasis on an even division. When a diplomat evaluates how large the gain (or loss) from a particular term of agreement would be, he will usually give special weight to that magnitude which seems to be equal to the opponent's gain (or loss). Each party will feel that its own advantage is small as long as the opponent receives more but that it is particularly large as soon as the opponent receives less. The same applies to disadvantages that both sides may incur as a result of an agreement. Indeed, the point of equality in itself is often felt to be particularly desirable. It is the point where an agreement becomes "equitable" or "fair." For diplomats who emphasize this criteria, it may almost appear more important that an agreement be "equitable" than that it enhance the national interest.

But whether two magnitudes are equal depends, of course, on the point from which they are measured. Terms can be made to offer equal advantages to both sides simply by shifting the break-even point.

In the Korean armistice negotiations, three different truce lines were advanced as being equitable, each one leading to an equal division of gains and losses in accordance with different criteria. At the very beginning of the armistice negotiations, the United Nations side proposed a truce line somewhat north (on the Communist side) of the line of ground contact, arguing that this would produce equality in terms of the military advantages and disadvantages. According to Admiral Joy, the senior delegate on the Western side, the UN team "contended that a northward adjustment of the ground-contact line was necessary to compensate for

<hr/>

[2] *Berlin in a Changing Europe,* Report of Senators Mansfield, Boggs, Pell, and Smith to the Committee on Foreign Relations (Washington: Government Printing Office, 1963), p. 8.

the withdrawal of United Nations Command air and naval operations, which ranged hundreds of miles north of the embattled ground forces." But somehow, the UN team felt ill-at-ease about this criterion and quickly shifted to another way of measuring equality. Admiral Joy wrote that this first proposal "was a bargaining position, and even while proposing it we made plain our interest in a solution on the line of ground contact."[3] This "solution" offered equality in the sense that neither side would gain territory, but it led to inequality in the sense that the United Nations forces would not be compensated for their withdrawal of air and naval operations.

The Communists thought of another criterion to make a truce line "equitable" that was more advantageous to them than this second UN proposal. They demanded that a line be drawn along the 38th Parallel, which would have given them territorial gains as compared with the line of ground contact. Although they argued for the 38th Parallel primarily on military grounds, the implication was clear that it would give equality in the sense that neither side would gain or lose in comparison with the status before the war. Incidentally, the Communists were not as shy about this proposal as the UN negotiators were about their first proposal. In contrast to what Admiral Joy reports about the way in which the UN team presented its case for a northward adjustment, the Communists did not "make plain their interest in another solution"; they vehemently and for a long time insisted on this southward adjustment of the line of ground contact.

Although a change in criteria can equalize the net gains of both sides for almost any set of terms, it may nonetheless be of great importance whether or not the negotiator thinks that the opponent's net gains are equal to his own. First, the point of imagined equality provides a focus for his expectations as to the outcome; it is like a resting point that can put an end to the infinite possibilities of dividing such things as territory, a sum of money, or voting power. Second, to depart from equality might have serious consequences for one's bargaining power. This is particularly true in antagonistic situations, where one does not wish to convey to the

---

[3] *How Communists Negotiate*, p. 60.

enemy—by accepting lesser gains than he—the idea that one evaluates one's own strength as being inferior to his.

In negotiation with an enemy, there is a further reason why the measurement of one's gains and losses is so uncertain. Whatever your foe gains in power, prestige, or wealth means a loss for you, even if you benefit yourself by cooperating with him at the time. And whatever your foe loses is *ipso facto* a gain for yourself because it weakens him. Hence, in evaluating whether an agreement—on balance—is to your advantage, you have to subtract something for your enemy's gains and add something to allow for the fact that his loss is your gain. What makes this evaluation so unstable is that the yardstick for measuring the opponent's losses often changes. First, you might measure whether he would suffer a loss compared with the situation before negotiation started, whereas later you might compare the possible outcome with the situation into which he maneuvered himself through his own bargaining moves. But have you gained if your enemy incurs a loss just because he breaks a commitment whose very purpose was to wrest a concession from you?

Where this slippery road of shifting evaluations might lead is illustrated by a report in the *New York Times* about a British proposal for an agreement with Khrushchev on Berlin. According to this story (which must be apocryphal!), the British Foreign Office reasoned in September, 1962, that the West should offer the Russians "presence" in West Berlin in exchange for a withdrawal of Soviet demands that the Western troops leave. Under one version, this Russian "presence" would have been established by permitting the Russian guards for the Soviet War Memorial (which lies in the British sector) to live in West Berlin and by giving the Russians control of a corridor from East Berlin to the War Memorial. Why this Western concession? Because, "for prestige reasons, the British believed Khrushchev could not give up his highly publicized demands for . . . removing the United States, British, and French garrisons unless he could show he had gained something in return."[4] That is, since your enemy would lose so much if he broke the commitment that he made in order to take something from you, you can reach a satisfactory agreement

[4] *New York Times,* Sept. 8, 1962.

by giving him only part of his "highly publicized demands," your loss being compensated by the fact that he will have to forgo the other part of his demands.

WHEN IS A COMMITMENT BROKEN?

When you have committed yourself not to yield on a certain point, your opponent may try to defeat the purpose of your commitment in two ways.[5] First, he may simply try to manipulate your threefold choice (e.g., by committing himself, erecting a deadline, or making threats) so that breaking your commitment will seem to you the lesser evil than the risks from holding on to your position. Second, your opponent may try to erode your commitment by permitting you to adhere to it in form while violating it in substance. The two methods are frequently combined: the first gives you the incentive to break the commitment; the second makes it easier to do so.

All commitments raise the question of criteria: What is the criterion that indicates whether or not a commitment has been broken? Since this criterion is frequently uncertain, the opponent can force his interpretation upon you, provided you are unable or unwilling to make a second commitment that will tie you to a firm interpretation of the first one.

Many commitments can be eroded because there is no firm criterion as to the time when the promised action should be taken. The fulfillment can thus be postponed indefinitely without incurring the costs of a clear-cut violation of one's commitment. The United Nations commitment to reunify Korea under free elections, which stemmed from the General Assembly resolution of October 7, 1950, was maintained in form in the Panmunjom Armistice agreement by adding an article which recommended to the governments concerned that they should hold a conference within three months "to settle through negotiation the questions of the withdrawal of all foreign forces from Korea, the peaceful settlement of the Korean question, etc."

Occasionally, however, it is possible to "freeze" firm criteria

[5] As defined before, a "commitment" is a move to convince one's opponent that one will maintain one's current position or implement one's prediction, by making it more difficult for oneself not to do so.

into one's commitment so as to prevent this erosion. On April 20, 1961, after the disastrous invasion attempt against Castro by Cuban refugees, President Kennedy declared: ". . . If the nations of this hemisphere should fail to meet their commitments against outside Communist penetration—then I want it clearly understood that this Government will not hesitate in meeting its primary obligations which are to the security of our Nation!" This commitment to act against Communist penetration was without firm criteria and hence did not strengthen the American bargaining position. However, on September 13, 1962, President Kennedy made a commitment that was much more specific, when he said: ". . . If Cuba should ever . . . become an offensive military base of significant capacity for the Soviet Union, then this country will do whatever must be done to protect its own security and that of its allies." As Khrushchev discovered a few weeks later in the negotiations following the Cuban crisis, this commitment provided the basis for a firm American position.

By way of example, a firm criterion could be "frozen" into the Western commitment to maintain troops in Berlin. The Western powers could promise to keep a specified number of troops in West Berlin rather than, as they do now, guarantee the presence of unspecified forces. Or to give another hypothetical illustration: In the test-ban negotiations, instead of insisting on "adequate inspection," President Kennedy could have declared that he would not accept an underground ban with less than, say, seven inspections. Yet these examples make it evident that commitments with "frozen" criteria suffer from another weakness. They make the negotiator vulnerable to the charge of clinging to symbolic positions. Whereas the criteria themselves cannot be eroded, the commitments as a whole might be scrapped more easily than if they had been based on broader principles that are more widely supported.

UNCERTAIN GOALS

The negotiator's evaluations depend of course to a large extent on his goals. As soon as he sets himself more modest goals, something that seemed to be a trifling advantage will look like a substantial profit; and should he choose new goals diametrically opposed to his old ones, anything that used to be evaluated as a gain will become a loss. This dependence of values on goals is common in everyday life and would not be worth mentioning if it were not for the fact that in negotiation the opponent often changes one's evaluations by changing one's goals.[6]

Naturally, governments frequently conceal their negotiating goals from their opponent. They may make only vague suggestions, even though they have a rather definite outcome in mind; or they may initially propose far more demanding terms (or deceptively modest ones), instead of revealing what they are trying to get. Nonetheless, the goals can be modified by a determined opponent.

WHAT IS WORTH NEGOTIATING FOR?

A government may enter into negotiation without having a specific outcome in mind. It may leave the initiative to its allies, or even to its opponent, and be concerned solely with the prevention of clauses that would be harmful to its interests. The defensive side in redistribution negotiations frequently takes such an attitude. It may only want to prevent a deterioration of the status quo without seeking any specific agreement. Likewise, the passive party in innovation negotiations may have come merely to see what the initiating party has to propose, planning to react to the alternatives as they unfold.

It is probably more common, however, for governments to pursue a more or less specific goal when they are negotiating. If it is an agreement they are trying to get, they will attempt to shape it in a certain way. Sometimes they may try to obtain one quite specific set of terms even though they are prepared to settle for less.

Given the diversity of objectives in foreign policy, it is natural that a specific negotiating goal, if it exists, must represent a compromise between several more or less conflicting aims of foreign policy. For example, in the negotiations that settled the Suez crisis in 1956, the American goal was to satisfy at least three partly

---

[6] Psychological experiments on bargaining behavior have investigated this dependence. See the literature on "level of aspiration" on p. 263 of the Bibliographic Note at the end of this book.

conflicting objectives of foreign policy: to restore harmonious relations with Great Britain and France, to safeguard the friendship of the Arab nations, and to preserve Israel's independence.

Sometimes, negotiating goals emerge within a government more by accident than by design. On other occasions, particularly if the government takes the initiative for an innovation agreement, a careful compromise among all relevant foreign policy objectives may be worked out. Thus, the United Nations Organization—an innovation largely the result of American initiative—was expected by American policymakers to solve a large number of urgent postwar problems. The State Department planners who formulated this initial American proposal for a world peace organization selected their negotiating goal from among a wide range of possibilities. They considered whether the world organization should be set up through a series of treaties or a single treaty, whether it should be a revised and strengthened League of Nations or a new organization, whether it should be based on regional groupings or have a universal structure, and whether it should be confined to issues of military security or include economic and other programs. All these alternatives were evaluated in the preparatory committees of the American government, long before the San Francisco Conference.[7] By contrast, when the French government entered the Geneva Conference on Indochina in 1954, it initially did not have any image of what it wanted. At first, French leaders had only vague ideas, such as to induce China to discontinue her aid to the Viet Minh by offering her economic assistance and French support for Peking's admission to the United Nations.

Governments usually do not negotiate for agreements that they consider highly unlikely. They might engage in pseudo-negotiations about totally improbable settlements for the sake of side-effects only (e.g., the East-West negotiations about a treaty for general and complete disarmament). But if a government is seriously trying to reach a certain agreement, the terms that it has in mind must not seem wholly unattainable. Partly, this is to conserve resources: governments are limited in the amount of attention, commitments, threats, and other pressures that they can

[7] U.S. Department of State, *Postwar Foreign Policy Preparation 1939–1945* (Department of State Publication 3580 [Washington, 1949]), pp. 112–13.

bring to bear on various negotiations at any one time. Partly, the goals are kept realistic in order to avoid failure: diplomats prefer to negotiate only for what they expect to get, because they want the satisfaction of getting what they negotiate for.

Communist governments, it seems, are more willing than Western governments to pursue unattainable goals. The comparison, however, is complicated by two factors. First, to the extent that Communists take seriously a view of history according to which their total victory is foreordained, the attainability of any intermediate goal toward that ultimate outcome must appear to be only a matter of time. Second, it is hard for Western observers to discover the real goals of Communist negotiators, as distinct from their asking position. For instance, did the Russians really want to replace the UN Secretary-General with a "troika" in 1960–61, or did they merely want to obtain more influence in the UN Secretariat? And in the summer of 1963, did they really want to combine the partial nuclear test ban with an East-West nonaggression pact, or was the demand for a nonaggression pact just a tactical move?

To select "realistic" goals, you as the negotiator must evaluate your opportunities for influencing your opponent and assess the chances for a change in his strength and preferences. If you are unable to see any hope for moving toward your goal today, maybe tomorrow your opponent will change his mind, and your goal becomes "negotiable." Without really trying, you cannot know whether you estimated his and your strength correctly.

Who Decides What Is Negotiable?

Your opponent, of course, has an interest in changing your goals. If he dislikes your aims, he will try to discourage you from negotiating by making your original goal seem unattainable. On issues he does not want to have raised, he may give the impression of being so firmly committed to preserve the existing situation that you feel neither threats nor inducements could lead to a change. Being realistic, you will not attempt to bargain for what seems impossible to obtain.

This has happened to the West on the issue of self-determination in Eastern Europe. Many Westerners feel that Russia is so committed to maintain Communist regimes wherever they have once been established, that a change—if it comes at all—can only evolve over decades or perhaps longer. Since the 1950s, the Western powers have assumed that this issue is not negotiable. In spite of new opportunities (such as the 1953 uprisings in the Soviet zone of Germany or the 1956 revolution in Hungary), and in spite of new negotiating contexts (such as the Soviet demand for a change in West Berlin), the West never made a serious attempt, through pressures and incentives, to strike a bargain that would improve the situation. To cite just one characteristic formulation of the Western view:

> It is, of course, virtually impossible for the Russians to accept the "self-determination" of the German people, which is understandably the only form of reunification the West Germans will entertain. To allow the Germans to vote down communism by a huge majority would be such a disaster for Russia's leaders in eastern Europe and in the struggle with the Chinese that it is out of the question.[8]

To convince the West that a political change in Eastern Europe would be such a disaster for Russia that it is "out of the question" constitutes perhaps one of the most successful commitments in history. Curiously, it is not even clear whether this commitment was entirely the making of the Communist rulers or whether it was in part invented in the West. According to Khrushchev, for example, the leaders in Moscow were not always unanimous that a non-Communist East Germany was "out of the question." Khrushchev once said in reference to the 1953 uprisings in East Germany that Beria, together with Malenkov, "made the provocative proposal to liquidate East Germany as a Socialist state, to recommend to the East German Communist Party to abandon the struggle for the building of Socialism."[9] Similarly, regarding the Hungarian Revolution the Chinese Communist Party wrote in 1963 that "for a time" the Soviet leadership "intended to adopt a policy of capitulation and abandon Socialist Hungary to counter-revolution."[10] If this Chinese story is true, we must now sadly realize that the West took a more Stalinist view of the world than Khrushchev did. In

[8] *Economist*, Aug. 24, 1963, pp. 643–44.
[9] Speech of March 10, 1963.
[10] *Peking Review*, Sept. 13, 1963, p. 10.

a sense, the West collaborated with the Chinese, by solidifying the Soviet commitment according to which Russia *must* maintain Communist control in Eastern Europe—even at the cost of the most violent intervention. If the Chinese *and* the West say a change is out of the question, how could Moscow dare to consent to one?

The tendency to negotiate only for what seems attainable can lead to a self-reinforcing cycle. A nation that would like to alter a situation through negotiation but expects slight improvement at best may formulate rather modest goals: it will try to negotiate for small adjustments instead of for major gains. The opponent will usually discover this restraint and accordingly expect that his contribution need not be large. Then, if the first party becomes impressed by the opponent's confidence—which it unwittingly created—it will lower its expectations even further, leading to still lower goals. And so forth. Should this cycle continue, its end point would be that the first party finds the outlook for negotiation so unattractive that it will decide to leave the issue as is.

However, modest goals can also have compensating advantages. To the extent that genuine modesty can be conveyed to the opponent, it will reassure him that he need not fear a major challenge to his interests. This may make him more relaxed and friendlier and lead to a more accommodating negotiating style which will benefit the first party. Conversely, if the first party had communicated far-reaching aspirations to its opponent, this might have put him on his guard and increased his resistance.

Whether modest goals or ambitious ones will in the end bring better results depends on the opponent's political style and ideology. Certain opponents might always push to the limit without ever becoming more accommodating. The dilemma is familiar: Even though you curtail your negotiating goals, you may fail to divert your opponent from his antagonistic aims (much as you may fail to make him observe rules of accommodation by observing them yourself). This is the perennial dilemma of Western policy toward the Soviet Union.[11]

---

[11] Some writers have suggested that the West make a more deliberate effort to reduce Russia's hostility and to get away from mutually antagonistic aims. They recommend that the West should not only avoid goals that are threatening

AN EXAMPLE: EASTERN EUROPE

It is easy to show that negotiators are adrift when they evaluate gains and losses. Their criteria of evaluation are unstable and subject to the opponent's influence. So are the goals that they pursue through negotiation and on which their evaluations depend.

It is more difficult, however, to demonstrate how the evaluations have shifted in some actual negotiation and to separate changes in criteria from changes in the objective situations to which the criteria are applied. Negotiators rarely write down how they measure gains and losses, why they consider certain terms acceptable or "fair" while rejecting others, and what their goals really are as distinct from their demands and proposals. And even if these evaluations survive the fleeting moment by being recorded in some government document, they are not collected systematically but are scattered by chance among the vast materials in government archives. They might appear as a passage in an inter-office memorandum, a sentence in a telegram instructing a delegate, or a brief notation in a diary.

The East-West negotiations concerning the fate of Central and Eastern Europe, during World War II and since, provide a dramatic illustration of how evaluations change. Since the Soviet archives remain closed, we can trace these changes only for the Western powers, and even there the evidence is incomplete. These shifts were fundamental in shaping the postwar world, comparable in importance to the great situational or "objective" changes that took place during the same period, such as the buildup of American military power from 1943 to early 1945, the sweeping advances of the Red Army, the economic recovery in Western Europe, etc.

The story begins in November, 1941. (However, the traumatic experience of the British in August, 1939, when their negotiations with Russia were suddenly cut off by the Stalin-Hitler pact, has a bearing.) In October, 1941, we must remember, the German

---

to the Russians but also undertake unilateral moves to demonstrate its benevolence. See Charles E. Osgood, *An Alternative to War or Surrender* (Urbana, Ill.: University of Illinois Press, 1962).

armies had come within twenty miles of Moscow, and the Soviet government had been evacuated to Kuibyshev. Yet Stalin, in these days of his greatest crisis, began the diplomatic offensive which gradually led to Western acceptance of his control over Eastern and Central Europe up to the Elbe. On November 8, 1941, scarcely a month after a British-American delegation had concluded an agreement in Moscow for supplying Russia with badly needed arms, Stalin sent a telegram to Churchill which was so rude that Churchill did not answer it till he had received an apology three weeks later. Stalin began his list of accusations and reproaches by complaining that Great Britain lacked an understanding with the Soviet Union on war aims and on the organization of peace and that there could be no "mutual confidence" until this was settled.[12]

Stalin's diplomatic offensive was not without effect in the British Foreign Office. It started the slow process by which the Western goals were adapted to what Western diplomats perceived to be the Soviet goals, and Western evaluations were changed accordingly. A Foreign Office Document of that time records how British officials began to develop new criteria for evaluating future negotiations with Russia: "We did not know the Russian aims; they would probably ask for access to the Persian Gulf, the revision of the Montreux Convention, and the establishment of Russian bases in Norway, Finland, and the Baltic States. If efficient arrangements were made for general disarmament and security, they might ask for less. At present they might be content with some general resolution; if they wanted more than this, they would have to define their ideas to us and to the United States. We ought to let them see that we were treating them on an equality, and that the peace settlement would be dictated largely by the three Powers."[13]

The impact of Stalin's rude telegram was enhanced by the tendency, common among diplomats, to conduct affairs of state as if they were interpersonal relations. Both Foreign Secretary Eden and the British Ambassador in Moscow, Sir Stafford Cripps,

[12] Winston S. Churchill, *The Grand Alliance* (Boston: Houghton Mifflin, 1950), pp. 528–31.

[13] Sir Llewellyn Woodward, *British Foreign Policy in the Second World War* (London: H.M.S.O., 1962), p. 160. The document has been paraphrased by Woodward.

favored making concessions to allay what, they felt, were Stalin's suspicions. As Eden explained in a memorandum to the American Ambassador a month later, when he, Eden, was leaving for negotiations in Moscow: "The terms of the message were such as to leave no doubt that Stalin was in a mood of suspicion and even resentment to a degree that might adversely affect the cooperation of the two Governments in the prosecution of the war, and His Majesty's Government decided that every effort must be made to dissipate these feelings."[14] And after his visit to Moscow, Eden sent to Washington the telegram cited before (p. 163), in which he again stressed Stalin's "suspicion" as a reason for consenting to a westward move of Russia's boundary of some hundred miles or more.

In the meantime, British evaluations continued to be recalibrated in response to Stalin's goals. Indeed, not only Stalin's stated demands, but his *potential* demands, were used to evaluate the terms at which it would be in the interest of both Russia and the West to reach agreement. In February, 1942, a telegram from the British Foreign Office to Washington pleaded in behalf of Stalin's territorial demands: "It seems to us that the right method both of meeting this [Soviet] suspicion and of guarding so far as may be possible against the risk of Russia following entirely independent policy is to emphasize to the Soviet Government that . . . we and the United States Government would wish . . . to reach tripartite solutions. It must be remembered that Stalin might have asked for much more, e.g., control of the Dardanelles, spheres of influence in the Balkans, one-sided imposition on Poland of Russo-Polish frontiers, access to the Persian Gulf, access to the Atlantic involving cession of Norwegian territory."[15]

Winston Churchill, at first, did not share the views of Eden and the Foreign Office. While visiting Roosevelt, Churchill cabled to Eden, who had just come back from his negotiations in Moscow:

We have never recognised the 1941 frontiers of Russia except *de facto*. They were acquired by acts of aggression in shameful collusion

[14] U.S. Department of State, *Foreign Relations of the United States, 1941,* Vol. I (Washington, 1958), p. 192.
[15] U.S. Department of State, *Foreign Relations of the United States, 1942,* Vol. III (Washington, 1961), p. 518.

with Hitler. The transfer of the peoples of the Baltic States to Soviet Russia against their will would be contrary to all the principles for which we are fighting this war. . . . About the effect on Russia of our refusal . . . to depart from the principles of the Atlantic Charter, it must be observed that they entered the war only when attacked by Germany, having previously shown themselves utterly indifferent to our fate. . . . No one can foresee how the balance of power will lie or where the winning armies will stand at the end of the war. It seems probable however that the United States and the British Empire, far from being exhausted, will be the most powerfully armed and economic *bloc* the world has ever seen, and that the Soviet Union will need our aid for reconstruction far more than we shall then need theirs.

Nor was Churchill taken in by the idea that Stalin's "suspicions" should be humored: "If they harbour suspicions of us, it is only because of the guilt and self-reproach in their hearts."[16]

Three months later, however, Churchill changed his mind. On March 7, 1942, he wrote to Roosevelt: "The increase in gravity of the war has led me to feel that the principles of the Atlantic Charter ought not to be construed so as to deny Russia the frontiers she occupied when Germany attacked her. . . . I hope therefore that you will be able to give us a free hand to sign the treaty which Stalin desires as soon as possible."[17] Why did Churchill change his evaluation as to what would be a satisfactory agreement with Russia? Russia's position had not become much stronger, and that of Great Britain and the United States was by no means weaker. We may speculate that Churchill was swayed in a manner in which negotiators are often influenced: by thinking in terms of historical analogy. He must have remembered how, in August, 1939, the Anglo-French negotiations in Moscow ended when Stalin made his pact with Hitler. He may have recalled his own words earlier that year, when he had warned Chamberlain quickly to conclude an agreement with Russia. The failure of the Ango-French negotiations in Moscow in 1939 must have also influenced the Foreign Office, since some of the same officials were involved then as were involved in 1942. As the American Chargé in London observed in March, 1942: "They are still bitterly con-

---

[16] *The Grand Alliance*, pp. 695–96, 473.
[17] Winston S. Churchill, *The Hinge of Fate*, p. 327.

scious that to their minds their own haggling tactics during the 1939 negotiations—and over these very Baltic States—were the real cause of Stalin's agreement with the Germans."[18]

Whatever caused Churchill to change his mind, he would have given in to the Russian demands when Molotov arrived in London in 1942 had it not been for American opposition. As it turned out, this opposition was sufficient to put the Russians off, and on May 26 a treaty of alliance was signed without any territorial provisions. To Churchill, who had just lowered his evaluation criteria in the last few months, this outcome now seemed like a gain: "This was a great relief to me, and a far better solution that I had dared to hope."[19]

Thus ended the first act. On the surface, the American position, that the Atlantic Charter should also apply to Eastern Europe, had won out. Underneath, however, the evaluation criteria had now been permanently altered. Russia was now expected to want these territories in Eastern Europe. Her goal gradually became the expected outcome, and the expected outcome became the new break-even point from which gains and losses would be measured in the future. By initiating his most successful series of negotiations at the time of his greatest weakness, Stalin had demonstrated the fallacy of the Western cliché that one must negotiate from strength.

The beginning of the second act might be traced to the first American-British review of war aims between Eden and Roosevelt in March, 1943. Eden told Roosevelt he thought that the Soviet Union would insist on absorbing the Baltic states. Roosevelt remarked that they might have to agree to this absorption but, if so, this ought to be used as a bargaining counter with Russia. On Poland, Eden thought that the Soviet Union would claim for itself some of the territory that had been part of Poland in 1939— possibly up to the Curzon line.[20]

Half a year later, Roosevelt remarked to Secretary of State Cordell Hull (who was about to leave for the Moscow Conference

---

[18] *Foreign Relations of the United States, 1942*, III, 533.
[19] *The Hinge of Fate*, p. 336.
[20] Herbert Feis, *Churchill-Roosevelt-Stalin* (Princeton, N.J.: Princeton University Press, 1957), p. 122.

of October, 1943) that his, Roosevelt's, inclination would be to tell Stalin, "that neither Britain nor we would fight Russia over the Baltic states. . . ." Although Roosevelt still wanted the Russians to promise a plebiscite over the absorption of the Baltic states, his earlier reluctance and the idea of a *quid pro quo* was gone. But on the Soviet-Polish boundary, Roosevelt still thought, as he told Hull, that it should be "somewhat east of the so-called Curzon line, with Lemberg going to Poland."[21]

This view prevailed in the American government up to the Yalta Conference in February, 1945. A U.S. policy paper in preparation for Yalta stated: "We should support a frontier settlement which in the east would take the Curzon Line as a basis but would, if possible, include the Province of Lwów [Lemberg] in Poland. . . . We should resist the exaggerated claims now being advanced by [the Polish Communists] for compensation from Germany which would include the cities of Stettin and Breslau in Poland and make necessary the transfer of from eight to ten million Germans." As to Hungary, another U.S. policy paper for Yalta evaluated possible gains and losses much as today they might be evaluated, say, for Finland. It recognized that the Soviet interest in Hungary was "more direct" than the American interest but added: "We do not, however, consider that the Soviet Union has any special privileged or dominant position in Hungary." Churchill, on the other hand, in his famous percentage deal with Stalin, had already agreed to a fifty-fifty sharing of dominance in Hungary. But even this was a far greater Western influence than the United States acceded to after the war and has taken for granted ever since.[22]

It would make this digression too long to trace the shifting Western evaluations regarding Eastern Europe through the Yalta and Potsdam Conferences and thence through the early postwar years. The story has been told often and well. But the vast changes in Eastern Europe have frequently been explained as though the only cause was that the Soviet forces got there first. Of course, without this military outcome most of the changes would probably

[21] *The Memoirs of Cordell Hull* (New York: Macmillan, 1948) II, 1266.
[22] *The Conferences at Malta and Yalta 1945*, pp. 230, 245. Churchill, *Triumph and Tragedy*, p. 227.

not have occurred. Yet the military outcome was in part determined by those negotiations in which the Western evaluations kept eroding.

Cause and effect are often intertwined. In a number of areas now part of Communist Europe, Western forces could have entered first, had these areas by that time not become regarded as belonging to the Soviet sphere of influence. In other areas, such as Bornholm and Northern Iran, the Soviets actually were in full military control, but were induced through negotiation to withdraw, partly because Western evaluations remained firm. By contrast, in Czechoslovakia, which was free of Soviet troops and far more accessible to American and British military strength than isolated Iran, the West tolerated Soviet interference and eventually the coup of 1948, precisely because Washington had already come to regard the Sovietization of Czechoslovakia as the expected and tolerable outcome.

Perhaps one more episode ought to be added to this tale, that of the 1948 Berlin blockade. Here, the Western evaluations changed in the opposite direction: at first it seemed like a gain if Stalin could be induced to settle for only a *limited* control over West Berlin, later any Soviet interference in West Berlin looked like a serious loss.

On July 30, 1948, a month and a half after Stalin had imposed the Berlin blockade, the Western powers started negotiating in Moscow in order to have the blockade removed. Stalin said he was willing to lift the blockade, provided the Western powers would simultaneously replace the West German mark in West Berlin with the Soviet mark.[23] The Western ambassadors accepted Stalin's proposal, but they reached an impasse with Molotov when trying to work out four-power control over the regulation of the Soviet marks that were to be used throughout Berlin. Stalin again intervened and assured the Western ambassadors that the bank in the Soviet zone which would issue and control the money for all

[23] Shortly after the first blockade measures, the Western powers had instituted a currency reform within their zones of Germany and a few days later introduced the new West German mark in West Berlin (after a new Soviet German mark had been introduced in East Berlin and in the Soviet zone of Germany).

of Berlin would itself be controlled by a four-power financial commission under the four commanders in Berlin.

What seems striking today is that in the summer of 1948 the Western evaluation criteria were such that it seemed worthwhile to accept Soviet currency in West Berlin (tempered with some Western controls) in exchange for Stalin's promise to discontinue the blockade. More than that, the American negotiator, Walter Bedell Smith, felt that Stalin's proposal "sounded very good indeed."[24]

As it turned out, this "very good" arrangement never materialized. The task of working out the practical implementation of the currency arrangement was left to the four military governors in Berlin. There, Soviet stubbornness saved the Western powers from what would have been a very undesirable trade (evaluated by today's criteria). The Soviet commander in Berlin not only objected to a four-power finance committee for controlling the bank in the Soviet zone that would have regulated the currency in West Berlin, but he wanted to restrict civil air traffic to Berlin and establish complete control over trade with Berlin.[25]

As W. P. Davison explained, the Western powers were so defeatist in the summer of 1948 because they greatly underrated the potentialities of the airlift and the strength of popular morale in Berlin.[26] But these erroneous estimates alone do not explain why, in August, 1948, Stalin's currency arrangement was acceptable to the Western capitals and looked "very good" to Ambassador Smith, whereas already in the spring of 1949 it would have looked like a serious loss. Parallel with the successful development of the airlift, but not just because of it, Western evaluations changed. For one thing, the very effort to preserve West Berlin made it seem more valuable. And the prolonged negotiations made the status quo assume permanent interest; it became the break-even point for measuring gains and losses. West Berlin was no longer

[24] Walter Bedell Smith, *My Three Years in Moscow* (Philadelphia: Lippincott, 1950), p. 249.

[25] Lucius D. Clay, *Decision in Germany* (Garden City, N.Y.: Doubleday, 1950), p. 371.

[26] W. Phillips Davison, *The Berlin Blockade* (Princeton, N.J.: Princeton University Press, 1958), p. 193.

a transient outpost behind the Russian lines accidentally left over from World War II.

Since then, Western evaluations regarding Berlin have continued to fluctuate. In 1959, for example, the Western powers proposed a new agreement on Berlin which would have guaranteed free access to West Berlin for five years (to expire in July, 1964!) and would have envisaged curbs on intelligence and "subversive" activities, with these controls to be monitored by the United Nations.[27] But the Russians saw to it that the Berlin negotiations would continue, and as a result the Western evaluations, instead of eroding further, became more assertive again. After 1961, the Western powers would certainly have considered their 1959 proposal a bad bargain.

There is nothing either a gain or a loss, but negotiating makes it so!

---

[27] When this interim agreement would have lapsed, the Russians could have refused to renew it except under conditions unacceptable to the West. Even though the old rights would then have been reinstated according to the Western view, the Western position would have seemed much weaker. As Henry Kissinger pointed out, it was doubtful that "the West would after a five-year interval defend rights for which it was not prepared to contend when they were first challenged and which were specifically altered by the interim agreement" (*The Necessity for Choice*, p. 143). And during the five years, the Communists could have used the curb on "subversive" activities to demand censorship and the restriction of political activity in West Berlin.

CHAPTER **11**

HOW THE PARTIES COME TO TERMS

UNTIL AGREEMENT EMERGES, EACH PARTY KEEPS PROPOSING terms to the opponent while trying to find out what terms he would settle for. It is an essential feature of negotiation that the process of finding out the opponent's terms (and of revealing one's own) is also part of the process of inducing him to soften his terms (and of making one's own terms more acceptable to him).

The Anticipated Minimum. People not familiar with the way in which nations negotiate assume that each party has its minimum position. They imagine the existence of a borderline dividing the terms at which a party would accept agreement from those at which it would inevitably reject. This borderline is thought to remain fixed except on those rare occasions when a government deliberately revises it up or down.

Reality is more complicated and more subtle. Objective minimum positions, in the sense just explained, normally do not exist for three reasons. First, governments do not face two choices only, agreement and no-agreement, that a minimum position could separate like a watershed. From the beginning of every negotiation to its very end, they keep choosing between three options, so that the watershed between the first two depends on the outlook for the third one: the prospects for further bargaining. Second, in deciding their threefold choice, governments must be concerned with more than the probable gains from further bargaining and the comparison of agreement with no-agreement. They must also consider how their negotiating will affect their bargaining reputation and to what extent they should observe or ignore rules of accommodation. Third, as discussed before, all evaluations and expectations—and even the goals—keep shifting.

Instead of fixed minimum positions, each party can have only an *anticipated minimum.* The negotiator anticipates that he will not choose agreement at terms below his "minimum," but he cannot know whether he might not eventually accept agreement at lesser terms or choose no-agreement even though the available terms were better than this "minimum." For example, in the negotiations about an inspection system for a ban on underground nuclear tests, the American negotiators might have anticipated that they would accept a treaty with, say, five inspections but not with four. If the time had come, however, either to sign a treaty prohibiting underground tests or to stop negotiating, even three inspections might have been found adequate or six insufficient.

There is a further complication: the anticipated minimum is usually blurred. Normally, the parties have only a vague anticipation of the terms that they expect to consider sufficiently desirable for preferring agreement over no-agreement. Frequently, this anticipation is very faint. Indeed, even when a negotiator has given up further bargaining and is actually choosing agreement (or no-agreement), he may not be fully aware how much worse (or better) the terms would have to be to reverse his choice. All the more reason to reject the popular notion of fixed minima, which stand immovable from the beginning to the end of a conference like goal posts in a ball game. To revert to the hypothetical example, should a treaty providing for six inspections be signed on underground tests, the American negotiators would probably not know whether they would have rejected the treaty if it had provided for only four, three, or one inspection.

It is not an uncommon negotiating tactic, however, to create a commitment to a position by treating it *as if* it were a fixed minimum. Government officials often talk about certain terms as being their firm minimum, pretending to know that agreement at inferior terms would *always* be undesirable. Actually, if these officials analyzed their beliefs, they would have to admit that they are not at all so clear as to where they should place the watershed between agreement and no-agreement. It is expedient for them, however, not to be fully aware of this indeterminacy and to talk themselves into believing that they know exactly where their "minimum position" lies. To cut short any erosive re-examination of this "minimum" among themselves, they might argue that "one has to stop somewhere."

THE FUNCTION OF PROPOSALS

Proposals play a key role in the process through which the parties come to terms. Indeed, the confrontation, revisions, and final acceptance of proposals at the conference table is sometimes all that is meant by "negotiation." Even in the broader definition used in this book, explicit proposals are an essential feature of "negotiation," for they distinguish it from tacit bargaining. Certainly, if there is to be an explicit agreement, there must first be at least one explicit proposal.

Proposals, however, are not the whole story of negotiation; rather, they are markers on the surface which indicate more substantial developments underneath. It should also be recalled that governments prepare proposals in part or entirely for the purpose of producing certain side-effects: to spread propaganda, to maintain contact, to stave off violent actions, or for similar reasons that do not concern agreement. Here these side-effects will be ignored in order to concentrate on the ways in which governments use proposals to reach favorable terms of agreement.

Ostensibly, proposals *always* represent an offer; they give a description of the terms that are allegedly being made available to the opponent. But in fact, proposals are frequently meant as an offer only toward the final phases of a conference. And even then they are binding only to the extent that the parties observe the rule of accommodation according to which an accepted offer should not be withdrawn. In contrast to business negotiations, governments can always withdraw their offers after they have been accepted, albeit with some cost to their bargaining reputation.

If you are engaged in international negotiation, many of your proposals do not serve as offers. Instead they are meant to influence your opponent so that he will make better terms available to you than he was originally disposed to or, conversely, so that he will come to accept greater demands of yours. In other words, your proposals serve either as path-breakers for an eventual offer of yours or as stimuli to make your opponent produce an offer favorable to you.

Your proposals must change your opponent's expectations. They must make him believe that you will insist on certain demands. More than that, they must accustom him to the idea that he wants to reach agreement by meeting what seem to be your irreducible terms. Thus your proposals should accomplish two things with your opponent: they should change his expectations about *your* anticipated minimum, and they should change his anticipations concerning *his* minimum terms. As suggested earlier, the first change will help to bring about the second change. If your opponent changes his expectation as to what *you* intend to settle for, he may change his mind as to what *he* is trying to get.

In the nuclear test-ban conference, for example, the Western insistence early in 1963 on more than just three on-site inspections may have changed Khrushchev's expectations as to the minimum inspection arrangements that the Western powers would accept for banning underground tests. And this may have helped to change his mind about his accepting a partial treaty permitting underground tests, once he had become anxious to have a treaty.

To keep the opponent interested in negotiating, diplomats often formulate their proposals in a flexible fashion. The marked preference for flexibility among many Western diplomats results, in part, from the fear that the opponent might suddenly choose no-agreement if faced with a firm position. In part, Western diplomats keep their proposals flexible because they feel that this is the proper way to negotiate.

But this tactic is self-defeating if the diplomats on the opponent's side want to prove their mettle by showing that they pushed you as far as possible. They cannot satisfy themselves (or their government) that they have reached the limit as long as you offer them a menu of choices, particularly if the menu keeps changing. This is the reason why Westerners have been warned against trying out many variant proposals in negotiating with the Russians. Occasionally, though, a variant proposal may have helped to get a satisfactory agreement with the Soviet Union, for instance the Western proposal for a partial test ban.

However, if your opponent is under domestic pressure to reach agreement and to demonstrate his own flexibility, your flexibility can be used to hasten agreement. You may ensnare him into accepting one of your proposals by putting many alternatives before him.

Tacit bargaining moves may add firmness to negotiations that are otherwise conducted in a flexible manner. The reason is that the opponent usually cannot tell how flexible or firm a tacit move is meant to be as long as it does not become the subject of explicit negotiation. Statesmen who feel constrained by tradition or by domestic opinion to maintain an appearance of flexibility, therefore, can profit from tacit moves that they link to, but do not mention in, their proposals. Also, whereas rigid explicit proposals might antagonize the opponent and cause him to break off negotiations, tacit moves might be tolerated by him because he does not know whether the lack of flexibility is intentional or not.

Such effects of tacit moves may have helped to resolve the Cuba crisis in 1962. Many observers feel that what really compelled Khrushchev to withdraw his missiles was the intelligence he received of American military preparations suggesting that an air strike against his Cuban bases was imminent. Since this threat was tacit (as far as can be judged from the published exchange between Khrushchev and Kennedy), it gave Khrushchev no hint as to how firm or flexible it was.[1] Therefore, it endowed the key American demand for the withdrawal of missiles (which was, of course, explicit) with particular firmness. All the other explicit positions —both the American and the Soviet ones—turned out to be so flexible that they practically melted away. Take the American demand for United Nations inspection. After being exposed to U Thant's mediation, Castro's haggling, and Khrushchev's counter-

---

[1] In a speech in 1963, Attorney General Robert Kennedy remarked that "notification" was sent to Khrushchev of "overwhelming retaliatory action" if the missiles were not pulled out. However, the *New York Times* quotes "high officials" as saying that the "notification" was by way of deeds, not words. "What got the message through to Khrushchev was action." The calling up of Air Force reservists and the movement of military equipment to Florida was deliberately done rather openly (*New York Times*, April 26, 1963).

offer for Red Cross inspection, it finally led to the curious agreement for distant and discreet observation of Soviet ships by the U.S. Navy. Likewise, Khrushchev's demand for the withdrawal of American missiles from Turkey was quietly abandoned. And his demand for an American pledge not to invade or interfere with Cuba became lost in the shuffle, when the UN inspection (on which American negotiators made such a pledge conditional) never materialized. (Khrushchev, however, likes to pretend that the pledge had actually been given.)

Firmness in negotiating proposals can be a deliberate tactic, just like flexibility. It may be used to make the opponent think that one's proposal is close to one's anticipated minimum or, at any rate, that one firmly expects to have one's proposal accepted and will not make further concessions. A way of expressing firmness —though not always a successful one—is repetition. Communist diplomats never tire of reiterating the same position over and over again. Westerners, on the other hand, often try to convey firmness by using new arguments and minor variations; perhaps the feeling that the public is listening in makes sheer repetition of their proposals embarrassing to them. Westerners feel free to be repetitious only when asserting a governing principle, such as the need for verification of disarmament measures or the legality of Western rights of access to Berlin.

But firmness is not always a tactic deliberately chosen to impress the opponent. Negotiators may be firm and keep on repeating their demands simply because their government is unable to furnish them with new instructions. When the representatives of the Algerian FLN negotiated with France about Algeria's independence, they first held on rigidly to sweeping positions (e.g., "complete independence") and could not come to grips with the many details that had to be settled to implement the granting of independence in an orderly fashion. This was not so much the result of their tenacity as of the inability of the Algerian rebels to make the decisions necessary for negotiation. The French practically had to teach their Algerian adversaries that concessions could be traded and that positions might be modified here or there without becoming less desirable.

THE FUNCTION OF ARGUMENTS

Anyone who has worked his way through verbatim records of an international conference must have wondered what, really, was the purpose of all the words that were exchanged over the green baize. At times diplomats seem to talk for the love of their own rhetoric, with no other purpose in mind than to make well-sounding speeches or to win a debating point. At other times they talk for the sake of some side-effect, say, to maintain contact with the opponent or to spread propaganda. Only part of their arguments serve the central purpose of improving the opponent's offers or of making him accept their own. Sometimes diplomats—like other human beings—talk without really knowing what they wish to accomplish with their words.

But, it is possible to concentrate on the arguments designed to improve the terms of agreement and to disregard all the talking done for other purposes or for no purpose at all. The negotiator can use such arguments in several ways, each of which represents a slightly different tactic. Quite likely he will mix these tactics intuitively, moving from one to the other like an experienced driver shifting gears, without consciously calculating what he is doing.

Arguments To Make One's Proposals Attractive

Of course, governments are not swayed by sales talk in the way a naïve consumer might be swayed by advertising. Nonetheless, a negotiator can say things about his offers that will make them seem more attractive to the opponent. One reason is that arguments may be like supplementary offers. That is, the words a negotiator uses in praising his proposal may be viewed as more or less binding amplifications which spell out further details of his offer. Such amplifications are binding for the same reason that an agreement itself is binding, though to a lesser extent. Should a party succeed in having its proposal accepted but later violate the interpretations and amplifications it has given, it will not be believed in the future when it tries to "sell" another proposal.[2]

---

[2] Decisions of the International Court support the notion that explanations given during negotiations are binding. The Court has held, however, that the

Another way in which a diplomat might make his proposals more attractive merely by talking about them is to convince his opponent that he is motivated by friendly intentions. This is particularly important for proposals aimed at a redistribution agreement, since the defensive side will be opposed to a redistribution that would strengthen an enemy but might tolerate one to win a friend.

Yet, in a way it is curious that talk at the conference table should make any difference. A customer shopping for a rug in a bazaar will not find the price more acceptable just because the merchant claims to be his friend. Perhaps the arguments of diplomats form part of the mosaic of intelligence on the basis of which governments try to size up their opponents. When a diplomat maintains that his proposals stem from the best of intentions, this will not be accepted as a definitive explanation, but it is an item that will be put on the plus side in evaluating his proposal. Remonstrations of good intentions are especially influential during those turning points in international relations when the question whether a country is one's friend or foe hangs in the balance.

Shortly after he became President, Harry Truman sent Harry Hopkins to see Stalin in Moscow. Truman considered this mission of "primary importance . . . to know whether the death of Roosevelt had brought any important changes in the attitudes of Stalin. . . ."[3] One of the most important problems for Hopkins to discuss was the disagreement about Poland. After Hopkins had explained the American desire for a free Poland, Stalin pointed out that in the course of twenty-five years the Germans had twice invaded Russia via Poland. It was therefore in Russia's vital interest that Poland should be both strong and friendly. And he added that "there was no intention on the part of the Soviet Union to interfere in Poland's internal affairs, that Poland would live under the parliamentary system which is like Czechoslovakia, Belgium, and Holland and that any talk of an intention to Sovietize

---

negotiatory history may be used for treaty interpretation only if the treaty itself is not clear and if all parties before the Court participated in the negotiations. (J. L. Brierly, The Law of Nations [Oxford: Clarendon Press, 1949], p. 235; Georg Schwarzenberger, International Law [London: Stevens, 1949], I, 218.)
    [3] Truman, Memoirs, I, 110.

Poland was stupid."[4] Hopkins' report did of course not fully persuade Truman as to the benevolence of the Soviet position, but neither was Truman convinced—as he became two years later—that Stalin did indeed want to Sovietize Poland.

About the same time, the Soviet government was engaged in some other redistribution negotiations. At the end of World War II Stalin tried to take some territory from Turkey. This aroused British and American opposition, and the way in which Soviet diplomats argued for their demand did not help. For instance, in a discussion with the Soviet ambassador in Ankara, the Turkish foreign minister inquired "whether the Soviet Union which possesses a respectable portion of the earth's surface really needed any additional territory." The Soviet ambassador replied that "the Soviet Union did not need additional territory but the Armenian Soviet Socialist Republic was very small and needed additional territory." The Turkish foreign minister simply retorted that he "could not accept such a statement."[5]

A more subtle way of making one's proposals more attractive is to influence the opponent's evaluation criteria, rather than to protest one's good intentions or to offer favorable amplifications.

Some time before the Soviets demanded a slice of Turkish territory, they had requested that the Montreux Convention be revised so as to remove all restrictions on the passage of Russian warships through the Turkish Straits. At Yalta, Stalin argued that "it was impossible to accept a situation in which Turkey had a hand on Russia's throat [but that the Convention should be revised] in such a manner as not to harm the legitimate interests of Turkey." Churchill did not deny the validity of these arguments and took a rather favorable view of the Russian request for a revision of the Convention. The Russian arguments also seem to have encouraged a re-evaluation in the U.S. government. A U.S. policy paper for the Yalta Conference argued that the Montreux Convention has "worked well" and that "any major changes probably would violate Turkish sovereignty." But a few months after Yalta, in preparation for the Potsdam Conference, another U.S. policy paper

---

[4] *Foreign Relations of the United States: The Conference of Berlin* (*Potsdam*) *1945*, I, 39 (quotation as paraphrased in the official minutes).
[5] *Ibid.*, p. 1025.

stated: "The Government of the United States believes that following the present war the Montreux Convention to some extent will be outmoded."[6]

On the issue of the revision of the Panama Canal Treaty, it is in Panama's interest to use arguments that will change the American evaluation criteria to make the treaty appear as an instance of colonialism—an inequity that ought to be remedied. Such an evaluation would make a redistribution in favor of Panama more attractive to the United States, because it would seem to be in line with a historical trend. Changes in favor of Panama would be viewed as an even outcome by the United States, not as a Panamanian gain and an American loss.

To sum up, arguments may induce the opponent to recalibrate his evaluations if he is already inclined to do so. He may be persuaded to shift his break-even point because he has no firm views as to where his gains and losses begin. But he will not be talked into reversing his preferences on major issues. Words are not enough to convert a government or the negotiators representing it.

Although experienced diplomats should know better, a great deal of time is wasted in international conferences as one delegate exhorts another delegate that his government should prefer what it dislikes and should shun what it pursues. International diplomacy is not like a high school debate where people change sides because they listen to some convincing sentences. Thus, one wonders what Secretary Byrnes sought to accomplish when he argued with Molotov that an independent Poland was better for Russia than one under Soviet control. Almost with disappointment Byrnes recalls: "I could not impress [Molotov] with my views that Soviet security would be better assured by having in Poland a people who are friendly, rather than a government that was friendly only because it was dictated by the Soviet Union. Unsuccessfully, I argued that governments would come and go, but that if the Soviet Government's conduct in Poland won the friendship of the people, the friendship of the government would be assured."[7]

---

[6] Ibid., The Conferences at Malta and Yalta 1945, p. 903 and p. 328; and The Conference of Berlin (Potsdam) 1945, I, 1014.

[7] Byrnes, Speaking Frankly, p. 32.

ARGUMENTS EXPRESSING FIRMNESS

An important function of arguments is to impress the opponent that one's proposal is firm and that no concessions can be forthcoming. A commitment may actually be reinforced by the act of explaining it in a public conference, because the negotiator will be afraid of domestic criticism if he makes a concession after having argued that his proposal was vital.

A common way of demonstrating one's commitment is to argue that domestic forces would oppose a change in one's position. Harry Hopkins, during his mission to Moscow in May, 1945, tried to demonstrate the firmness of the American position on Poland primarily by pointing out that public opinion in the United States was disturbed and that Truman might lose the public support that Roosevelt enjoyed for a friendly policy toward the Soviet Union. However, Hopkins probably weakened his argument by dissociating himself from this body of opinion and by implying that the President, for himself, really had no strong views on Poland. He told Stalin that "rightly or wrongly" there was a strong feeling among the American people that the Soviet Union wished to dominate Poland but added that this was not his point of view. Hopkins argued that friendly American-Soviet relations were threatened by the public reaction in the United States to the events in Poland but reminded Stalin that "many minority groups in America" were not sympathetic to Russia anyhow, "that Poland was only a symbol," and that Stalin "should not assume that the *Chicago Tribune* or the Hearst Press had any real influence on American public opinion."[8]

The domestic-opinion argument is effective only if it conveys the idea that the domestic views are held by people who can influence policy. At the 1955 summit meeting Bulganin used a domestic-opinion argument on Eden that seemed to meet this requirement. He told Eden in private—as if he were imparting a great secret— that "it would really not be possible for his Government to return to Moscow from this Conference if they agreed to the immediate unification of Germany. They were a united Government and

[8] *The Conference of Berlin (Potsdam) 1945*, pp. 56–58 (quotes as paraphrased in Bohlen's memorandum).

reasonably solidly based in the country, but this was something that Russia would not accept; and if they were to agree to it neither the army nor the people would understand, and this was no time to weaken the Government."[9]

The domestic-opinion argument was again used on Eden by Secretary Dulles during the Suez crisis in 1956. According to Eden, Dulles "stated that he could not release us from our obligation to withdraw [the British forces from the Canal zone], since to do so would be 'in some sense a breach of faith on the part of the Administration with Congress and United States public opinion.' He maintained that our action had caused revulsion throughout the United States." But this time Eden was not impressed with the argument: "This was strong language," he writes, "and at variance with the reports of our own representatives, who considered that the sharp feelings displayed at that time in Washington had not really represented American opinion."[10]

Another way of expressing firmness is to maintain that one's position accords with legal or scientific principles. At least, this is the principal function of legal and scientific arguments; for you do not usually make your proposal more attractive to your opponent by telling him that what you are proposing is in accordance with scientific facts or international law. However, if you make your opponent believe that *you* think your proposal is grounded on such principles, you may have conveyed to him that your proposal is firm. If your opponent believes that you view your position as being part of a larger, coherent system, he must expect that you will refuse a concession for fear of undermining other positions that are connected with this system of yours. The American negotiators in the nuclear test-ban conference may have used scientific arguments with some success for this reason. They were able to demonstrate a strong commitment to many minor details of the inspection system because they maintained the stance that the system, in its entirety, had to be in accordance with scientific requirements. During the early part of the test-ban negotiations the Russians gave in on several such details, not so much because they cared whether or not the system was scientifically sound, but

[9] Anthony Eden, *Full Circle*, p. 334.
[10] *Ibid.*, p. 664.

because they were impressed with the American commitment to a scientifically grounded system.

Procedural arguments or arguments against a new precedent are often used for the same purpose. If you can show that a concession would violate established procedure or set a new precedent, your position may look firmer than if your opponent thought that you would only be conceding some of the substance of your position.

Another tactic for dissuading your opponent from further bargaining is to argue that you know he is willing to settle for your terms, if pressed to do so. In other words, you pretend to know that his anticipated minimum terms are compatible with your offer, thus suggesting that you will be quite stubborn in clinging to your terms.

Firmness can also be expressed by telling your opponent that you are not at all eager to reach agreement, so that he will think he has to meet your terms to make agreement worthwhile for you. Up to the atomic bombing of Hiroshima, the United States was anxious to obtain Soviet participation in defeating Japan. This wish resulted from faulty intelligence about Japan's military strength, ignoring of Japanese peace feelers, and the unimaginative insistence on "unconditional surrender." But these errors are not the ones that concern us here.

American diplomacy committed another error in negotiating with Stalin for Soviet entry into the war against Japan—regardless of whether or not Soviet participation was necessary for a quick victory. This was the American belief that Stalin was not eager to come into the war and hence would do so only if rewarded by territorial gains. Foreign Secretary Eden, for one, did not share this view, as he explained to Secretary of State Stettinius when they met at Malta to prepare for the Yalta Conference (where Stalin was promised his reward for entering the war against Japan). According to the minutes of the Malta meeting, Eden told Stettinius: ". . . if the Russians decided to enter the war against Japan they would take the decision because they considered it in their interests that the Japanese war should not be successfully finished by the U.S. and Great Britain alone. There was therefore no need for us to offer a high price for their participation, and if we were prepared to agree to their territorial demands in the Far East we should see to it that we obtained a good return in respect of the points on which we required concessions from them."[11]

At Yalta, Stalin skillfully avoided giving any support to Eden's thesis that it was in Russia's own interest to enter the war against Japan. He argued that if his demands in the Far East were not met, "it would be difficult for him and Molotov to explain to the Soviet people why Russia was entering the war against Japan . . . ; however, if these political conditions were met, the people would understand the national interest involved and it would be very much easier to explain the decision to a Supreme Soviet."[12] And when Hopkins came to see him in Moscow a few months later, Stalin, to make sure that his conditions would be met, again used the argument that he was not eager to enter the war against Japan.

ARGUMENTS ABOUT RULES OF ACCOMMODATION

Negotiators argue a great deal about rules of accommodation. Appeals are made to the opponent that he ought to be more flexible, that he should not impugn one's motives, that it is his turn to reciprocate a concession, and so forth. Negotiators of the European Communities are wont to plead for their proposals by appealing to the *esprit communautaire,* implying that a higher standard of accommodation should apply within the Communities.

In multilateral negotiations, arguments about rules of accommodation have greater effect than in bilateral ones. The other parties may act as mediators who will turn against a party that can be shown to have violated these rules. Hence, negotiators not only will argue that the opponent ought to observe certain rules (or has failed to do so) but will try to demonstrate that they themselves are beyond reproach. They will use what is sometimes called "diplomatic language"—meticulously polite, never blunt, and always flexible. A negotiator who wants to veto a proposal in a multilateral conference without incurring blame may say, for example, that the issue has not yet been adequately discussed and therefore must be postponed.

[11] *The Conferences at Malta and Yalta 1945,* p. 501.

[12] *Ibid.,* p. 769 (quote as paraphrased in the minutes). Earlier, at Teheran, Stalin had promised to participate in the Pacific war without mentioning territorial compensation. (For further details of this story, see Herbert Feis, *The China Tangle* [Princeton, N.J.: Princeton University Press, 1953], pp. 226–39.)

Moreover, to gain the approval of third parties who might have a mediating influence in multilateral negotiation, diplomats will usually see to it that their arguments sound reasonable. They will not commit gross violations of logic, brazenly distort well-known facts, or offend common standards of justice and fairness. Western participants in the Eighteen-Nation Disarmament Conference felt that the presence of neutral nations forced the Communist negotiators to use more reasonable arguments than in earlier conferences without neutral participation. By contrast, if there are no mediators around, it sometimes pays to use a totally unreasonable argument to demonstrate that one's position is independent of the reasons that are being discussed and therefore cannot be shaken by the opponent's arguments. This is what Tsarapkin may have had in mind when he maintained at the nuclear test-ban conference (prior to the participation of neutral nations): "I must repeat that whether the staff of control posts, or of other parts of the control system, consists of foreigners or of citizens of the country on whose territory the control post is located, the work of control will not suffer in any way. This is an absolutely indisputable proposition, which you cannot possibly refute."[13] The question whether citizens could be trusted to report a violation by their own country is blithely ignored.

REACHING POINTS OF AGREEMENT

As the parties bring their positions into agreement, they adapt their proposals to a single agreed set of terms, out in the open at the conference table. But this is only the surface manifestation of the process of reaching agreement. The rest takes place in the negotiators' minds and in the inner councils of governments. The terms of agreement are reached through a contest of wills, wits, and interests—much of which remains concealed from the opponent—in which the parties keep revising their expectations about each other, shift their evaluations for measuring gains and losses, and continually weigh (as long as they seek agreement) the

[13] Conference on the Discontinuance of Nuclear Weapon Tests, 23d Plenary Meeting, Dec. 11, 1958, p. 16.

choice between accepting the available terms and further bargaining.

The open confrontation of proposals may be clarified by, first, examining how parties come to terms on a single, indivisible issue and by, later, considering how they connect several issues to arrive at more complex agreements. A variety of different maneuvers are used to come to terms on a single issue. These maneuvers usually take place in various combinations, but for the sake of clarity they will be discussed one by one.

THE COMPROMISE

Edward Stettinius wrote in defense of the Yalta Conference, which he attended as Roosevelt's Secretary of State, that the Russians made more concessions than the United States and Great Britain made to them. "On certain issues, of course," he goes on to say, "each of the three Great Powers modified its original position in order to reach agreement. Although it is sometimes alleged that there is something evil in compromise, actually, of course, compromise is necessary for progress as any sensible man knows. Compromise, when reached honorably and in a spirit of honesty by all concerned, is the only fair and rational way of reaching a reasonable agreement between two differing points of view."[14]

It is a recurrent theme in Western writings on diplomacy that compromise is not only desirable but even necessary for reaching agreement. The fact is that agreement can be reached in other ways, some of which might well be considered more desirable. The Yalta Agreement should be neither defended nor attacked because parts of it were reached through compromise. Moreover, it is an egregious error to call compromise a "fair" or "rational" method without comparing the "fairness" of the initial positions from which the parties started. Perhaps Stettinius' phrase "in a spirit of honesty" implies such a comparison. But honesty is not the discriminating criterion here, since all negotiation naturally includes some deception.

A "compromise" usually means an agreement reached through

---

[14] Edward R. Stettinius, Jr., *Roosevelt and the Russians* (Garden City, N.Y.: Doubleday, 1949), p. 6.

concessions by both sides. And a party is said to make a "concession" when it changes its proposal so as to bring it closer to that of the opponent. However, the fact that a party has made a concession only means that it has lowered the terms it first stated —not the ones it expected to get. When a party reaches a compromise, its expectations may actually move in a direction opposite to the movement of its proposals. While the proposals become more modest, the expectations may become more demanding. For example, a negotiator may have been ready to make a large concession when he discovers that the opponent is asking much less than expected. The negotiator will then *raise* his expectations, while *lowering* his demands by only the small concession necessary to reach agreement. Evidently, there is nothing either fair or foul in moving one's proposal closer to that of the opponent, nor does an agreement become reasonable merely because it has been reached through such mutual revisions of proposals.

The mutual concessions required for a compromise, moreover, may have quite a different meaning for each of the parties. Your opponent may never have expected to obtain more than the point of compromise, but he asked for more initially in order to have a "bargaining position." You, on the other hand, may have expected to settle at your initial position, or very close to it, and therefore had to change your expectations when you saw how far apart you were from your opponent and how determined he was. Now, from your point of view, surely, this compromise maneuver did not make the outcome particularly "fair."

It is one of the most common negotiating tactics to ask for more than one expects to receive, in order to move the point of compromise in one's favor. Of course, if both sides use this tactic, its effect may well cancel out. Your opponent will not accept your proposal as long as he thinks that it is only a "bargaining position"; in fact, he may not even make concessions from his "bargaining position" until you have lowered yours. It is still worse for you if your opponent thinks that you have been asking for far more than you would settle for, whereas actually you have left yourself very little room between your initial proposal and your anticipated minimum. Khrushchev alleged that this was happening to him with his proposals on Berlin:

They [Adenauer and Brentano] say that negotiations with the Soviet Union should follow the principle of concession for concession. But that is a mercantile approach. When working out our proposals we did not approach the matter as hucksters would, who name the price with a "margin," at thrice the cost, and then, after bargaining, sell their goods at a much cheaper price than the one they named at the beginning. . . . We have no reason to make any concessions, since we have not made our proposals for the purpose of bargaining.[15]

A special form of the compromise maneuver is *haggling* (also known as "bazaar" bargaining and, in French, as *marchandage*). In haggling, both parties more or less admit that they are starting with "bargaining positions." They alternate in making many separate, and usually small, concessions until the point of compromise is reached. Haggling is rather customary for reaching agreement on numbers, such as amounts of money or tariff rates. The region of compromise can often be projected long before the compromise has been settled, because both sides may reveal the rate at which they are making concessions. If this is the case, a tentative agreement has in fact been reached in the initial phases of haggling, and the exchange of the additional concessions merely confirms and perhaps refines the point of compromise. For this reason, if you are involved in a situation where the opponent expects you to haggle and you have made the first proposal, you may refuse to make any concessions until your opponent has raised his initial proposal to a level from which your joint haggling promises to converge on a point that will meet your expectations. If your opponent should fail to improve his first counter-offer, you will tell him that you "refuse to consider it," because you know that a compromise between his and your position would not satisfy you.

Sometimes negotiators try to reach a favorable compromise by asking for something that is of little value to them but highly undesirable to the opponent. The objective is not to obtain part of what they are asking for but to receive a concession from the opponent in return for abandoning their demand entirely. One might call such positions "extortionary" demands.

[15] Speech in Tirana, May 30, 1959 (N. S. Khrushchev, *World without Arms, World without Wars*, Book 1, p. 374).

In the Korean truce talks the United Nations negotiators were faced with such a demand. After prolonged wrangling, it was agreed that a Neutral Nations Supervisory Commission be established to check on the implementation of the truce terms and that each side was to nominate three neutral nations acceptable to the opponent. The United Nations nominated Sweden, Switzerland, and Norway; the Communists nominated Poland, Czechoslovakia—and the Soviet Union! The Communists did not need Soviet members in the Supervisory Commission in addition to Czechs and Poles, and they must have been well aware that the West could not accept the Soviet Union as a neutral nation. Nonetheless, they argued stubbornly in favor of their proposal: "If the Soviet Union could not be nominated as a neutral nation, there would be no neutral nation at all existing in the world. What is more strange is that your side should object to the Soviet Union when it has agreed to Poland and Czechoslovakia."

For some strange reason the U.S. government (which instructed the UN Command) forbade the UN negotiators to mention the real reason why the Soviet Union was unacceptable as a neutral nation—namely, that it was the main logistics base for the Communist forces. This inhibition did not go unnoticed by the Communists: "Why do you give no logical reason for opposing the great, peace-loving U.S.S.R. as a member of the Neutral Nations? You give no reason because you have none. You are unable to deny that the U.S.S.R. is a true neutral in the Korean conflict."

While the UN labored under its self-imposed handicap, this debate went on for weeks and weeks. The UN side tried to eliminate the Soviet Union as a neutral nation by suggesting that both the Soviet Union and Norway be dropped. But this was rejected, and the UN Command did not insist. In the end, the UN Command felt it had to pay the ransom to get rid of this "extortionary" demand and swapped a position to which it had attached great importance: the prohibition of the repair and construction of airfields after the truce.[16]

A more effective riposte to an "extortionary" demand is to raise an "extortionary" demand of one's own. With a little more

[16] Vatcher, *Panmunjom*, pp. 108–13, and Joy, *How Communists Negotiate*, pp. 89–99.

daring and imagination, the U.S. government could have instructed the UN negotiators differently. It could have replied to the Communists, for example, that the inclusion of the Soviet Union among the neutral nations required that it be balanced with another Far Eastern power—namely, Nationalist China (while explaining to its allies that it expected to trade the nomination of Nationalist China against that of the Soviet Union). Since Communist China would not have accepted Nationalist China as a neutral nation, this coupling—if maintained with firmness—might have saved the UN side from buying off the Communist demand by conceding something that it really wanted.

Like all evaluations in negotiation, evaluations of a compromise are dependent on, and changed by, the negotiation process. What started out as your "bargaining position" may later become an essential part of your anticipated minimum and vice versa. Your opponent may consider your "bargaining position" as a modest demand on one issue, but on another issue he may mistake for an "extortionary" demand a position that you consider essential. Since the difference between a "bargaining position" and an essential position or between a modest and an immodest one depends on expectations and evaluation criteria, and since these expectations and criteria change as a result of negotiation, all the bench marks for assessing a compromise are really adrift.

CATCHING UP WITH RISING DEMANDS

A compromise is not the only way in which parties can converge on the terms of agreement. One party, far from making concessions, may add new demands to its proposal. If the other party wishes to reach agreement nonetheless, it will have to continue conceding and in the end settle for less favorable terms than those initially proposed by the first party.

This tactic was already known in ancient mythology. The prophetess Sibyl of Cumae offered Tarquin the Proud, last of the legendary kings of Rome, nine books containing prophecies. Tarquin thought the price so high that he refused to buy. Sibyl then burned three of the books and offered the remaining six at the same price. When Tarquin refused again, she burned three more, and Tarquin, fearing that she might destroy them all, bought the last three books at the price originally asked for the nine.

The tactic of the Sibylline Books serves to discourage the opponent from further bargaining. He may quickly accept the offered terms for fear of continually missing better opportunities. It is particularly effective when the prospects for no-agreement look increasingly worse to the opponent.

This happened to the Finns when they were defending themselves against the Russian invasion in the winter of 1939–40. The Finnish government continued to negotiate with Moscow in order to halt the Soviet attack. The Soviets, too, preferred a negotiated settlement, since they had discovered that conquering all of Finland would be very difficult (owing to the surprisingly effective Finnish resistance) and risky (because of the possibility of Anglo-French intervention). When Molotov made his first peace offer, he warned the Swedish Foreign Minister who acted as intermediary: "If these terms are not now accepted, the demands will be increased." Two weeks later, he repeated this warning and made no concessions at all. And when the Finnish negotiators arrived in Moscow a few days later, new demands, indeed, were added. The Finns felt forced to accept.[17]

In other situations, the Sibylline Books tactic may have the advantage of drawing the opponent into the negotiations through the modest initial proposals, whereas starting with the more demanding final position might have repelled him. Once the opponent is negotiating, the gradually increasing demands may help shift his evaluations and eventually make the final position acceptable to him. This happened during 1961–62 in the prolonged nuclear test-ban conference. On the detection system, the Russian position for a while moved further away from the Western position, while the Western powers, up to a point, were catching up with the rising demands. (The issue of the detection system became immaterial, however, when the partial treaty was signed in 1963.)

The Sibylline Books tactic violates rules of accommodation and hence may antagonize public opinion or stir up the opponent's

[17] Max Jakobson, *The Diplomacy of the Winter War* (Cambridge, Mass.: Harvard University Press, 1961), pp. 234–35, 249–50.

hostility. If this is a drawback, however, it can be minimized by couching the initial proposal in ambiguous language and by arguing that the ensuing demands are justified by changed conditions. In this way it will also be easier for the opponent to swallow the increased demands because his bargaining reputation will be less impaired.

ACCEPTING THE FIRST PROPOSAL

When negotiating an agreement, you may settle many of its terms simply by accepting the first proposal that your opponent puts forward, either immediately or after having made some proposals of your own. You may do so because (1) you have no desire to improve the terms, (2) you fear the opponent might add to his demands, or (3) you are convinced that your opponent will not improve his first offer. Your opponent may even present his first proposal as an ultimatum; that is, he may commit his bargaining reputation to his prediction that he would rather break off negotiations than change his proposal.[18]

Not just minor points but important issues are frequently settled through acceptance of the first proposal. In fact, more examples could probably be found than of settlements through compromise. To cite just one instance, the purchase price for Alaska was fixed in this manner. Secretary of State Seward offered $5,000,000, but the Russian Ambassador asked initially for $7,000,000 and refused to lower his price (although he was authorized to go down to $5,000,000). Seward therefore accepted the initial Russian demand for $7,000,000. (Afterwards Seward also purchased the cancellation of all claims that the Russian-American Company had in Alaska by adding another $200,000.)

---

[18] In labor-management negotiation, an elaborated version of the tactic of making one's first proposal the final one has become known as Boulwareism (after Lemuel Boulware of the General Electric Corporation). The company carefully prepares a proposal which in many ways corresponds to the wishes and attitudes of the employees, takes precedents and analogous situations into account, and is widely advertised among the employees. Naturally, labor leaders dislike this procedure because they cannot obtain better terms than those originally offered by management. See Carl M. Stevens, *Strategy and Collective Bargaining Negotiation* (New York: McGraw-Hill, 1963), pp. 34–37, and Allan Weisenfeld and Monroe Berkowitz, "A New Look in Collective Bargaining," *Labor Law Journal* (Aug., 1955), pp. 561–71.

Focal Points and Mediation

Among the many alternatives for settling an issue, there are often a few which seem particularly prominent to the parties. These focal points are like a notch where a compromise might converge, a resting place where rising demands might come to a halt, or a barrier over which an initial proposal cannot be budged. In *tacit* bargaining, focal points help the parties to coordinate their expectations and positions. In negotiation, since coordination can be achieved through the exchange of proposals, focal points serve to reduce the alternatives that the parties must consider.[19]

Round figures in monetary settlements, apart from satisfying the common preference for simplicity and neatness, are easier to justify. Secretary of State Seward and the Russian Ambassador might have agreed on a purchase price for Alaska of $6,000,000 or $8,000,000 without needing any reason for the particular last six digits. But had they settled on, say, $7,169,315, they would have wanted to justify the $169,315. Indeed, the final price for Alaska of $7,200,000 was the sum of two separately justifiable round figures.

Another reason why negotiators tend to agree on focal points is that they can better anchor their commitments at places that are set apart from neighboring points by some particular feature. Boundary disputes are frequently settled on focal points based on precedent or geographic features. For example, in settling the Oregon boundary dispute of 1846 between the United States and Great Britain, the line was drawn along the 49th Parallel up to the Juan de Fuca Strait and thence through the middle of the Strait to the Pacific. The 49th Parallel was prominent because it extended the U.S.-Canadian boundary that existed east of the disputed area, and the Strait was an obvious geographic feature.

Where precedents or geography do not provide focal points, negotiators often construe some points so as to make them prominent. For example, delegates haggling about import quotas often first decide to reduce the infinite number of quantities on which they could possibly agree to a few figures, such as a quota

[19] Focal points, and particularly their role in coordination, have first been dealt with by Thomas C. Schelling (*The Strategy of Conflict,* pp. 67–73).

equal to last year's imports, one equal to the average of the last five years, and perhaps one equal to the import quota of a third country. As if by tacit agreement, bargaining will then be confined to these artificially created focal points.

In multilateral negotiation, a preliminary agreement between some of the participants can act as a focal point. Those who have reached a preliminary accord will look at their point of agreement as the prominent feasible solution and be reluctant to change their positions. Unless the disagreeing parties give in, they may find themselves excluded from the agreement or at least being blamed for obstructing unanimity. To prevent this, it may sometimes seem preferable to withdraw from negotiations or to break them up before the other parties have formed such a focal point. When President de Gaulle suddenly vetoed Britain's application for entry into the Common Market in January, 1963, many people wondered why he had not chosen the more "subtle" method of insisting on terms that would be rejected by Great Britain. The answer may be that he expected the other five Common Market members and Great Britain soon to agree on a set of terms, so that France would have had to veto a "ready agreement" instead of breaking off "fruitless negotiations."

A related effect occurs in *mediation:* the mediator's suggestions are influential mainly because they create focal points.[20] This becomes particularly evident when the parties are trying to arrive at a complex agreement which has to settle many interrelated details. The Common Market agreements on agricultural integration of January, 1962, and December, 1963, were both based on a comprehensive proposal by the Common Market Commission. On both occasions, the Commission made its proposal before formal negotiations among the six member states had started (as it was requested to do), and as the negotiators approached their deadline while their draft agreement was still full of gaps, the original Commission proposal—with some revisions—was the only complete arrangement on which they all could quickly converge. The mediating power of the Commission is enhanced by the fact that it possesses better technical knowledge about such intricate agreements than any of the six governments.

[20] *The Strategy of Conflict,* p. 144.

DEDUCTION FROM A FRAMEWORK AGREEMENT

Friendly nations often use a two-stage process to arrive at points of agreement. By means of a compromise (or some other maneuver involving a confrontation of proposals) they first reach agreement on a framework of broad objectives and principles. Then they deduce detailed points of agreement from this framework by applying mutually acceptable methods of reasoning (simple logic, methods of an appropriate scientific discipline, or legal reasoning).

Since the outcome from the application of these methods is roughly predetermined, the parties, by settling on the framework, in fact agree on a certain range within which the final terms will fall. Thereafter they leave the determination of the specific terms to the deductive process. Of course, even the most scrupulous application of mutually acceptable methods of deduction frequently leaves some uncertainties that will have to be settled in other ways (through a compromise, for example).

In a climate of acute antagonism, the "deductive method" is likely to break down because the opponents will be tempted to depart from the agreed framework or from the methods of deduction in order to shift the outcome to their advantage. The "deductive method" is most effective when the parties observe many rules of accommodation.

In negotiations between Western nations deduction from an agreed framework is often delegated to experts who are more conversant with the applicable methods than political negotiators. This does not mean that the experts are impartial; they may have strong preferences regarding the outcome and may feel obligated to seek favorable terms for their government. However, each party expects its experts not to violate the standards of their profession —at least not flagrantly.

Between East and West, a famous attempt to delegate the "deductive method" to experts was the 1958 Experts' Conference for a nuclear test-detection system. This conference was expected (at least by the Western participants) to settle various details of a detection system by applying the methods of physical sciences to the framework agreement, according to which the system should discover nuclear weapon tests in any environment that seemed physically accessible for testing. The restriction in methods to physical sciences excluded, for example, consideration of psychological questions, such as the capabilities and national bias of the technical and administrative staff. Almost at once, however, the participants were dealing with topics which do not ordinarily crop up in a physics colloquium. In part, personnel questions were settled by exchanging proposals. For instance, the American participants proposed that inspection posts should have thirty technicians, and the Soviets accepted this number. In part, personnel questions were called "political," meaning that they were out of bounds for the Experts' Conference. Thus the American participants insisted that the experts ought to say nothing about the question of whether the control posts should be manned by technicians who were *not* nationals of the country in which the posts were to be located.

A notable instance where the 1958 Experts' Conference departed from the "deductive method" was in singling out a detection system which was expected to have only a poor capacity for underground tests below five kilotons. The selection of this particular system could, of course, not be based on the laws of physics, nor did the agreed principles (terms of reference) justify it. The solution appropriate to the "deductive method" would have been to show how the system had to vary depending on the size of tests to be detected. This is what the American participants initially favored. But in order to keep the number of control posts acceptable to the Russians, the Americans and the British suggested settling for a system with a reduced performance. In doing this, they acted as negotiators, not as scientific experts.[21]

[21] This change in roles need not be criticized if it was authorized and fully understood in Washington. See Robert Gilpin, *American Scientists and Nuclear Weapons Policy* (Princeton, N.J.: Princeton University Press, 1962), pp. 202–14; and Earl H. Voss, *Nuclear Ambush* (Chicago: Regnery, 1963), pp. 183, 214–19. A comprehensive analysis of the 1958 Experts' Conference and the subsequent role of experts will be found in Harold Jacobson and Eric Stein, *Diplomats, Scientists and Politicians: The United States and the Nuclear Test Ban Negotiations* (Ann Arbor: University of Michigan Press, 1964). On the difficulties of separating "political" from "technical" issues see Ciro E. Zoppo, *Technical and Political Aspects of Arms Control Negotiation: The 1958 Experts' Conference* (RAND Corporation Research Memorandum 3286 [Santa Monica, Calif., 1962]).

NON-CONTROVERSIAL SOLUTIONS

Diplomats like to stress that in practicing the art of negotiation one must be able to overcome sticky issues of conflict through the discovery of "new solutions" or the invention of "new formulae." What is usually meant by a "new solution" is an outcome that is less controversial than any of the alternatives which have been the subject of dispute. By contrast, a compromise is "controversial" because it picks an outcome from a range of alternatives where each improvement for one party means some deterioration for the other party. A "non-controversial" solution avoids this choice entirely: it puts an end to the dispute by picking an outcome so that the losses and gains of the parties remain unaffected or indeterminate.

In 1943, Great Britain, the United States, and the Soviet Union formed the European Advisory Commission, which served as an important negotiating body for detailed agreements on the termination of hostilities in Europe. Lord Strang, the British representative at this Commission, reports that it was often possible to reach agreement with the Russians by changes in wording which they found objectionable but which was of little consequence to the other parties. Lord Strang wrote that when the parties had reached an impasse:

I would sometimes suggest that we should leave our formulae entirely aside for the moment and try to explain to each other exactly what were, in practice, the results that we wished to achieve by this particular clause in the agreement. If each of us could have his own way, what was it that we wanted to see happening when the time came to apply the clause? By this procedure, it would sometimes appear that, for all that we were at variance in our drafting, our practical aims were in fact not irreconcilable. On this basis, a new and usually simpler form of words could be found which was acceptable to all.[22]

Another form of a non-controversial solution is to leave the settlement to a chance process. This maneuver is well known in everyday life. If two people cannot agree on how to allocate between themselves some indivisible piece of property, they may

[22] Lord [William] Strang, *Home and Abroad* (London: André Deutsch, 1956), pp. 205–6.

nonetheless agree on flipping a coin or drawing lots to settle the issue. The counterpart in international negotiation is to turn an issue over to arbitration or to let it be decided by a plebiscite, provided the outcome of either of these processes is unpredictable for both parties (if it is predictable, the solution will be controversial).

Arbitration is widely used for settling boundary disputes. In the Venezuelan boundary dispute of 1897 between the United States and Great Britain, the parties were unable to foresee the outcome of the arbitration procedure to which they agreed. Great Britain, in fact, accepted arbitration only reluctantly but then was awarded most of the disputed territory. In the prolonged Franco-German dispute about the Saar, the French and German governments agreed in 1954 to let the Saar population vote on a statute providing for the Europeanization of the Saar. The rejection of this statute came somewhat as a surprise for both governments and paved the way for the return of the Saar to Germany.[23] In the Kashmir dispute between India and Pakistan, the Indian government has withdrawn its consent to a plebiscite precisely because it considers its outcome predictable.

MANIPULATION OF ISSUES

Governments usually have considerable freedom in the way in which they formulate the issues. Their delegates may spend more time and effort in trying to agree on what the issues are than in settling them. For good reason! The formulation of an issue may stake out the starting points and limits for concessions, fix the bench marks for evaluating gains and losses, and circumscribe the areas where pressures, threats, and inducements can be used.

At the beginning of the Korean truce talks the Communists proposed the following four-point agenda: "(1) The establishment of the 38th Parallel as the military demarcation line. . . . (2) Withdrawal of all armed forces of foreign countries from Korea. (3) Concrete arrangements for the realization of a cease-fire. . . . (4) Arrangements relating to prisoners of war follow-

---

[23] Jacques Freymond, *The Saar Conflict, 1945–1955*, pp. 172 ff.

ing the armistice."[24] Evidently, the first two agenda items were not issues for negotiation but the Communist-preferred terms for a settlement. The UN side was not deceived by this tactic and rejected this "agenda."

When Panama broke diplomatic relations with the United States after the disturbances in the Canal Zone in January, 1964, it tried to maneuver the United States into accepting revision of the 1903 Treaty as a subject of negotiation. Presumably this would have focused negotiations on the question of how extensively the 1903 Treaty should be revised. Failing agreement on this question, the United States might then have been accused of breaking its promise to revise the treaty, and third countries as well as many people in Panama and the United States would thereafter have considered the treaty less valid.

Instead of formulating an issue so that one's terms are already built into it, one may protect one's position by making it into a condition for negotiation. Jean Monnet, as noted before, successfully made the acceptance of the principle of a supra-national authority a condition for participation in the negotiations on the Schuman Plan. In the Free Trade Area Negotiations in 1957–58, the countries in favor of a free trade area (Great Britain and the present EFTA members) tried to confine the negotiations to the detailed implementation of their objective to avoid a dispute about its desirability and feasibility. However, the tactic failed in this case.

In the 1958 Experts' Conference the Russians initially maintained that the conference should start by coming out in favor of test cessation. As the leader of the Soviet delegation put it: "If we do not assume that tests must and will be halted, then our work is quite fruitless."[25] The American scientists countered that the Experts' Conference should only examine techniques for detecting nuclear tests without reaching a conclusion on the desirability of test cessation. The American position won out, and the issue whether or not tests were to be stopped was left to the political test-ban conference.

The order in which issues are dealt with has several implica-

[24] Vatcher, *Panmunjom*, p. 33.
[25] Conference of Experts, July 2, 1958, P.V. 2, p. 46.

tions. To increase the chances for agreement, negotiators tend to take up the less controversial issues first, in the hope that the parties will become increasingly desirous of an agreement and therefore willing to make greater sacrifices in solving the hard issues. With only a few refractory issues left, the negotiators may take pride in seeing their efforts succeed and be afraid of public censure should they fail. When the six members of the Common Market had to settle a long list of tariff positions in 1959–60, the Common Market Commission carefully arranged to start with discussion of those products on which agreement could be reached most easily. In the end, when the parties were left with only a few remaining products, they felt under pressure to compromise their differences.[26]

Proposals for an agenda can of course be confronted with counter-proposals. This may permit a compromise maneuver on some issues before they have even been debated. For example, "extortionary" demands and counter-demands may be canceled out at this stage rather than after the substantive matter has been brought up by both sides.

A related tactic is to make the inclusion of an undesirable agenda item so difficult that other parties will not find it worthwhile to press the issue. Stalin succeeded in preventing the British from bringing up the Yugoslav question at the Potsdam Conference by exploiting Truman's impatience. When Eden first wanted to put this question on the agenda, Stalin argued that Yugoslavia was an allied country and that it was not possible to settle this matter without the Yugoslavs being present. Since Truman wondered whether the matter was serious enough to warrant sending for Yugoslav representatives, Churchill pointed out that the Yalta agreements on this subject had not been carried out: there had been no elections, juridical procedure had not been restored, etc. Stalin then reiterated he would agree to discuss the subject but that it was "not possible to try the Yugoslav state without hearing its representatives." Here Truman intervened and said that "he

[26] Leon N. Lindberg, *The Political Dynamics of European Economic Integration* (Stanford, Calif.: Stanford University Press, 1963), p. 215. The tariff positions were those of the so-called List G. This list was in itself a refractory residue from the Treaty of Rome negotiations.

was here as a representative of the United States to discuss world affairs. He did not wish to sit here as a court to settle matters which will eventually be settled by the United Nations Organization. If we do that, we shall become involved in trying to settle every political difficulty and will have to listen to a succession of representatives, De Gaulle, Franco, and others. He did not wish to waste time listening to complaints but wished to deal with the problems which the three Heads of Government had come here to settle."[27] This marked pretty much the end of the Yugoslav question at Potsdam.

As noted before, however, an agreed agenda is important only to the extent that the parties feel constrained to observe the rule that one ought to adhere to it. In multilateral negotiation this rule is more difficult to violate than is the case in two-party meetings. Furthermore, partial agreement is harder to reverse in multilateral negotiation, since all the parties would have to consent to the change. Hence, the ordering of issues tends to be more important than in a bilateral conference.

In the Paris Peace Conference of 1919, the British war aims were dealt with at the beginning, and Clemenceau was criticized for being tardy in securing the French demands. But as John Maynard Keynes pointed out (in his biographical sketches of Clemenceau, Lloyd George, and Woodrow Wilson), the more modest British aims served to accustom the President to the controversial French demands. Furthermore, this order of procedure also laid Lloyd George "open to the charge, whenever he seemed too critical of French demands, that, having first secured every conceivable thing that he wanted himself, he was now ready with characteristic treachery to abandon his undertakings to his French comrades. In the atmosphere of Paris this seemed a much more potent taunt than it really was."[28]

An accentuation of this tactic is the *last-minute demand*, which a party presents in a multilateral conference only after all the other outstanding issues have been settled and the agreement is ready for signing. If the other parties are anxious to preserve and conclude the agreement reached, they may feel forced to give in. At the end of the 1954 Geneva Conference on Indochina, the Cambodians waited until last, after the French, the Chinese, and all the other parties had practically settled the agreements on Laos and Vietnam. Anthony Eden recalled that he, Molotov, and Mendès-France, already exhausted from negotiating all the other settlements, had to hold a long meeting with the Cambodians and the Viet Minh. "It was a gruelling session. At two o'clock on the morning of the 21st [of July], after hard bargaining and some surprising last-minute concessions by Molotov, we succeeded in resolving the remaining differences between them."[29]

The government whose demands are dealt with at the end of a conference does not, of course, always gain. If it cannot convincingly threaten to choose no-agreement, its demands may be left unsatisfied, particularly if it should come under pressure at home not to become responsible for a breakdown in the negotiations. This seems to have happened to the Dutch when the detailed agricultural accords were settled in Brussels in December, 1963. After the other Common Market countries had accepted in part the proposal of the Commission and in part agreed to modify this proposal here and there, the Dutch still held on to a position that differed from the "focal point" created by the Commission proposal. Unfortunately, the disagreement was about the unlofty subject of the price difference between butter and margarine. When it came to the showdown, the Dutch government did not want to become responsible (as the French negotiators skillfully made it appear) for holding up the progress of Europe because of the price of margarine.[30]

More important perhaps than the ordering of issues is the linking of separable issues into *package deals* and *tie-ins*. In a package deal a party proposes simultaneously to settle several issues that are considered part of the agreement under negotiation. In a tie-in a party introduces an issue considered extraneous by the opponent and offers to accept a certain settlement provided this extraneous issue will also be settled to its satisfaction. For example, in 1961 the new American administration offered the Russians a package

[29] *Full Circle,* p. 159.
[30] *Le Monde,* Dec. 24, 1963, p. 1.

deal to settle some of the important outstanding issues of the test ban; whereas in the summer of 1963 Khrushchev first wanted a tie-in between a partial test ban and a nonaggression pact.

The time to propose a package deal is when your opponent fears that he may not get his way on an issue of particular interest to him unless he concedes you something in return. If you are willing to give in on the first issue anyhow, you might as well tie it together with another issue where you could make some gains. There was an interesting incident at the Potsdam Conference which suggests that President Truman may have missed an opportunity for a package deal in which he could have made his consent to the new Western frontiers of Poland conditional on Soviet concessions on German reparations. Truman and Churchill, after all, did accept the Polish frontiers that Stalin had asked for. Before this issue was settled, however, President Truman made a remark which Stalin seems to have misunderstood as a hinted proposal for a package deal. Stating that the German occupation zones should not be changed in favor of Poland, Truman argued that "any other course will make reparations very difficult, particularly if part of the German territory is gone before agreement is reached on what reparations should be." According to the minutes of this meeting, Stalin replied "that the Soviet Union was not afraid of the reparations question and would if necessary renounce them." Instead of exploring whether Stalin was indeed willing to make a package deal Truman simply added "that the United States would get no reparations anyhow. This made no difference. We were trying to keep from paying more, as we did before [after World War I?]."[31]

The opposite of a tie-in is to carve an issue out of a larger context, leaving the related issues unsettled. This involves certain risks, however. The related issues may be settled by default because postponing them may make a temporary arrangement permanent or the limited settlement may create a strong precedent for the issues which have been left out. In addition, by settling one issue in isolation, the negotiator may surrender his leverage for obtaining a satisfactory settlement of the other issues—the opportunity for a package deal will be permanently lost.

[31] *The Conference of Berlin* (*Potsdam*) *1945*, II, 209.

Excluding underground tests from the nuclear test-ban treaty surely facilitated agreement. But until the summer of 1963 Khrushchev vigorously opposed this separation of issues. He must have realized that once a partial treaty had been signed, the Western powers would feel under much less pressure to accept his minimal detection arrangements for banning underground tests.

Apart from avoiding disputes that are hard to resolve, the separation of issues may make it easier for both parties to offer concessions. If the issue appears to be isolated, the terms on which it is settled will not create "focal points" that might affect the outcome of other disputes.[32]

[32] For a stimulating discussion that stresses the advantages of separating issues, see Roger Fisher, "Fractionating Conflict," in *International Conflict and Behavioral Science,* ed. R. Fisher (New York: Basic Books, 1964).

NEGOTIATING SKILL: EAST AND WEST

IT IS MEANINGFUL TO CONTRAST THE SOVIET STYLE OF NEGOTI-
ation with that of Western governments, for there are enough
unique characteristics to set the two apart. But between the styles
of Western governments the differences are normally overshadowed
by those between individual negotiators. In the current era something like a national style emerges in the West only in a case
such as De Gaulle's France, where the particular style of the man
at the top is executed in detail by a centralized government with
disciplined and experienced officials.

Western diplomats differ of course in their training and cultural
traditions. These differences may find some reflection in their
methods of negotiation, but usually they are not pervasive enough
to produce a distinctly recognizable negotiation style. More important are the differences in government structure determining
the domestic constraints under which each negotiator must operate.
These, however, vary from issue to issue. An example of a somewhat more constant national characteristic is the high sensitivity of
American diplomats to public opinion, which might derive both
from cultural factors and the particular features of American
political life. French diplomats are prone to elaborate historical-
philosophical themes as a background to their negotiating strategies, perhaps because their education puts such stress on the
composition of synthesizing essays. German and American negotiators at times place a greater emphasis on legal aspects than the

diplomats of most other Western countries, probably because of the important role that lawyers play in the conduct of foreign policy in Bonn and Washington.[1]

HOW SHREWD ARE SOVIET NEGOTIATORS?

Soviet foreign policy has been highly successful in the last twenty years, if measured by the expansion of the Communist-controlled area and by Russia's newly won influence in many parts of the world. Yet the combined military and economic strength of the West has remained superior to that of the Communist camp during this same period of expansion. Small wonder that many people think Soviet negotiators are far shrewder and more skillful than their Western opponents and that conferences with the Russians are traps to be avoided rather than opportunities to be sought.[2]

Undoubtedly, Soviet negotiators have certain advantages over their Western adversaries because they are backed by an authoritarian government. Western capitals, and Washington in particular, cannot develop a negotiating position on a major issue without letting the public in one some of the internal controversies. This gives Soviet delegates valuable intelligence about the strength

[1] Kenneth W. Thompson stresses this point for the American diplomatic style (*American Diplomacy and Emergent Patterns* [New York: New York University Press, 1962], pp. 37–38). Charles W. Thayer also believes that one can scarcely distinguish different styles of diplomacy among the great powers, except for the Soviet style (*Diplomat* [New York: Harper, 1959], pp. 83–84). Harold Nicolson, however, maintains that there are certain constant characteristics that distinguish the practice of negotiation by such powers as Great Britain, Germany, France, and Italy. As a good Englishman, Nicolson of course finds that the British type of diplomacy "is on the whole the type which is most conducive to the maintenance of peaceful relations"; but as not such a good historian he forgets 1914 and the 1930s when he writes that the British diplomatist "almost always succeeds" (*Diplomacy*, pp. 144, 131). Raymond Aron contrasts the methods by which the British and the French negotiate with the United States: the British try to influence American policies through discussion and public opinion, the French through obstructions (i.e., the threat of no-agreement) (*Paix et Guerre entre les Nations* [Paris: Calmann-Lévy, 1962], pp. 461–63).

[2] Apart from additions and changes, this section has appeared as an article in the *New York Times*, Dec. 9, 1963 (Magazine section). © 1962 by The New York Times Company. Reprinted by permission.

with which Western positions are held. Moscow, of course, permits no leaks about any differences that might exist between, say, Gromyko and Malinovsky over how to approach the West on disarmament or on Berlin. Its fall-back positions remain secret, not only from newspapermen but frequently also from its own delegations. Western diplomats often complain about this wall of secrecy that makes it so difficult to find out how firmly a Soviet position is held and what sort of modifications in the Western position might lead to agreement.

Moreover, Soviet diplomats need not feel constrained by domestic public opinion as much as Westerners do. The public in Communist countries is normally poorly informed about negotiations. Knowing their lack of influence on foreign affairs, Soviet citizens hardly attempt to make their views heard—or even to formulate a view of their own. This permits Soviet diplomats to choose their negotiating tactics with greater freedom. Only in the long run, perhaps, do Communist leaders require some domestic backing for their foreign policy.

Soviet negotiators enjoy a further advantage in that they can support their long-term strategy and day-to-day tactics with fully coordinated propaganda machinery, whereas Western countries speak always with many voices. Frequently at conferences the Russians delight in citing statements by Western opposition leaders, scientists, or journalists to refute a position of a Western government.

In short, Soviet negotiators seem to command all that is required for carrying out the most cunning strategies: complete secrecy in planning, freedom from domestic interference in execution, and the coordinated support of a powerful authoritarian regime. Given all these advantages, have Soviet negotiators really shown proportionate cunning and skill? An examination of their record, comparing some of their opportunities with the results they actually obtained, is in order.

The Marshall Plan, to take one case, will long be remembered as one of the most successful and farsighted programs of American foreign policy. What is almost forgotten is that the Russians were initially invited to participate. After Marshall's historic speech in June, 1947, British Foreign Secretary Bevin quickly seized the initiative, met with his French colleague Bidault, and asked Moscow to join in a conference at which Europe would work out its answer to the American offer. Stalin sent Molotov to Paris with a delegation of eighty-nine aides.

What did the skillful Soviet negotiator make of this decisive opportunity? He did not try to postpone West European recovery and European-American cooperation by more than five days!

True, Bevin made it clear that he would not be delayed by Soviet stalling. But why did Molotov make it so easy for Bevin? Why did he reject outright the American offer for a coordinated recovery program, instead of accepting it in principle and then discussing the details later? Why did he fail to exploit the suggestion made by some groups in the West that the United Nations should play the leading role in European recovery? Or he could have shown some interest when Bidault (conscious of pressure on his government by the powerful French Communist Party) made a last-minute effort to save the conference. With reluctant agreement from Bevin, Bidault's proposal attempted to meet some of the Soviet objections by emphasizing that the organization for European recovery would not interfere with a country's internal affairs. Yet Molotov would not give an inch, and the conference broke up. Thus Russia lost its chance to delay or influence an integrated West European recovery.

To realize the enormity of this Russian blunder, we must recall that the implementation of the Marshall Plan was not assured at that time. On the one hand, U.S. Congressional support was far from certain. On the other hand, there was considerable European backing for Russia's participation. Prior to the conference which brought Molotov to Paris, an editorial in the London *Times* said: "The strongest argument which could be placed in Mr. Marshall's hands for delivery to Congress would be the firm hope of a sound integration of the whole European economy effected by all the countries which are to benefit from American aid, and led by Britain, France, and the Soviet Union." Similarly, the *Economist* proposed that the United Nations Economic Commission for Europe be used—"in spite of its shortcomings"—as the machinery to administer Marshall aid: "Might it not therefore be the course of wisdom to reach a compromise between the Russian and the Western views?"[3]

Khrushchev showed himself an equally unskillful negotiator with his tactics on the Berlin issue, though his mistakes were of a different kind from Stalin's and Molotov's. As noted before, Khrushchev spoiled his bargaining reputation by repeating again and again his threat to sign a peace treaty with the Communist regime in East Germany, each time specifying the period within which he would do so but doing nothing each time his bluff was called. An explicit threat with a time limit can be a potent weapon; however, prudent negotiators use it only when they are fully prepared to carry it out or are certain that they will not be challenged. A time limit makes it all too apparent if they are caught bluffing, and this damages the credibility of their threats in the future. History recounts few examples of a senior statesman who squandered and blunted his power to use such threats so completely as Khrushchev did.

This was not Khrushchev's only blunder. When he broke up the summit meeting in May, 1960, he spoiled a unique opportunity to extract concessions from the United States. Only a few days before he flew to Paris to meet with Eisenhower, Macmillan, and De Gaulle, he was able to denounce the United States roundly for the U-2 flights, causing major repercussions in the whole world and skillfully trapping the U.S. government in a lie. On the first day in Paris, Khrushchev played his cards well; with righteous indignation he asked for an apology from the President, which he must have known he could not get. But he did get the promise

[3] The *Times* (London), June 24, 1947; the *Economist*, June 28, 1947. A French diplomat noted in his diary just a few days before Molotov's final *nyet:* "With a little Machiavellism, the Soviets ought to . . . insert themselves in the preparatory plan because their accession would immediately provoke its failure" (Jacques Dumaine, *Quai d'Orsay: 1945–51* [Paris: Julliard, 1955], p. 204). And two years later McGeorge Bundy reflected: "How much of the original impetus of the plan would have survived if Molotov had really sat down at Paris, deployed the enormous retinue he took with him (and one still wonders what they were doing there if this notion was not considered) and cooperated in form but not in fact?" In the mood of 1949 Bundy goes on to ask: "And if we are grateful, are we perhaps also safe for the present, from the effects of a policy of deceptive friendliness by Russia?" ("The Test of Yalta," *Foreign Affairs* [July, 1949], pp. 627, 629.)

that the U-2 flights would be discontinued, while Macmillan and De Gaulle pleaded with him to start the summit meeting.

What a reversal of roles, after Khrushchev had been calling for a summit conference so long! What a chance for Khrushchev to drop the demand for apology grudgingly, as if making a generous concession, and then to confront the Western statesmen and ask for reciprocal concessions!

Khrushchev chose another tactic. He put on his rambunctious show in Paris, throwing away his dignity and his trump card. In the end it was, in a sense, he who apologized—two days later in East Berlin. To the glum East German Communists who had expected the long-announced peace treaty, he said the existing situation would have to be preserved until another summit meeting could take place.

Later, Khrushchev hinted that he had anticipated the failure of the Paris summit meeting but that his colleagues wanted him to go all the same. Perhaps Khrushchev realized that his earlier expectations were too optimistic and that the Western powers would not abandon Berlin completely. But this was a poor reason for bringing back from Paris even less than he could have gotten. Had he chosen a shrewder tactic, generously "forgiving" the U-2 incident, the Western powers could not have broken up the meeting without making at least some concessions—perhaps quite substantial ones.

According to a recent Soviet handbook on diplomacy:

[Communist diplomacy] is invariably successful in exposing the aggressive intentions of the imperialist governments. . . . It does this from the tribunes of diplomatic conferences, in official diplomatic statements and documents, as well as in the press. [This] is one of the important methods of socialist diplomacy by means of which it mobilizes democratic social opinion and the masses of people all over the world against the aggressive policies of the imperialist governments.[4]

Yet, when faced with some unusual opportunity for mobilizing "the masses of people all over the world," Soviet diplomacy is not "invariably successful."

[4] *Diplomaticheskii Slovar* (Moscow: State Publishing House for Political Literature, 1960), I, 466.

Along came the issue of atmospheric nuclear tests in the spring of 1962, for example. For the previous six months the United States had confined itself to underground testing, although the Soviet Union had resumed nuclear tests in the atmosphere the summer before. But in March, 1962, the American government decided the self-imposed handicap was too great, and President Kennedy announced twelve days before the disarmament conference convened that the United States would soon have to resume nuclear testing in the atmosphere. He promised, however, that if the Soviet Union would accept a treaty with appropriate controls, "sign it before the latter part of April, and apply it immediately . . . , there would be no need for our tests to begin." Some people feared that the Russians might take advantage of that offer and make some last-minute concessions which would trap the American government into further negotiations whose only result would be postponement of its tests.

As it turned out, the Soviets were far too clumsy. Whatever their real aims, they failed to delay the U.S. tests, they did not inflict a propaganda defeat on the West, and they did not get a control-free ban against underground nuclear testing. Although at the time they probably preferred to remain free to resume their own tests later in 1962 rather than to commit themselves at once to test cessation under a treaty, they must surely have been interested in making propaganda gains and in increasing dissension between the United States and neutralist nations. For this, they had some real opportunities.

They could have encouraged the interest the British negotiators showed in a further reduction of the inspection system. "We are ready to negotiate upon any proposals for an adequate minimum of international verification," said the British Foreign Secretary Lord Home. "We are flexible and ready for reasonable compromise." Nyet—no international verification at all, was the Soviet reply.

Opportunity for the Soviets to make some political and propaganda gains became even greater when the eight neutral nations proposed their compromise plan for a test ban. That plan essentially accepted the Soviet position that there should be no foreign inspectors in Russia but added an "international commission" to evaluate the data from national systems. The commission could, in a vaguely defined way, call on a suspected country to furnish more information and *perhaps* arrange an on-site inspection. Obviously, the United States had some serious reservations about the proposal but refrained from rejecting it.

At that juncture, Premier Khrushchev could have announced dramatically that he was not only ready to accept the neutrals' proposal but also that he would consent to combine it with the "best elements" of the Western draft, provided President Kennedy kept his word and did not start atmospheric tests, now that a treaty could be signed "before the latter part of April." Had the President rejected this outright, beginning the tests a few days later, he would have met with a worldwide storm of protest and probably with serious disagreement from Macmillan. On the other hand, had the President postponed the tests, Khrushchev would not have been committed to any treaty he did not want. As the Western negotiators were urgently trying to nail down a specific treaty text (while the expensive task force in the Pacific was kept waiting), the Soviet negotiators could have become evasive or simply have stuck to the neutrals' proposal until American patience ran out. In the end, the United States might have been forced to resume atmospheric tests with a propaganda loss far greater than it actually suffered in April, 1962.

The Soviet negotiators were not imaginative enough to try for these almost riskless gains. To be sure, they urged negotiations on the basis of the neutrals' proposal, but they refused to accept obligatory international inspection (although, without detailed specifications, "international inspection" is just a vague phrase). And while they made some threats to discourage the American tests, they failed to couple them with a dramatic offer.

Another tactical mistake of Soviet negotiators is that they often fail to exploit an "extortionary" demand before it has become obsolete. After World War II they maintained their opposition to the cession of the Saar to France, apparently in the hope that France would have to ransom the Saar from the Soviet veto at a high political price. As late as 1947 it looked as if this tactic would work. Secretary Byrnes expected that: "Russia will maintain its opposition to the cession of the Saar until the final hours and then seek to secure, in exchange for agreement, French support on some other question."[5] The Soviet negotiators missed this final hour. Instead they unwittingly made possible the transfer of the Saar to Germany and thus contributed to Franco-German reconciliation.

Related to the mistake of letting an "extortionary" demand become obsolete is the failure to revise an unacceptable demand in time to make gains through a compromise. For example, in 1945 Stalin faced Turkey with a double demand. As we have seen, he not only requested a revision of the Montreux Convention but also asked for a slice of Turkish territory and a Russian base in the Straits. Originally, the United States was willing to support a revision of the Montreux Convention in Russia's favor, Great Britain was ready to go along, and Turkey would probably not have been able to resist by herself.

But Stalin's additional demands for a slice of Turkish territory and a base stirred up British and American opposition. As a result, Stalin failed at the Potsdam Conference to consolidate any gain regarding the Straits. All he obtained was American and British consent to "recognize" the need for revision of the Montreux Convention. It was agreed that the next step should be the subject of direct conversations between the three powers and Turkey. But then in 1946 Stalin made the fatal mistake of renewing *all* his demands against Turkey. This aroused American opposition, and a year later Turkey received full American support under the Truman Doctrine. When in 1953 the Russians at last withdrew their demands for Turkish territory and a base in the Straits, what good was this belated concession? Turkey was now firmly in NATO, and the Western support for changing the Montreux Convention had long since evaporated.

The mistake of clinging to unacceptable demands for too long is related to the self-defeating way in which the Russians sometimes negotiate a tie-in. The tactic of a tie-in will not work if the opponent is asked to surrender more than he expects to receive.

---

[5] *Speaking Frankly*, p. 170.

When the French negotiators at Brussels linked their consent to the Second Stage of the Common Market with an agreement on agriculture, they managed this tie-in successfully, because the sacrifices they asked of the Germans for the common agricultural policy were not such as to outweigh German interest in continued progress of the Common Market. But when Russian negotiators tried to obtain more influence in the United Nations Secretariat, they totally mismanaged the tie-in tactic. As discussed earlier, they tried to tie their consent to a successor for Dag Hammarskjöld to their demand for a "troika." A troika, however, would have canceled all interest the United States and other United Nations members had in replacing Hammarskjöld, whereas a more modest Soviet demand (such as for a "troika" of Deputy Secretaries) might have been accepted, particularly if it had found favor with the uncommitted nations. (In fact, the Western nations did accept some changes in the UN Secretariat in favor of the Afro-Asians.)

We can find some common elements in the shortcomings of Soviet negotiators. They often ask for a whole loaf where they could get half a loaf—and wind up with nothing. They fritter away the credibility of their threats and the value of their promises, the two key tools for every diplomat. They cannot find the right dosage of demands and inducements. Curiously, they walk out of negotiations when they should stay in, while at other times they keep on talking in violation of their own deadlines. They insult those whose good will they ought to cultivate, and become self-righteous and rigid where they ought to be ingratiating and inventive. They fight furious battles against an empty phrase or a vague principle, although they are past masters at twisting the meaning of words and at utilizing agreements-in-principle for their own ends.

In short, the shrewd and skillful negotiating style of the Soviet government turns out to be a myth. However, Western diplomats should not be too sanguine about Soviet blunders, for many of these blunders are simply a failure to take advantage of Western vulnerabilities. On such occasions the East-West performance resembles that of two novice chess players. If one player leaves his queen unprotected and the other fails to take it, neither can be called a master.

Moreover, the very idiosyncrasies of Soviet negotiators that account for their blunders can also work to their advantage. If they are careless in having their bluffs called, they are also carefree in trying to gain through bluffing. If they miss many a chance to obligate the West by being a little more generous, they correspondingly feel no obligations to be generous where it would hurt them. And if they do not have the French dexterity in managing a tie-in so as to come out ahead, their rigidity also prevents them from becoming entangled in an exchange where they are left holding the short end. It is true, sometimes they are so stubborn that they cling to an unacceptable demand until they have missed the opportunity for a profitable compromise. But at other times, they are stubborn enough to repeat what seems to be an unacceptable demand until the opponent has changed his evaluations and accepts all or most of what they asked for. Sometimes, certainly, they are too obtuse to force Western governments into a substantial concession by beguiling Western opinion with a small concession of their own. At other times, nonetheless, this obtuseness saves them from disaster, when they can salvage a crucial position only by defying public opinion throughout the world.

Contrary to a popular image in the West, Soviet negotiators are bold rather than shrewd, brazen rather than cunning. It is not the skills attributed to a Talleyrand that the West must fear from Communist diplomats, nor are the Russians brilliant disciples of Machiavelli. What the West must beware of is the brazenness that allowed Stalin to negotiate for his East European empire while the Germans were at the gates of Moscow, the boldness that permitted Khrushchev to make this empire "unnegotiable" while trying to negotiate for Communist control over West Berlin and for the retention of his troops (if not missiles) in Cuba.

WESTERN TALENTS

Dante's description of Heaven may strike us as somewhat lackluster and contrived in comparison with the rich detail and vividness of his Hell. Whoever has tried to describe Heaven will understand why even a Dante might fail. Certainly, for as mundane a topic as negotiating skill, Hell is much easier to paint than Heaven.

Perhaps the faults of negotiators can be more readily identified than their virtues, because in diplomacy failure usually makes news while success is undramatic. Perhaps the weaknesses of our negotiators stand out more sharply because they are spiced with our frustrations, whereas their strengths seem so bland since they are taken for granted. Perhaps the Faustian devil in all our souls, who makes us sooner tire of one page of praise than of a hundred pages of criticism, beguiles us into thinking that in any comparison of virtues and vices, the vices alone tell an interesting story.

It seems natural to evaluate the diplomatic talents and faults of Western governments primarily by comparing them with those of the Soviet government, because among modern negotiating styles the principal distinction is that between East and West. Actually, the Western fortes show up mainly in negotiations with other Western governments but are of little value with Communist opponents; and conversely, the Western faults are harmful in dealing with Communist diplomats but less serious in negotiations within the West. That is to say, the talents of Western diplomacy are largely confined to negotiations with more or less friendly nations, whereas its weaknesses show up in coping with an adversary.

An important talent of Western diplomats that Communists largely lack is the ability to negotiate within the framework of an international organization and to take advantage of international institutions for settling disputes. Through various alliances, Western nations are able to coordinate their activities and to maintain an effective unity in policy execution, even though they might never be fully agreed on all the details of a policy or on a unified doctrine. In fact, it is precisely because they do not insist on a unity of dogma that they can negotiate their differences so as to avoid both schism and *diktat*. The Warsaw Pact cannot embrace Yugoslavia, and for all practical purposes it now excludes Albania. But NATO was able to survive the Suez crisis, it has lost neither Greece nor Turkey so far in spite of their quarrel over Cyprus, it contains such diverse nations as Norway and Portugal, and unless Paris and Washington descend to the negotiating methods used between Mao Tse-tung and Khrushchev, NATO will also be able to weather the American-French dispute.

Western diplomats are skillful also in dealing with conflicts in isolation. Within an alliance tied by an intimate fabric of military, commercial, financial, and cultural relations, they understand how to negotiate about a conflict in one of these spheres without impairing their relationship in the other spheres. This means they must be willing not to bring in other matters even when this might strengthen their case.

Related to the adeptness with which Western diplomats negotiate within international organizations is their capacity for utilizing rules of accommodation. Many rules are observed among Western allies as a matter of routine, thus preserving a tradition of reciprocation that is both efficient and profitable in the long run. Perhaps their familiarity with constitutional procedures in domestic affairs helps Western officials to work with and benefit from an accommodating style in international affairs. Of course, this presumes a mutual and lasting willingness to use restraint in making gains at the expense of the other parties. When this restraint breaks down, all the short-run accommodations nevertheless proffered become gratuitous losses.

Negotiation in this *esprit communautaire* is greatly facilitated through legal arrangements which set limits to the parties' expectations and thus to the range of conflict over which they bargain. It is also helped by common institutions that can take on a mediating function or provide experts to settle terms of agreement through the "deductive method." And as Jean Monnet pointed out, the life of institutions is longer than the life of people, so that institutions can, if they are well constructed, accumulate and transmit the wisdom of succeeding generations.[6] In the case of negotiations between France and Germany, for example, the special relationship based on the rapport between De Gaulle and Adenauer is already a thing of the past. But the collaboration based on the common institutions in Brussels has survived, and in the long run it may well turn out to be the principal driving force for Franco-German unity.

[6] Jean Monnet, *Les Etats-Unis d'Europe Ont Commencé* (Paris: Laffont, 1955), p. 22.

As with Soviet diplomacy, however, the idiosyncracies that account for Western negotiating skill are, on other occasions, responsible for Western weaknesses. Most of the Western talents cannot weather highly antagonistic situations.

WESTERN WEAKNESSES

The following inventory of Western weaknesses is illustrated mostly with examples from American and British diplomacy. Perhaps other Western negotiators—be they French or Finnish, Turkish or Italian—might protest that this portrait does not fit them. But since the diplomacy of the United States (and to a somewhat lesser extent that of Great Britain) plays such a leading role, American or British weaknesses are certainly highly relevant for the West.

LETTING THE OPPONENT DETERMINE THE ISSUES

In a news conference on July 12, 1962, Secretary of State Rusk complained, when talking about the Berlin issue, that "the other side seems not to want to talk about a great many things which are of interest to us, the permanent peace settlement for Germany as a whole, for example, or arrangements with respect to Berlin as a whole, because they have simply said that certain matters are just not discussable." One of the newspaper correspondents present thought he had detected something new. He started fishing for more: "You have now reintroduced the elements of an all-German settlement and of a Berlin accord that involves all of Berlin. Is this perhaps an interesting outcome of your recent European trip?" But the Secretary retreated quickly: "No, I didn't intend to make that much news with that remark. I was reflecting on the general attitude of the West over a considerable period of time. . . . The West has been trying to . . . find a permanent satisfactory German settlement which would bring peace to Central Europe. But that has not been pursued because, as you will recall, I did say that was the kind of thing that the other side has not been willing to discuss. They say, 'This is not discussable. Now let's talk about your position here in West Berlin.' "[7]

[7] *Department of State Bulletin,* July 30, 1962, pp. 172–73.

And what does the West do? It talks about its position in West Berlin and agrees that East Berlin and Eastern Europe are not discussable.

It is, of course, often impossible to prevent the opponent from making an issue out of something that one would prefer to have left alone. And if the opponent can make no-agreement unpleasant enough, it may even be desirable to negotiate about such issues. But this does not mean that one must abstain from raising other issues where the tables would be turned.

The neutralization of Laos was an unavoidable issue. Because the Communists committed more force than the United States was willing to commit, they could have achieved an outcome favorable to them without an agreement. Likewise, the neutralization of South Vietnam has become an issue for the United States, in part because of the difficulty of achieving a military victory and in part because of De Gaulle's attempt to gain influence at the expense of his American ally. Yet the West scarcely tries to make an issue out of the neutralization of North Vietnam. During the Laos Conference of 1961–62, the neutralization of North Vietnam was never seriously raised as an issue, and in connection with the possibility of a negotiated settlement for South Vietnam it was raised only belatedly and rather gingerly. For example in his press conference of February 1, 1964, President Johnson said that if there was a proposal from any side to neutralize both North and South Vietnam, "the United States would consider it sympathetically." Why not *make* a proposal for a neutral North Vietnam and press for it?

Similarly, it may be impossible for the United States to prevent the notion of returning Okinawa to Japanese control from persisting as at least a latent issue. There seems to be no need, however, to accept as a law of nature the point of view that the return of the Soviet-held Kuril Islands to Japan is no longer an issue.

To compare the case of the Panama Canal Zone with that of the formerly Finnish port of Petsamo is instructive. In both cases there is the same overwhelming disparity of strength between the country in possession of each of the areas (the United States and the Soviet Union) and the country that claims or might claim the area (Panama and Finland, respectively). In both cases the country in possession acquired permanent sovereign rights through a clear-cut treaty (although Stalin showed more foresight than Teddy Roosevelt in not leaving Finland "titular sovereignty" over Petsamo). And the difference in the history of the two treaties is not such that the renegotiation of one should be an obvious issue whereas the renegotiation of the other is never mentioned. The Soviet-Finnish treaty ended a war, it is true, in which Finland had joined in an attack on the Soviet Union. But the Soviet Union had attacked Finland and taken territory from her only fifteen months earlier, whereas Panama owes its existence as a nation independent of Colombia to Theodore Roosevelt's intervention.

It can be said, of course, that little Finland is anxious not to make an issue out of the return of Petsamo (although without this port Finland has no access to the Arctic Sea), because she would rather live in peace with Russia and because she has not the faintest hope of ever getting Petsamo back anyway. But this is precisely the point. The Finns know that Soviet negotiators would not permit them to make an issue out of Petsamo;[8] the Panamanians know that it is quite profitable to make an issue out of their treaty with the United States.

The tendency to let the opponent determine the issue shows itself not only in the selection of subjects for negotiation but also in the terminology adopted and the concepts used. This may be a more serious consequence, for it can affect the thinking of negotiators without their being aware of it.

An interesting illustration is the development of the concept "colonialism." Western negotiators talk and think of "decolonization" only in reference to areas in Africa, Asia, or Latin America that have been colonized by a Western country. When referring to Eastern Europe, on the other hand, they talk in terms of "stabilization," or at best "liberalization," and it is a rather rare occasion when they bring up the very recent colonization of Tibet or the nineteenth-century colonization by Russia of vast areas in Central Asia. Western diplomats maintain that it would be futile to make an issue out of Tibet or Uzbekistan or to compare the

---

[8] Actually the Russians did relent on other issues. For example, in 1962 the Finns succeeded in getting permission to lease the Saimaa Canal, which they had lost in the peace treaty with Russia.

desirability of self-determination for Angola with that for East Germany. The Western effort to win the support and friendship of Afro-Asian nations, it is argued, would not be helped by raising such issues, because the Afro-Asians do not wish to become involved in the East-West "cold war" but are only interested in those manifestations of colonialism that are part of their own experience.

Western negotiators who think this way seem to forget that whether or not a subject seems relevant to one's own experience depends on how it is presented. When the U.S. government consented in December, 1962, to the removal of the Hungarian question from the UN agenda and to having the position of a UN Representative on Hungary abolished, it merely intended to abandon what seemed like a useless irritant against the Soviet Union. But unintentionally, it confirmed the view of the Afro-Asian nations that colonialism in Hungary had nothing to do with the colonialism they were fighting.

Mental associations are formed by repetition. If the West consents to the removal of the Hungarian question from the UN agenda (which has a long and growing list of other colonial issues) and almost never raises such issues as the fate of the Asian Muslims in Soviet Uzbekistan, it teaches the Afro-Asians to associate "colonialism" only with those issues in which it is the accused party.

SHY ABOUT COUNTER-DEMANDS

Western negotiators assume that it would be clearly improper not to be flexible. It is widely felt in the West that concessions ought to be reciprocated and that compromise is the ideal way of reaching agreement. At the same time, Western governments (except France under De Gaulle) are reluctant to refuse negotiation if confronted with a redistribution demand. However, if one engages in redistribution negotiations while observing the rule of flexibility, there is only one way of avoiding a net loss: to make counter-demands. But this, Western negotiators are reluctant to do.

Counter-demands are requests for a redistribution in one's favor, either on an issue related to the one raised by the opponent or possibly on a quite unrelated issue. They are essential, not only to permit oneself to be flexible without incurring a net loss, but also to protect oneself against mediators who simply split the difference between the opposing proposals—as most mediators are wont to do. How, for example, would U Thant have mediated the Berlin negotiations? "There are various other issues like Berlin," he said on December 2, 1962, "on which it may become imperative to reach solutions on the basis of compromise and the principle of give-and-take on both sides."

On those rare occasions when Western negotiators do confront the opponent with a counter-demand, they tend to convey a lack of conviction—almost as if they acted with a bad conscience. They do not push the counter-demand with the same vigor that the opponent puts behind his initial demand, nor do they repeat it anywhere nearly as often.

For example, after the Soviet demands against West Berlin in November, 1958, the Western allies, in their notes of December 31, 1958, hinted at a counter-demand for the areas now in East Germany which were evacuated by the Western troops:

> The Soviet Union has directly and through its [East German] puppet regime . . . consolidated its hold over the large areas which the Western Alliance relinquished to it. It now demands that the Western Alliance should relinquish the positions in Berlin which in effect were the *quid pro quo*. The three Western Powers are there as occupying powers, and they are not prepared to relinquish the rights . . . , just as they assume the Soviet Union is not willing now to restore to the occupancy of the Western Powers the position which they had won in Mecklenburg, Saxony, Thuringia and Anhalt and which, under the agreements, of 1944 and 1945, they turned over for occupation by the Soviet Union.[9]

But little has been heard of this potential counter-demand since.

Similarly, after the Berlin wall went up, the Western allies occasionally suggested that freedom of circulation should be restored in all Berlin in accordance with the Four-Power Agreements. But this has remained a wish rather than a demand, and even the wish was quickly suppressed when it met with the expected Soviet rebuff.

[9] U.S. note to the Soviet Union of Dec. 31, 1958 (*Department of State Bulletin*, Jan. 19, 1959, p. 79).

The reluctance to make counter-demands is not confined to East-West negotiations. The United States made no counter-demands, for example, in the negotiations with Panama after the riots in the Canal Zone in January, 1964. It is true that the incident touching off these riots can be blamed on the American side (the refusal of American students to observe the U.S.-Panamanian agreement on flags). But afterwards, mobs from Panama attacked the Canal Zone, and sniper fire from *outside* the Zone caused casualties among U.S. forces. As President Johnson pointed out, the role of the U.S. forces "was one of resisting aggression, and not committing it."[10]

Resisting aggression? The negotiations were opened with Panamanian charges of U.S. aggression, and the United States made no demands of its own. One wonders whether American interests might not have been better protected, and the negotiations actually facilitated, had the U.S. government immediately come forth with a series of counter-demands. For example, Washington might have requested that Panama take steps to prevent a recurrence of mob attacks on the Canal Zone; it might have raised the question of compensation for the property destroyed; and it might have hinted that the violence by Panamanian mobs made it inadvisable to offer further concessions, inasmuch as the flag incident would not have occurred had the United States refused to accept Panamanian flags in the Zone a number of years ago. In short, Washington could have assumed the posture of the aggrieved party instead of meekly accepting the role of the accused. By abstaining from any counter-demands, the U.S. government might actually have done a disservice to the Panamanian government, because for domestic reasons the Panamanian government needed to win concessions from the United States, and counter-demands would have allowed Washington to concede more.

Western negotiators give various justifications for not raising counter-demands or for abandoning them so meekly. Counter-demands, it is said, would widen the area of conflict. This is of course true when they are first raised. Indeed, it is the purpose of counter-demands to prevent the area of conflict from lying entirely on one's

[10] President Johnson's statement of Jan. 23, 1964.

own side of the fence. But later, counter-demands may facilitate agreement by putting some pressure on the opponent and permitting greater flexibility in one's own position.

Another justification for avoiding counter-demands, which is used primarily in the United States, is that Congress and the public would object if the counter-demand were later dropped in exchange for the withdrawal of the opponent's original demand. This justification is weak for three reasons. First, effective negotiation requires a willingness to become committed and to occasionally absorb the cost of breaking one's commitment. Second, the objections to dropping counter-demands can often be avoided by identifying one's counter-demands as such. Where this is feasible, the public will accept, if not urge, that they be dropped as soon as the opponent withdraws his original demand. Third, there is something disingenuous in arguing that Congress or the public would not accept the withdrawal of counter-demands. Unless the negotiator also refuses to be flexible, he is in fact implying that a concession on a counter-demand would be noticed, whereas a concession at the expense of the status quo could be concealed.

As a result of their shyness about counter-demands, Western negotiators frequently miss opportunities for making tie-ins. (Unlike the counter-demand in redistribution negotiations, which wards off the opponent's demand, the counter-demand in a tie-in is used to gain some objective by making the fulfillment of a demand by the opponent conditional on the fulfillment of one's own demand.)

In the postwar negotiations with the Soviet Union on European problems, the Western powers were anxious to work out a treaty for re-establishing Austria's independence. In 1946 the Western powers and the Soviet Union negotiated the peace treaties with Bulgaria, Romania, Hungary, and Italy, about which the Russians were just as anxious. The Soviet Union wished to conclude peace treaties with the three Balkan states in order to solidify and formalize Communist control, and it wanted a peace treaty with Italy in order to obtain Italian reparations.

While these peace treaties were being negotiated, Secretary Byrnes tried in vain to bring up the Austrian treaty. At the first session of the Council of Foreign Ministers meeting in April,

1946, Byrnes asked that the Austrian question be included on the agenda, but Molotov immediately objected, saying he was not ready to give it consideration at this time. Byrnes tried again in April and at the next session of the Council of Foreign Ministers in June. At this latter session, Molotov contended that it was inadvisable to consider the Austrian treaty because the parties would have their hands full with the treaties under consideration. As Secretary Byrnes recalled in his memoirs, Molotov exclaimed: "May God help us to complete the work on the treaties which are now before us." And then Byrnes continued in his memoirs: "Since it was clear that Mr. Molotov was lending little assistance, I could only reply that I hoped, indeed, that God would do so."[11]

But this was not the only reply Byrnes could have given. He could have firmly refused to discuss any other treaties unless the Austrian treaty were included. Since the Soviet Union still had considerable interest in these other treaties, the tie-in might have worked.

A more recent example of neglecting a tie-in is provided by the British negotiations with Egypt in 1954, concerning the Egyptian demand for the withdrawal of British troops from the Suez Canal area ahead of the time specified in the Anglo-Egyptian treaty. Surely, the British negotiators must have thought about the possibility that Egypt might want to nationalize the Canal. Yet, they did not attempt to tie guaranties against nationalization to the withdrawal of their troops. They were of course under American pressure to give in to the Egyptian demand, and even if they had obtained an Egyptian promise against nationalization, it might later have been broken. Nonetheless, by tying in their counter-demand at that time, they might have accomplished one of two things. With an Egyptian promise against nationalization, British intervention against a breach of this promise would have been easier to justify at home and harder to oppose by the United States (and Egypt, knowing this, might well have kept the promise). If, on the other hand, Egypt had refused to give such a promise, the British-Egyptian conflict would have come to a head at a time far more favorable to Britain: there would have been no need to attempt a landing of troops in the Suez Canal Zone, for the troops were still there.

[11] *Speaking Frankly*, p. 164.

AFRAID OF MAKING UNACCEPTABLE PROPOSALS

Related to the shyness about counter-demands is the aversion of Western negotiators to push proposals that they consider unacceptable to the opponent. This aversion applies to major positions only, not to proposals on some details within a larger position. On details, Western diplomats of course frequently make demands which they expect to be unacceptable—only in order to have room for concessions when seeking a compromise.

As noted before, Communist negotiators are more willing to exert themselves for unattainable goals. Or perhaps they are more aware of the fact that what the opponent will ultimately accept is in part a function of what is being proposed to him. Sometimes they even admit that they do not expect their proposals to be accepted. Khrushchev once wrote to Macmillan: "In sending this message [suggesting a German peace treaty and withdrawal of foreign forces], I ask myself the question, what will be your reaction? Will you accept our proposals? I will tell you frankly, I have no belief in this because I do not believe in the wisdom of those circles which now determine the policy of the Western powers. It seems that the time is not yet ripe. . . ."[12]

Various reasons may account for the aversion of Western diplomats to unacceptable proposals. They may feel that it would look foolhardy to advance such proposals. They may fear they would needlessly antagonize the opponent. Or they may think that they could be accused of not negotiating "in good faith."

The notion that one should not push unacceptable proposals has for Westerners almost the quality of a moral rule, even where this "moral" way of negotiating comes in conflict with the morality of one's negotiating position. Paradoxically, this rule—far from facilitating negotiation—may sometimes destroy the possibility for negotiating at all. On certain issues, Western diplomats prefer to avoid negotiation altogether because they would either have to push unacceptable proposals or take the initiative in proposing an outcome that would be inferior to no-agreement.

What these Western negotiators overlook is that by refusing to press a certain proposal because it seems unacceptable, they may

[12] Letter to Macmillan of April 12, 1962.

actually make it so or at least maintain it so. They strengthen the opponent's commitment by conveying to him that he is not expected to yield. And they forgo pressures that might erode the opponent's evaluations.

Western diplomats could learn a lesson from their colleagues in the new African states. There are several similarities between the posture of the new African states with regard to their grievances about the Union of South Africa and the posture of the Western powers with regard to their grievances about Eastern Europe. The goals that the Africans favor—abolishing apartheid and wresting Southwest Africa's independence from the Union of South Africa —are now totally unacceptable to the government of South Africa. Likewise, the goals that the Western powers favor in Eastern Europe are now totally unacceptable to Moscow: self-determination in the Soviet Zone of Germany and independence in Eastern Europe such that, say, the Hungarians could choose neutrality as they tried to in 1956. The African states have nowhere near the military and economic powers needed to force the government of South Africa to give in. In the same way, the local populations in East and Central Europe do not have the power to force Moscow to give in (as demonstrated on June 17, 1953, and in October, 1956). If South Africa were to be defeated by a full-scale Soviet intervention, this might bring an East-West war into the heart of Africa. And if the West attempted a full-scale military intervention against Soviet control in Eastern Europe, this, correspondingly, would probably lead to an East-West war in the heart of Europe that might well become nuclear.

The difference between the African negotiators and the Western ones is that the Africans keep pushing day after day their proposals for abolishing apartheid or detaching Southwest Africa from the Union, whereas Western negotiators act in the belief that self-determination for the Soviet Zone of Germany or full independence for Budapest is out of their reach, if not out of the question. The Africans feel confident that the trend of history is in their favor, regardless of the present imbalance in power. The Western powers either do not look for a favorable trend (they settle for "stabilization"), or they hope for internal "liberalization" (a trend which would permit them to continue their passive role). Thus they forget that historical trends are shaped by the expectations of men and that these expectations can be shaped, in part, by pushing unacceptable proposals.

But what about the objection that unacceptable proposals will make a favorable outcome even less likely by provoking the opponent and exacerbating his feelings of hostility? There is, of course, no pat answer to this familiar risk. The choice between modesty and aggressiveness depends on the merits of the issue and on the prospects for changing the opponent's attitudes. It is not a foregone conclusion that relations with the opponent will become more difficult if he is being confronted with unacceptable proposals. Westerners often wish that the Soviet Union were more of a "status quo power"—that is, interested in preserving only its present influence and possessions, not in adding to them. Is it not possible to stimulate such an interest more by challenging the Soviet stake in the status quo than by guaranteeing it?

DENYING ONESELF AVAILABLE THREATS

From April, 1939, until the announcement of the Hitler-Stalin pact on August 21 of that year, the British and the French tried to negotiate an agreement with Russia against the likelihood of German aggression. This was not an easy assignment, since the Poles, Romanians, and Baltic states—the potential victims of Hitler's next move—were adamantly opposed to automatic Soviet assistance, fearing (not unreasonably as shown by later events) that once Soviet armies entered their countries to fight the Germans, they might never leave.

According to a Foreign Office memorandum of May 22, 1939, the British in their own right were not sanguine about negotiating with Moscow: "Even though we may not be able to count implicitly on the Soviet Government either honestly wishing to fulfill, or being capable of fulfilling, their treaty obligations, nevertheless, the alternative of a Soviet Union completely untrammelled and exposed continually to the temptation of intriguing with both sides . . . might present a no less, perhaps more, dangerous situation than that produced by collaborating with a dishonest or an incompetent partner."

Nor did the British have much confidence in the strength of their negotiating position. On July 20, 1939, William Strang, the British emissary in Moscow, reported to London:

Our need for an agreement is more immediate than theirs. Unlike them we have assumed obligations which we may be obliged to fulfill any day; and some of the obligations we have undertaken are of benefit to the Soviet Union since they protect a good part of their Western frontier. Having committed ourselves to these obligations, we have no other policy open to us than that of building up the Peace Front. The Russians have, in the last resort, at least two alternative policies, namely, the policy of isolation, and the policy of accommodation with Germany.[13]

By assuming that they had "no other policy open" to them, the British denied themselves the capacity to threaten. Scarcely nine months before, the same British government and the French had signed an agreement with Hitler at Munich, in violation of their commitment to Czechoslovakia and excluding the Soviet Union, permitting the Germans to expand eastward while keeping peace in the west. If the Soviets were as suspicious as Strang reported they were in his dispatch from Moscow, it should have been easy for the British to make the Soviets suspect that unless they showed more interest in reaching agreement on the Peace Front, there might be another Munich which would bring the German army up to the Soviet border. The British seem to have forgotten that a threat has to be credible only to the opponent; it does not have to be agreeable to oneself or satisfy all one's commitments. Who can say whether hints of such a threat would not have led to an Anglo-French-Soviet agreement before Stalin signed the pact with Hitler? The puzzling thing is that the British never even considered whether or not they should make use of it.

Western negotiators have no particular difficulty in using threats that are merely an extension of warnings (i.e., when the threatened action is an addition only to the action that would be taken anyhow in one's self-interest if the opponent failed to comply). Such threats Western negotiators often use to good effects, and, in contrast to Khrushchev's negotiating style, they wisely prefer to leave them implicit, where feasible, instead of making explicit threats.

[13] E. L. Woodward and R. Butler (eds.), *Documents on British Foreign Policy 1919–1939* (Third Series), V, 646; VI, 422.

On those occasions, however, when the Western negotiator could make an effective threat only by envisaging a radical departure from his basic policy, he often denies himself the capacity to threaten, even though these occasions are frequently decisive junctures in important negotiations. Of course, if you are pursuing certain aims through negotiation, it is not an inviting prospect to contemplate a complete reversal of your policies in conflict with your present aims—merely for the purpose of hurting your opponent. But your opponent may not know how attached you are to your present policies and how unlikely such a reversal is. Just because you do not wish to switch to the opposite policy does not mean that you should guarantee to your opponent that you will not do so.

Such self-denial is desirable only in dealing with close allies or trustworthy friendly nations, when it is more important to maintain the opponent's long-term confidence than to exert pressures by threatening a reversal of one's joint policies or a reversal even of the alliance itself. Where this long-term confidence is lacking, nothing is lost by letting your opponent fear that you might do an about-face unless he becomes more accommodating. In 1942, to cite a previous example, Churchill was won over to Eden's idea that Stalin should be granted territorial gains in Eastern Europe in exchange for a pact with Great Britain. Churchill changed his mind not because he felt confident about Stalin's long-term policies but for precisely the opposite reason: he feared Stalin might make another deal with Hitler.

American negotiators have deprived themselves of threats on a number of occasions because they did not want to envisage reversing a basic policy. In the Far East as in Europe, the United States has adhered to the policy of leaving the Communists certain sanctuaries—areas where it will not interfere—to avoid a direct great-power conflict, to reduce the risks of expanding hostilities, and occasionally to preserve Western sanctuaries as a *quid pro quo*. Much as this may have been a wise policy, it was foolish to guarantee to the opponent in every instance that this policy would not be reversed.

The Korean armistice negotiations might have ended faster or on terms more favorable to the West had Peking been left in greater doubt whether or not the Chinese mainland (then exceedingly vulnerable) might be attacked from the air or the sea. At least the threat should have been kept alive that the United Nations forces would try to regain part of North Korea. On February 3, 1951, months before the armistice talks had even started, the State Department declared (according to the *New York Times*) "that the restoration of peace in Korea would not be helped by 'speculation' about whether U.N. forces would or would not cross the 38th Parallel if they reached it in a new offensive." The restoration of peace might indeed have been helped if just such speculation had been encouraged very loudly in Washington!

Again, in the negotiations for the neutralization of Laos in 1961, the Americans would have been in a stronger bargaining position if they had not deprived themselves so much of their capacity to threaten. When the American negotiators set out to attend the Laos Conference, Washington could simply have expressed mild interest in neutralization. Instead, the United States gave obvious signs that it would pursue nothing but neutralization and make no more attempts, for instance, to include Laos in a Western alliance. Nor were the Communists given much reason to fear an expansion of hostilities into their sanctuary in North Vietnam.

The Russians, by contrast, do not give the United States the comfort of curtailing their capacity to threaten. One reason why the United States is cautious in asserting itself in Panama or in helping anti-Communist forces in Cuba is the fear that the Russians might intervene, either by supporting local opposition or with action elsewhere. Khrushchev likes to encourage speculation about Soviet intervention rather than to snuff it out. Even after his retreat in the 1962 Cuba crisis, he promised to intervene in Cuba if the United States ever acted against Castro.

But when asserting themselves on Eastern Europe, the Russians have no American threats to worry about. In October, 1956, while the Kremlin leaders formulated plans to crush the Hungarian Revolution, they might at first have been somewhat worried that the West would help the Hungarians. Then, as the West continued to negotiate only for propaganda effects in the United Nations, this risk must have looked increasingly smaller. And, as if to assure everyone that the United States all along had been negotiating merely for side-effects, President Eisenhower guaranteed to the Russians that as long as they maintained superior local force, their sanctuary in Eastern Europe was under no threat from the West, either at that time or on any similar occasion in the future. "Nothing, of course, has so disturbed the American people as the events in Hungary," he remarked in his press conference on November 14, 1956. "Our hearts have gone out to them, and we have done everything it is possible to, in the way of alleviating suffering. But I must make one thing clear: the United States doesn't now—and never has—advocate open rebellion by an undefended populace against force over which they could not possibly prevail."

Robert Murphy's account of the atmosphere in the U.S. State Department during the Hungarian Revolution is much to the point. There were "fears of terrible reprisals" by the Soviet army against the Hungarians, but no thought seems to have been given as to how the United States might instill some fears into the Soviet leaders when they debated whether to order military intervention. There was much concern that "the Russians were trying to blame Americans for the human slaughter" [sic!]—this concern, in fact, prompted the Eisenhower statement just quoted—but little concern that the United States might be blamed for having lost all interest in the liberation of Eastern Europe. The idea of flying supplies to the Hungarians was conveniently dismissed by the argument that Austria opposed any overflights, but how many planes would Austria have shot down? And the suggestion of *threatening* American intervention was equated with the *certainty* of war. Although it is obvious that "the American people did not desire to go to war against the Soviet Union," would the Russian leaders have desired to go to war against the United States if offered a more attractive compromise settlement? During the Cuban missile crisis in 1962, President Kennedy could also have argued that the American people did not "desire" to go to war against Russia and confined himself to negotiating for ephemeral side-effects in the United Nations.[14]

---

[14] Robert Murphy, *Diplomat among Warriors* (Garden City, N.Y.: Doubleday, 1964), pp. 428–32. Murphy's pages merely reflect State Department thinking during those days. Had Murphy been in charge of the Hungarian crisis, he might have acted differently. His memoirs suggest that he did not usually share the

We can detect some underlying characteristics that the weaknesses of Western negotiators have in common. There is a somewhat passive attitude toward conflict, a tendency to avoid conflict rather than to win it and a readiness to quit while gains might still be made. Where the West has to negotiate from weakness, it often lacks the self-confidence and boldness to push for success; where it can negotiate from strength, it is frequently too squeamish to exploit its advantages. More fundamental, however, is the tendency to overlook the fact that negotiation changes evaluations. He who mistakes his eroding evaluations for the trend of history can be made to believe that slowing down his retreat is a gain, that preventing further enemy advances must be the limit of his ambitions, and that trying to recover what has been lost would be utter recklessness.

THE COMPLEAT NEGOTIATOR

The compleat negotiator, according to seventeenth- and eighteenth-century manuals on diplomacy, should have a quick mind but unlimited patience, know how to dissemble without being a liar, inspire trust without trusting others, be modest but assertive, charm others without succumbing to their charm, and possess plenty of money and a beautiful wife while remaining indifferent to all temptations of riches and women.

It is easy to add to this garland of virtues, but difficult in the real world to judge a good negotiator from a bad one. One cannot evaluate a negotiator merely by asking how close he came to realizing the aims of his government; for if he came close, he may owe his success to modest aims or favorable conditions rather than to his skill. Nor can one be sure that he has done well just because his gains and losses compare favorably with those of the opponent; for it is an essential task of negotiators to change the evaluation of gains and losses.

Frequently one judges a negotiator by comparing the results he obtained with results he might have obtained had he acted differently. In doing so, however, one should distinguish between

---

Western weakness of denying oneself available threats (e.g., his recommendation to challenge the 1948 Berlin blockade on the ground, pp. 316–17).

errors in negotiation, on the one hand, and errors in prediction and foreign-policy planning, on the other. Furthermore, one has to allow for domestic constraints which limit the alternatives that the negotiator could have chosen. Even though a skillful negotiator will guide and strengthen his domestic support, he cannot escape these constraints completely.

On occasion, the outcome of an international conference seems predetermined by the balance of military strength, by economic factors, or by other forces beyond the negotiator's control. For example, George Kennan argued that the establishment of Soviet military power in Eastern Europe and the entry of Soviet forces into Manchuria did not result from the wartime conferences of Moscow, Teheran, and Yalta, but from the military operations during the concluding phases of the war when the Western democracies were not in a position to enter these areas first.[15] One can surely agree with Kennan that only a limited range of alternatives was open at these conferences. But one should question how narrow this range actually was and whether the negotiators did not take for granted bounds that they drew themselves.

Imagine, for instance, a reverse of the situation in Iran and in Korea—that Iran was the country divided into a Communist North and a pro-Western South but that Korea was unified under a government friendly to the West. If this were the situation today, we would probably feel that the Western democracies could have done nothing to prevent the Russians from staying in Northern Iran (an area they occupied first, after all!) but that in Korea the West had a better chance to keep the country unified and friendly (obviously! Russia having entered the war against Japan so late and Korea being more accessible to American military strength than Iran).

Many of the clichés about the perfect negotiator might be revised rather than discarded. A good negotiator should be *realistic,* yes, but not in the sense of accepting an outcome as being determined by the balance of forces without trying to re-interpret

[15] George F. Kennan, *American Diplomacy, 1900–1950* (Chicago: University of Chicago Press, 1951), p. 85. Regarding Europe, Kennan conceded that "the postwar line of division between East and West might have lain somewhat farther east than it does today, and that would certainly be a relief to everyone concerned" (*ibid.,* p. 87).

this "balance" in his favor. Instead of taking a situation for granted, he should be realistic in recognizing that his opponent's evaluations as well as his own are constantly adrift, that issues are not created by Nature but by himself and by his opponent, and that there are ways of negotiating from weakness as well as from strength.

A good negotiator should also be *flexible*—not by being without a firm position but by utilizing both firm and flexible proposals. He should be flexible in his tactics by discriminating between occasions when it pays to adhere to rules of accommodation and when it does not. He must distinguish situations where it would be disastrous to make a threat from others where it is essential to threaten or even to bluff. He must know when to humor the personal quirks of his opponent and when to ignore them. He must be willing to disregard propaganda losses at one time and to negotiate merely for propaganda at another time. He must be prepared to follow domestic opinion at home as well as to encourage a new consensus both in his government and in his country.

And a good negotiator should be *patient*—though not primarily in order to sit in Geneva for months at a time hearing the opponent repeat speeches and repeating his own. He should be patient in working for seemingly lost causes, because by doing so he may slowly change the opponent's views and objectives. He should be patient to live with conflict and uncertainty and know that he may have succeeded even if (or precisely because) his negotiations failed. Above all, he must maintain the will to win.

BIBLIOGRAPHIC NOTE

TECHNIQUES OF DIPLOMATIC NEGOTIATION

The formalities of negotiation are listed in the traditional manuals on diplomat practices. For example: Sir Ernest Satow, *A Guide to Diplomatic Practice* (rev. ed.; London: Longmans, Green, 1958); and Graham H. Stuart, *American Diplomatic and Consular Practice* (New York: Appleton-Century-Crofts, 1952).

The *history* of diplomatic practices and of the conduct of foreign relations is dealt with in Garrett Mattingly, *Renaissance Diplomacy* (London: Jonathan Cape, 1955); and Harold Nicolson, *The Evolution of Diplomatic Method* (Glasgow: The University Press, 1954). Heinrich Wildner, *Die Technik der Diplomatie: L'art de négocier* (Vienna: Springer-Verlag, 1959) treas both history and current aspects of negotiation techniques and contains an extensive, annoted bibliography of earlier guides for the "perfect negotiator." In view of this bibliography, only three such guides are here mentioned that contain observations still of some interest today: François de Callières, *De la Manière de Négocier avec les Souverains* (1716 [English translation published by University of Notre Dame Press, 1963]); Fortune-Barthelemy de Félice, *Des Négociations ou de l'Art de Négocier,* reproduced in Karl von Martens, *Le Guide Diplomatique,* Vol. I (Paris: Gavelot, 1851); Antoine Pecquet, *De l'Art de Négocier avec les Souverains* (The Hague: J. van Duren, 1738).

On modern problems of negotiating methods: Dean Acheson, *Meetings at the Summit: A Study in Diplomatic Method* (Durham, N.H.: University of New Hampshire, 1958), an address at the University of New Hampshire, is excellent on summitry. Wipert von Blücher, *Wege und Irrwege der Diplomatie* (Wiesbaden: Limes Verlag, 1953); Jules Cambon, *Le Diplomate* (Paris: Hachette, 1926); Sir Maurice Hankey (Lord Hankey), *Diplomacy by Conference, Studies in Public Affairs, 1920–1946* (London: E. Benn, 1946); Sir William Hayter, *The Diplomacy of the Great*

Powers (New York: Macmillan, 1961), impressions of U.S., Soviet, French, and British negotiating styles; Norman L. Hill, *The Public International Conference* (Stanford, Calif.: Stanford University Press, 1929), interesting observations on pre- and post-World War II conferences and on the role of experts. *Journal of International Affairs,* special issue on "Diplomacy in Transition," XVII, No. 1 (1963); Stephen D. Kertesz and M. A. Fitzsimons (eds.), *Diplomacy in a Changing World* (Notre Dame, Ind.: University of Notre Dame Press, 1959); R. B. Mowat, *Diplomacy and Peace* (London: Williams & Norgate, 1935); Harold Nicolson, *Diplomacy* (New York: Harcourt, Brace, 1939); Dean Rusk, "The President," *Foreign Affairs,* XXXVIII, No. 3 (April, 1960), 353–69 on summitry; Charles W. Thayer, *Diplomat* (New York: Harper & Brothers, 1959).

For a novel on negotiating techniques: Francis Walder, *Saint-Germain ou la Négociation* (Paris: Gallimard, 1958 [English translation: *The Negotiators,* published by McDowell, Obolensky in 1959]).

For a sweeping analysis of the relation between diplomatic and military bargaining, with many keen observations on methods of diplomatic negotiation: Raymond Aron, *Paix et Guerre entre les Nations* (Paris: Calmann-Lévy, 1962).

FOREIGN POLICY, PUBLIC OPINION, AND THE CONDUCT OF FOREIGN AFFAIRS

Even though the literature on foreign policy is vast, not many of the books deal with methods and principles of negotiation. A recent bibliography can be found in Elmer Plischke, *Conduct of American Diplomacy* (Princeton, N.J.: Van Nostrand, 1961), and this book also describes the organization of U.S. diplomacy. Special aspects of U.S. diplomacy are dealt with in Michael H. Cardozo, *Diplomats in International Cooperation: Stepchildren of the Foreign Service* (Ithaca, N.Y.: Cornell University Press, 1962); and Robert Gilpin, *American Scientists and Nuclear Weapons Policy* (Princeton, N.J.: Princeton University Press, 1962).

For the influence of domestic opinion on negotiations: Andrew Berding, *Foreign Affairs and You! How American Policy Is Made and What It Means to You* (Garden City, N.Y.: Doubleday,

1962), which is illustrative but uncritical of the public-opinion influence; Bernard C. Cohen, *The Political Process and Foreign Policy: The Making of the Japanese Peace Settlement* (Princeton, N.J.: Princeton University Press, 1957); Bernard C. Cohen, *The Press and Foreign Policy* (Princeton, N.J.: Princeton University Press, 1963); Cecil V. Crabb, Jr., *American Foreign Policy in the Nuclear Age* (Evanston, Ill.: Row, Peterson, 1960), Chap. 7; H. Bradford Westerfield, *Foreign Policy and Party Politics* (New Haven: Yale University Press, 1958).

The following deal with the American negotiating style and recent problems in U.S. diplomacy: Dean Acheson, *Power and Diplomacy* (Cambridge, Mass.: Harvard University Press, 1958); Henry Kissinger, *The Necessity for Choice* (New York: Harper & Brothers, 1960), which contains many interesting observations on the weaknesses of the American style; Thomas Molnar, *The Two Faces of American Foreign Policy* (New York and Indianapolis: Bobbs-Merrill, 1962); Kenneth W. Thompson, *American Diplomacy and Emergent Patterns* (New York: New York University Press, 1962).

The atmosphere of the late 1950s is recaptured in Coral Bell, *Negotiation from Strength: A Study in the Politics of Power* (London: Chatto and Windus, 1962). In contrast with the inability to negotiate from strength, case histories of skillful negotiation from weakness are most instructive, such as Annette Baker Fox, *The Power of Small States: Diplomacy in World War II* (Chicago: University of Chicago Press, 1959).

Applicable to the conduct of diplomacy in general (not just U.S. diplomacy) are: Joseph Frankel, *The Making of Foreign Policy: An Analysis of Decision-Making* (London: Oxford University Press, 1963); Lester B. Pearson, *Diplomacy in the Nuclear Age* (Cambridge, Mass.: Harvard University Press, 1959); and Arnold Wolfers, *Discord and Collaboration: Essays on International Politics* (Baltimore, Md.: Johns Hopkins Press, 1962). A rich but diverse source of historical material is Alfred Vagts, *Defense and Diplomacy; The Soldier and the Conduct of Foreign Relations* (New York: King's Crown Press, 1956).

The Communist Style of Negotiation

Primarily analytical: Dean Acheson, "On Dealing with Russia: An Inside View," *New York Times* (April 12, 1959), Magazine section, pp. 27, 88–89; McGeorge Bundy, "The Test of Yalta," *Foreign Affairs*, XXVII, No. 4 (July, 1949), 618–29; John C. Campbell, "Negotiation with the Soviets: Some Lessons of the War Period," *Foreign Affairs*, XXXIV, No. 1 (Jan., 1956), 305–19; Philip E. Mosely, *The Kremlin and World Politics* (New York: Vintage, 1960), Chap. 1, "Some Soviet Techniques of Negotiation," and Chaps. 5 through 10, for an excellent analysis; Gordon Craig, "Techniques of Negotiation," in Ivo J. Lederer (ed.), *Russian Foreign Policy, Essays in Historical Perspective* (New Haven, Conn.: Yale University Press, 1962), pp. 351–73; Gordon Craig, "Totalitarian Approaches to Diplomatic Negotiation," in A. O. Sarkissian (ed.), *Studies in Diplomatic History and Historiography in Honour of G. P. Gooch* (London: Longmans, Green, 1961), pp. 107–25, for an interesting comparison between Soviet and Fascist style; Stephen D. Kertesz, "American and Soviet Negotiating Behavior," in Stephen D. Kertesz and M. A. Fitzsimons (eds.), *Diplomacy in a Changing World* (Notre Dame, Ind.: University of Notre Dame Press, 1959), pp. 133–71, for good contrasts between East and West; Raymond Dennett and Joseph E. Johnson (eds.), *Negotiating with the Russians* (Boston: World Peace Foundation, 1951); John W. Spanier and Joseph L. Nogee, *The Politics of Disarmament: A Study in Soviet-American Gamesmanship* (New York: Praeger, 1962); William H. Vatcher, Jr., *Panmunjom: The Story of the Korean Military Armistice Negotiation* (New York: Praeger, 1958).

Primarily memoirs: James F. Byrnes, *Speaking Frankly* (New York: Harper & Brothers, 1947); General George Catroux, *J'ai vu tomber le Raideau de Fer: Moscou 1945–1948* (Paris: Hachette, 1952) French Ambassador; Mark W. Clark, *Calculated Risk* (New York: Harper & Brothers, 1950), relating to 1946–47; Mark W. Clark, *From the Danube to the Yalu* (New York: Harper & Brothers, 1954), Korea and criticism of policies in Washington; John R. Deane, *The Strange Alliance* (New York: Viking Press, 1947), lend-lease negotiations; Admiral C. Turner Joy, *How*

Communists Negotiate (New York: Macmillan, 1955), Korean armistice; U. S. Ambassador Walter Bedell Smith, *My Three Years in Moscow* (Philadelphia: J. B. Lippincott, 1950); Lord F. William Strang, *Home and Abroad* (London: André Deutsch, 1956), on Franco-British negotiations in Moscow in 1939 and European Advisory Commission, 1943–44.

EUROPEAN INTEGRATION

Since this book contains many illustrations from the history of European integration, some studies relevant for these negotiating methods deserve to be listed here: Achille Albonetti, *Préhistoire des États-Unis de l'Europe* (Paris: Editions Sirey, 1963); Miriam Camps, *The Free Trade Area Negotiations* (Occasional Paper No. 2 [London: Political and Economic Planning, 1959]); Amitai Etzioni, "The Dialectics of Supranational Unification," *The Amercan Political Science Review*, LVI, No. 4 (Dec., 1962), 927–35; Great Britain, *Negotiations for a European Free Trade Area; Documents Relating to the Negotiations from July, 1956, to December, 1958* (Cmnd. 641 [London: H.M.S.O., 1959]); Ernst B. Haas, *The Uniting of Europe* (Stanford, Calif.: Stanford University Press, 1958); Ernst B. Haas, "International Integration, The European and the Universal Process," *International Organization*, XV, No. 3 (Summer, 1961), 366–92; Karl Kaiser, *EWG und Freihandelszone; England und der Kontinent in der Europäischen Integration* (Leiden: A. W. Sythoff, 1963); Leon N. Lindberg, *The Political Dynamics of European Economic Integration* (Stanford, Calif.: Stanford University Press, 1962); Anthony Nutting, *Europe Will Not Wait: A Warning and a Way Out* (London: Hollis & Carter, 1960).

ACCOUNTS OF SPECIFIC NEGOTIATIONS, BIOGRAPHIES, AND OTHER SOURCES

It would be pointless to begin listing here memoirs of senior negotiators and statesmen, such as those by Churchill, Truman, Eden, Cordell Hull, etc. These autobiographies are, of course, important sources for the study of negotiations. So are good biographies. To list just a few that are particularly relevant for methods of negotiation: Gordon A. Craig and Felix Gilbert (eds.), *The*

Diplomats: 1919–1939 (Princeton, N.J.: Princeton University Press, 1953); Alexander DeConde, *The American Secretary of State, an Interpretation* (New York: Praeger, 1962) contains good essays on the relationship between Secretaries and their Presidents; Harold Nicolson, *Curzon: The Last Phase 1919–1925* (London: Constable, 1934), which gives a fascinating analysis of Curzon's techniques at the Lausanne Conference; Charles Webster, *The Art and Practice of Diplomacy* (New York: Barnes & Noble, 1962), content is less ambitious than title, on Palmerston and autobiographical.

The literature on many specific conferences is also large. Specialized bibliographies can be consulted for the Congress. of Vienna, the Paris Peace Conference of 1919, etc. For more recent conferences: Herbert Feis, *Between War and Peace, the Potsdam Conference* (Princeton, N.J.: Princeton University Press, 1960); Edward J. Rozek, *Allied Wartime Diplomacy: A Pattern in Poland* (New York: John Wiley, 1958); Amelia C. Leiss and Raymond Dennett (eds.), *European Peace Treaties after World War II: Negotiations and Texts of Treaties with Italy, Bulgaria, Hungary, Rumania, and Finland* (Boston: World Peace Foundation, 1954); Jacques Freymond, *The Saar Conflict, 1944–1955* (New York: Praeger, 1960); Jean Edward Smith, *The Defense of Berlin* (Baltimore, Md.: Johns Hopkins Press, 1963), which offers a bibliography of other studies on Berlin.

Two studies on financial negotiations are: Edward W. Bennett, *Germany and the Diplomacy of the Financial Crisis, 1931* (Cambridge, Mass.: Harvard University Press, 1962); and Richard N. Gardner, *Sterling-Dollar Diplomacy* (Oxford: Clarendon Press, 1956).

On disarmament negotiations: Merze Tate, *The Disarmament Illusion, the Movement for a Limitation of Armaments to 1907* (New York: Macmillan, 1942); Andrew D. White, *The First Hague Conference* (Boston: World Peace Foundation, 1912); Calvin De Armond Davis, *The United States and the First Hague Peace Conference* (Ithaca, N.Y.: Cornell University Press, 1962); Raymond G. O'Connor, *Perilous Equilibrium: The United States and the London Naval Conference of 1930* (Lawrence, Kan.: University of Kansas Press, 1962); Bernard G. Bechhoefer, "Negotiating the Status of the International Atomic Energy Agency," *International Organization,* XIII (Winter, 1959), 38–59; Bernard G. Bechhoefer, *Postwar Negotiations for Arms Control* (Washington: The Brookings Institution, 1961); Joseph L. Nogee, *Soviet Policy towards International Control of Atomic Energy* (Notre Dame, Ind.: University of Notre Dame Press, 1961); and Spanier and Nogee listed above in Section 3; Earl H. Voss, *Nuclear Ambush* (Chicago, Ill.: Regnery, 1963) on test-ban conference; Harold Jacobson and Eric Stein, *Diplomats, Scientists and Politicians: The United States and the Nuclear Test Ban Negotiations* (Ann Arbor, Mich.: University of Michigan Press, 1964).

BARGAINING THEORY AND ANALYSES OF DECISION-MAKING

Some of the more recent publications presenting or making use of game theory and related approaches are: Kenneth E. Boulding, *Conflict and Defense: A General Theory* (New York: Harper & Row, 1962); James Buchan and G. Tullock, *The Calculus of Consent* (Ann Arbor, Mich.: University of Michigan Press, 1962); John C. Harsanyi, "On the Rationality Postulates Underlying the Theory of Cooperative Games," *The Journal of Conflict Resolution,* V, No. 2 (June, 1961), 179–96; R. Duncan Luce and Howard Raiffa, *Games and Decision* (New York: John Wiley, 1957), which is an excellent and comprehensive treatment of game theory but, as with all pure game theory, scarcely relevant for political negotiation; J. Pen, "A General Theory of Bargaining," *American Economic Review,* XLII (March, 1952), 24–42, which makes interesting points on the bargainer's satisfaction and the "ludic" element in bargaining; Anatol Rapoport, *Fights, Games, and Debates* (Ann Arbor, Mich.: University of Michigan Press, 1960); William H. Riker, *The Theory of Political Coalitions* (New Haven: Yale University Press, 1962); Thomas C. Schelling, *The Strategy of Conflict* (Cambridge, Mass.: Harvard University Press, 1960), highly relevant for tacit bargaining as well as negotiation; Martin Shubik (ed.), *Game Theory and Related Approaches to Social Behavior* (New York: John Wiley, 1964), a collection of articles.

Analyses of the decision-making process are: Richard C. Snyder, H. W. Bruck, and Burton Sapin, *Foreign Policy Decision Making*

(New York: The Free Press, 1962); Charles E. Lindblom, "The Science of 'Muddling Through,'" *Public Administration Review*, XIX (Spring, 1959), 74–88; and David Braybrooke and Charles E. Lindblom, *The Strategy of Decision* (New York: The Free Press, 1963), the latter two deal more with domestic policies.

Psychologists have developed the concept "level of aspiration," representing a level of future performance that an individual explicitly undertakes to reach. Satisfaction (or dissatisfaction) results if this level is reached (or cannot be attained). The level tends to be revised in response to previous performance. Evidently there are some similarities between this concept and the ideas in this book of evaluations and of objectives that are adjusted to changing expectations. Selwyn W. Becker and Sidney Siegel, "Utility of Grades: Level of Aspiration in a Decision Theory Context," *Journal of Experimental Psychology*, LV, No. 1 (1958), 81–85, gives a bibliography. Jerome D. Frank, "Recent Studies of the Level of Aspiration," *Psychological Bulletin*, XXXVIII, No. 4 (April, 1941), 218–26, discusses the earlier literature. Sidney Siegel and Lawrence E. Fouraker, *Bargaining and Group Decision Making* (New York: McGraw-Hill, 1960), relates level of aspiration to bargaining situations. In the experiments on which most of these studies are based, however, the "level of aspiration" has frequently been artificially rigged (e.g., as a peak in rising rewards) so that modifications of this level in response to the bargaining process could not be adequately studied.

Unfortunately, there are few studies of how psychological or personality factors affect negotiations. Sidney Verba, "Assumptions of Rationality and Non-Rationality in Models of the International System," in Klaus Knorr and Sidney Verba (eds.), *The International System: Theoretical Essays* (Princeton, N.J.: Princeton University Press, 1961) offers an excellent abstract discussion of the problem of defining "rationality." Irving L. Janis, "Decisional Conflicts: A Theoretical Analysis," *The Journal of Conflict Resolution*, III, No. 1 (March, 1959), 6–27, is a most promising beginning where one wishes for more. An outstanding example is Alexander L. George and Juliette L. George, *Woodrow Wilson and Colonel House: A Personality Study* (New York: John Day, 1956).

LABOR-MANAGEMENT NEGOTIATIONS

There are a number of parallels between labor-management and intergovernmental negotiations, for instance the shifting evaluations, the effect of the negotiator's personality, and the influence of domestic affairs or intra-union and intra-management affairs respectively. One of the principal differences between intergovernmental and labor-management negotiations is that the latter take place under constraints enforced by higher authorities. Also, the issues in labor-management negotiations are much simpler.

The most comprehensive and systematic analysis is Carl Stevens, *Strategy in Collective Bargaining Negotiation* (New York: Mc-Graw-Hill, 1963), which puts proper stress on the fact that evaluations keep shifting (although the story might have been told just as precisely in simpler terminology).

Interestingly, there seem to be more studies of the bargaining process in labor-management negotiation than in international negotiation. Neil W. Chamberlain, *Collective Bargaining* (New York: McGraw-Hill, 1951), and J. T. Dunlop and J. J. Healy, *Collective Bargaining: Principles and Cases* (Homewood, Ill.: R. D. Irwin, 1953), both deal, in part, with the bargaining process. Ann Douglas, *Industrial International Peacemaking* (New York: Columbia University Press, 1962), contains case material. Elmore Jackson, *Meeting of Minds: A Way to Peace through Mediation* (New York: McGraw-Hill, 1952) on methods of mediation. James W. Kuhn, *Bargaining in Grievance Settlement* (New York: Columbia University Press, 1961); Edward Peters, *Strategy and Tactics in Labor Negotiations* (New London, Conn.: National Foremen's Institute, 1955).

INDEX

BOOKS

The Soviet Bloc, by Zbigniew K. Brzezinski (jointly with the Russian Research Center). Cambridge, Mass.: Harvard University Press, 1960.

The Necessity for Choice, by Henry A. Kissinger. New York: Harper & Row, 1961.

Strategy and Arms Control, by Thomas C. Schelling and Morton H. Halperin. New York: Twentieth Century Fund, 1961.

Rift and Revolt in Hungary, by Ferenc A. Váli. Cambridge, Mass.: Harvard University Press, 1961.

United States Manufacturing Investment in Brazil, by Lincoln Gordon and Engelbert L. Grommers. Cambridge, Mass.: Harvard Business School, 1962.

The Economy of Cyprus, by A. J. Meyer, with Simos Vassiliou (jointly with the Center for Middle Eastern Studies). Cambridge, Mass.: Harvard University Press, 1962.

Entrepreneurs of Lebanon, by Yusif A. Sayigh (jointly with the Center for Middle Eastern Studies). Cambridge, Mass.: Harvard University Press, 1962.

Communist China 1955–1959: Policy Documents with Analysis, with a Foreword by Robert R. Bowie and John K. Fairbank (jointly with the East Asian Research Center). Cambridge, Mass.: Harvard University Press, 1962.

In Search of France, by Stanley Hoffmann, Charles K. Kindleberger, Laurence Wylie, Jesse R. Pitts, Jean-Baptiste Duroselle, and François Goguel. Cambridge, Mass.: Harvard University Press, 1963.

Somali Nationalism, by Saadia Touval. Cambridge, Mass.: Harvard University Press, 1963.

The Dilemma of Mexico's Development, by Raymond Vernon. Cambridge, Mass.: Harvard University Press, 1963.

Limited War in the Nuclear Age, by Morton H. Halperin. New York: John Wiley, 1963.
The Arms Debate, by Robert A. Levine. Cambridge, Mass.: Harvard University Press, 1963.
Africans on the Land, by Montague Yudelman. Cambridge, Mass.: Harvard University Press, 1964.
Counterinsurgency Warfare, by David Galula. New York: Praeger, 1964.
People and Policy in the Middle East, by Max Weston Thornburg. New York: W. W. Norton & Co., 1964.
Shaping the Future, by Robert R. Bowie. New York: Columbia University Press, 1964.
Foreign Aid and Foreign Policy, by Edward S. Mason (jointly with the Council on Foreign Relations). New York: Harper & Row, 1964.
Public Policy and Private Enterprise in Mexico, by M. S. Wionczek, D. H. Shelton, C. P. Blair, and R. Izquierdo, ed. Raymond Vernon. Cambridge, Mass.: Harvard University Press, 1964.
How Nations Negotiate, by Fred Charles Iklé. New York: Harper & Row, 1964.

OCCASIONAL PAPERS
(Published by the Center for International Affairs)

1. *A Plan for Planning: The Need for a Better Method of Assisting Underdeveloped Countries on Their Economic Policies,* by Gustav F. Papanek, 1961.
2. *The Flow of Resources from Rich to Poor,* by Alan D. Neale, 1961.
3. *Limited War: An Essay on the Development of the Theory and an Annotated Bibliography,* by Morton H. Halperin, 1962.
4. *Reflections on the Failure of the First West Indian Federation,* by Hugh W. Springer, 1962.
5. *On the Interaction of Opposing Forces under Possible Arms Agreements,* by Glenn A. Kent, 1963.
6. *Europe's Northern Cap and the Soviet Union,* by Nils Orvik, 1963.
7. *Civil Administration in the Punjab: An Analysis of a State Government in India,* by E. N. Mangat Rai, 1963.

MOONGLADE

MAINE SHORE CHRONICLES

MOONGLADE

MARY FREMONT SCHOENECKER

FIVE STAR
A part of Gale, Cengage Learning

GALE
CENGAGE Learning

Detroit • New York • San Francisco • New Haven, Conn • Waterville, Maine • London

GALE
CENGAGE Learning

LIBRARY OF CONGRESS CATALOGING-IN-PUBLICATION DATA

Schoenecker, Mary Fremont.
 Moonglade / Mary Fremont Schoenecker. — 1st ed.
 p. cm. — (Maine Shore chronicles ; 2)
 ISBN-13: 978-1-59414-885-9 (alk. paper)
 ISBN-10: 1-59414-885-6 (alk. paper)
 1. Maine—Fiction. I. Title.
PS3619.C4493M66 2010
813'.6—dc22   2009046961

First Edition. First Printing: March 2010.
Published in 2010 in conjunction with Tekno Books.

Printed in the United States of America
1 2 3 4 5 6 7 14 13 12 11 10

To Tom
for sharing the journey

ACKNOWLEDGMENTS

I especially want to thank my muse, Carylee Caputo, for her insight and suggestions that I could not do without. She read all parts of the manuscript and, whenever my writing flagged, nudged me on. Thank you, Cary, from your "Auntie M."

Many people helped to create an authentic time and place for *Moonglade,* Maine Shore Chronicles. Barbara Swartzlander, Public Service Director at University of New England Libraries, led me to helpful references. Officers of the Maine Marine Patrol, the US Coast Guard, and the Maine State Police Bureau of Information gave anonymous help with procedural law enforcement regulations. Any mistakes in interpretation are mine.

I extend gratitude to Ed Rea, Ocean Park Association Executive Director, for helpful information about Ocean Park, a Chautauqua community. Thanks also to the Blue Hill Brass Quintet for sharing live performance concert tapes at the Temple in Ocean Park, and the musicians for their willingness to be a small part of the story.

Trusted friends with keen instincts provided encouragement and help. My special thanks to Marge Boos, for an artist's advice and Dottie Otting, my kindred spirit, for her unflagging moral support.

For so much of the above, and the many research trips involved in the writing of *Moonglade,* I will be forever grateful for the patience and support of my husband, Tom. He was there every step of the way.

AUTHOR'S NOTE

Moonglade takes up where *Finding Fiona* left off. This second book in the Maine Shore Chronicles series features Maddy's friend, Clare Chamberlaine. Known to her friends as "CeCe." *Moonglade* is Clare's story.

The general setting of *Finding Fiona* exists again in *Moonglade*, with the addition of a seaside Chautauqua community, Ocean Park. Ocean Park is a real community. I have stayed in the village and found it to be quintessentially Victorian, still abounding in Christian faith, old fashioned courtesy, and charm. I take author's liberty for all incidents and places mentioned in *Moonglade* to be products of my imagination.

The characters in *Moonglade*, with two exceptions, are fictitious. Reuben Bell, the co-owner of the Blue Elephant Café and Catering, gave permission for inclusion, as did the musicians of The Blue Hill Brass Quintet.

CHAPTER ONE

A scream tore from Clare's throat as she leaned over the bow, boat hook in hand. "OhmyGod. Turn away! Hard to starboard," she called, her voice wavering on the wind.

"Hey!" Paul shouted "What's wrong?"

Clare bolted from the pulpit rail, shrieking, "There's a corpse on the buoy!"

Paul shot up from his seat at the wheel, straining to see over the cabin trunk. "A corpse? I think you've had too much sun, CeCe. It's probably dead fish."

Clare walked shakily aft along the narrow deck space, one hand sliding along the coaming. "Uh-uh. Fish don't have hair. It is a dead body. I've seen enough of them in the ER, and I'm not putting a boat hook near that marker." She dropped the hook into the cockpit locker and sank down on the bench. "No way to end a sailing lesson, Cap."

Paul Fontaine stared back at the marker buoy as the boat churned about fifteen feet astern. A bloated head, face down, bobbed from a shadowy torso, long swaths of hair streaming out like seaweed.

"Holy Mother, it *is* a body."

"So what do we do now, Paul?"

"We bring this boat to shore for starters, but first, I better notify the Coast Guard, or maybe the police. Somebody! Geez, I don't know, CeCe, this is a first for me. I'm gonna head out a ways and circle around while I radio the Coast Guard."

Paul fumbled with the VHF mic. "Pa used to leave the radio on scan when we sailed, but I haven't used it in so long it's lucky I remember the distress signal."

Clare could hear radio Coast Guard answering, "Sector Northern New England Command Center." Paul switched to a working frequency, and then his steady voice reported their location. The drone of the motor competed with the back and forth from Operational Control at South Portland. Clare was concentrating on where Paul was steering in Wood Island Harbor when she heard the Coast Guard request *Julie's Dream* drop anchor and stay in the location of the marker.

Her stomach was doing flip flops, and her mind was churning. *This isn't really me, getting rattled over a dead body. We've been sailing for three hours . . . much longer than my first two lessons. I guess the sun and the strain of learning to crew is getting to me.* Clare struggled with her emotions. She rolled her eyes, shook her head, and pointed to the cabin.

Paul must have understood because she heard him radio back that his passenger needed to get home to Biddeford. He asked if he could dock at Biddeford Pool and wait for the Coast Guard vessel to reach him there.

Clare stopped in her tracks when she heard him get the okay. "Thank God, Cap. My stomach is a little queasy. This is more than I bargained for."

Paul shot her a concerned look. "I thought nurses had strong constitutions, but I have to say you don't look so hot, Cec. Come and sit tight for a bit."

Clare checked her watch. "I'm supposed to be picking *Tante* up at six, and it's already five o'clock."

"As long as the Coast Guard is allowing me to wait for them at the Pool, you can go on home right after we dock."

"Then how will you get home?"

Paul was quiet. He wiped a hand over his forehead.

"Would it be too much to ask you to stop at the house and tell my father what happened? There's friction between us lately, and he'll take it a lot easier from you than me."

"I can do that, but there's no way your father would blame you for something like this. Shall I ask him to come down to the docks?"

"No! It'll probably be late, and that's too much tension for him. I'll get a ride home. Right now I need to put you to work if you're up to it. Today's lesson has obviously changed. No mooring. We need to get the fore and aft ropes and fenders ready. I've got to ease Pa's boat through 'The Gut' to a floating dock at the Pool."

Paul had no problem maneuvering into the basin at Biddeford Pool. *Julie's Dream* was a sleek Bermudan sloop. He'd been sailing it with his father since he was twelve, and the Pool was home. After tying up at the floating dock, he walked Clare to her car. Their heads were inches apart as Paul leaned in, resting his arms on the open window, close enough for Clare to smell the sea in his hair.

"Pa will be glad to see you, Clare, 'cause you make him think of Maddy, and he doesn't see as much of her as he'd like to."

"Hey. 'Course not," she shrugged. "Maddy and I are as close as sisters, but I don't see much of her either since the wedding. As it should be, I suspect. Patrick is the coolest guy I know." She wiggled her eyebrows and smiled. *C'est la vie*, eh, Paul."

"Got to agree." Inching forward he brushed his lips across her cheek.

"Mmm. Salty with a trace of lavender." His warm brown eyes fastened on her breast under a damp t-shirt emblazoned with Nurses are the Best. His brows danced up, Groucho Marx style. "Uh-huh, agree again, CeCe."

Clare shook her head and gave him a little shove. "Go watch for the Coast Guard, Skipper. Everything will be okay." She started the engine, and Paul backed away. "Call me later, okay?" she called, wiggling her fingers at him.

Jacques Fontaine called to her from the wrap-around porch as soon as Clare pulled up in the side drive of the big beach house.

"I heard you drive in, Clare. Come on up. I want to hear all about your lesson. Where's Paul?" he asked as Clare climbed the steps to the porch of the Fontaines' sprawling Victorian they called Francois's Fancy.

"Paul is at the floating dock at the Pool, and I need to explain why." She let Jacques lead her to a porch rocker to sit next to him. "We had a great sail down to Goose Rocks Beach and back. We were on the water quite a while, and Paul said the boat handled beautifully. He also said I was a fast learner." Clare shot him a smile that belied the jittery feeling in her gut.

"I'm sure of that, Clare. What did you work on today?"

She drew in a deep breath. "Mainly I practiced tacking and learned how to lower the sails on approach. There was a light breeze all afternoon and a dropping sun when we came in to pick up a mooring in the harbor. I was ready with the boat hook while Paul was at the wheel, but then something unbelievable happened." Clare watched Jacques's face carefully, hoping not to shock him too much. "There was a dead body tangled on the marker buoy."

"A body!" Jacques Fontaine's brows furrowed with concern. He stopped the rocking chair and looked straight at her. "Good Lord. A dead body was at our marker? What did you do?"

"Well, I'm used to DOAs that come into ER, but I have to admit this one kind of threw me. The unexpected, you know. I was concentrating on holding the boat hook correctly to pick up the buoy rope, and I could hardly believe my eyes. It . . . er . . . she, uh, didn't look human. There it was, though, a body float-ing face down, and I guessed it probably was a female, long hair and all. I couldn't pick up the marker."

"Well, of course not. What did Paul do?"

"He notified the Coast Guard over the radio. They requested *Julie's Dream* stay at the scene, but Paul told them his passenger had to get back to town so they allowed him to come in to the Pool and moor at the dock. He's waiting there for a Coast Guard vessel to come down from South Portland."

Jacques Fontaine shook his head and sank back in the rocker. "I can't imagine. A dead body tangled on our mooring? That will shake up the locals, for sure. Paul did the right thing. The Coast Guard will immediately notify the Maine Marine Patrol, and I'm sure they'll handle things." He took her hand in his. "I'm so sorry it happened with my boat and especially to you, Clare."

Professor Fontaine looked thoughtfully at her. "Do you really have to get back to Biddeford? Kathleen is on her way home with lobster, and I can go down and pick Paul up in a little while."

Clare looked away for a second. "Paul said to tell you not to come to the harbor. He expects it will be late, and he'll get a ride home. I wish I could say I can stay, but this is the first full weekend I've had off in a month, and I promised *Tante* we'd go out to dinner tonight." She rose and planted a kiss on his cheek. "Thanks, Papa Jacques, but I'm already late, and I really have to go now. Can I have a rain check on the lobster?"

"Of course you can, my dear. You know you're welcome here any time."

"See you soon then, okay?"

"You bet." Jacques stood and smiled, slipping his arm around Clare to give her shoulder a squeeze. "Be sure to give your aunt Margaret my love," he said as Clare hurried down the porch steps. "And if you see that daughter of mine any time soon, tell her to call."

She noticed his smile had turned sad when she waved to him from the car. She tried to relax as she drove past the big summer homes on Mile Stretch Road, but her mind was a bee hive. First the dead body, then Paul. *He's beginning to give me funny feelings I'd rather not have . . . at least not with him! I wonder if it's only flirting.*

That house holds too many memories that I'm not anxious to think about, either. Tricky doings there last year when Maddy got lost in time. Francois's Fancy is like most of the other houses along the dune ridge, only it's not a summer home and the people in it are not your typical summer people. Professor Fontaine will always be Papa Jacques to me. And his daughter, Maddy . . . you don't get much tighter than Maddy and me . . . that is until Miss Madelaine Fontaine became Mrs. Patrick Donovan.

The light was flashing with two calls on the answering machine when Clare got to her apartment. She pushed play and listened to time and day.

Saturday, five P.M. "Hi, it's me," said Maddy's voice. "How'd it go today? I'd love to have been aboard *Julie's Dream* with you. Call us."

"No, no. You wouldn't want to be aboard, babe. Not this time." Clare spoke to the receiver in her hand while the second call beeped Saturday, six P.M. "Hallo, *ma chérie.* I made reservations for six-thirty. Are we going to be late?"

Clare dialed *Tante's* number. "Sorry, *Tante.* We are going to be a little late. I was delayed, but I'll be there to pick you up in about twenty minutes."

"Is something wrong, Clare?"

"No. Just sit tight and let me get ready, okay?" She hung up the phone and headed for the shower.

The water felt like little needles pelting her sunburned face and neck, harsher than the salt spray that stung her cheeks sailing on Saco Bay. She loved sailing. Loved the wind that filled

16

the sails and sent Paul's boat skimming across the water. *Paul. He could become a major distraction in my life . . . Nope. I'm not gonna let that happen.*

Out of the shower, Clare dressed quickly and dug in her purse for keys. *Tante will probably be on tenterhooks waiting to pounce on me for being on the water in Paul's boat.*

Sometimes Clare had to treat *Tante* Margaret with kid gloves. Sometimes the woman's persistence knew no end, and, always, she was the mother whom Clare lost at age three. The only mother Clare had ever known, Margaret Chamberlaine was a force to be reckoned with. Genes from her half-breed, French seer grandmother didn't get lost on Margaret.

Tonight Margaret had a hidden agenda. Thankfully, the Seaview restaurant was crowded, and they were turning tables over fast for a waiting line. *Tante* knew everybody in the place, so, although they were late, their reservation was honored.

Tante ordered her favorite, Coquille St. Jacques and talked all through dinner about the perils of sudden Atlantic storms and fishermen, like Clare's uncle Jean, losing lives at sea. Clare knew the hidden message was *stop sailing with Paul Fontaine.*

When *Tante*'s caution drew a line, Clare usually pummeled ahead full speed. This time she didn't dare. She listened quietly with a few "uh-huhs," and they were in and out of the restaurant in record time. Margaret thought Clare's unusually quiet demeanor meant she didn't feel well, so Clare played it up to be a little too much sun and let *Tante* believe it. There were no objections to being brought home early.

A message from Paul was blinking when Clare got back to her apartment. His voice sounded stressed.

"A State Marine Patrol sergeant brought me home after the body went to the coroner. Seems the Patrol is the chief investigating unit. The Coast Guard Station notified them as soon as I called in the distress signal. Both units conducted a search of the water to try and determine where the body came from. Local police combed the shore looking for anything related to the incident. It took a hell of long time, so it was very late when I got home.

"Because Pa's boat was involved, they wanted statements from us, and you about finding the body. I hope you didn't say anything to your aunt Margaret yet. Call me on my cell phone when you get back from the restaurant."

"Dammed straight, I didn't let *Tante* in on this—yet," Clare said aloud to the receiver.

She dialed Maddy's number first. Maddy's take on the whole episode with her brother was essential before she spoke to Paul.

Patrick answered the phone. "Hi Clare. Got your sea legs yet?"

"I got them early on today, but I'm not so sure I want them now."

"Sounds like King Neptune dished up a little surprise, huh? Hold on. Madelaine's been wondering about you all afternoon. Here she is."

"Hey, CeCe. Don't tell me you've been out on the water all this time?"

"No, but the sun and the sea have finally caught up with me. You won't believe what happened out there today."

"It was perfect sailing weather. What could have happened?"

"Well, everything went smoothly until we came in to pick up a mooring at the end of the afternoon. There was a dead body tangled on the marker buoy."

"A dead body! Are you kidding me?"

"I'm not kidding, and your husband pegged it right a minute ago. King Neptune dished up an ugly surprise today."

"Good Lord, Clare. What did you do?"

"Me? Nothing. Paul notified authorities, and he brought me to shore. He had to wait there for the Coast Guard to arrive,

18

and I had to leave for a dinner date with *Tante*."

"Paul handled things okay?"

"Until we tied up at the wharf, yes. That's when he asked me to stop at the house and explain to your dad what happened. He said something about friction between them, and he definitely didn't want Papa Jacques to come to the harbor. As I was leaving, your dad asked me to tell you to call him."

"Hmm. Well, it hasn't been easy for Paul at the house these last few weeks, and I know he's been trying to avoid situations that cause stress for Papa."

"But your father looked pretty good, Mad. He was shocked, of course, when I told him the news, but he seemed okay to me. A little sad, but you told me yourself that Doc Halliday told him to stop worrying about his heart."

"That's true. Papa's life was pretty stress free until July, but Paul feels that his coming home has changed things. You know Paul. Everything he does seems to turn into a disaster. First he loses his job, and then there's this *Julie's Dream* thing with Kathleen."

"What d'ya mean, *Julie's Dream* thing?"

Maddy lowered her voice. "I can fill you in on all the details later, just not right now. We're due at Patrick's mom's for a birthday party. You've got tomorrow off and I'm going to be alone, so come over in the morning and we'll go to mass and come back here for brunch. Okay?"

"Gotcha. Sounds good, babe. See you tomorrow."

Clare dialed Paul's cell phone.

"Hey, Paul. Sorry to get back to you so late. I did follow your advice, though. I didn't mention one word to my *tante*. Just told her I had another sailing lesson. That led to my listening all through dinner about the perils of Atlantic storms and how my uncle Jean's boat should never have been out in the storm that took his life."

"Sorry, CeCe, but unfortunately, your aunt Margaret may learn about another tragedy sooner than we like. The body will probably be in the newspaper. The Maine Marine Patrol officers and the Coast Guard did a thorough search of the area before the corpse went off to the coroner."

"So you said before. What did they find?"

"They found zilch. *Nada*. They were looking for debris from a boat or an oil slick in case a vessel went down in the area. The search took so long it was dark before I got back to Pa. A sergeant brought me home, took my statement and verification from Pa about the boat. I told it straight—just like it happened. There's no way what you say can be any different than my words, right?"

"Of course not."

"I was obligated to give the officer your address and told him you probably wouldn't be home until late. He may wait till morning."

"Thanks for the heads-up, Paul, and chill out, okay? Sounds like they're just following routine, and I'll be ready, whenever. Back to you, tomorrow."

CHAPTER TWO

The doorbell rang at seven-thirty in the morning. Clare opened the door a crack. A man wearing yellow rubber boots and a tan uniform towered over the lintel. Clare slanted her head, looked up and stared. He removed his hat and sunglasses. High, carved cheekbones, full, wide mouth, and black-fringed eyes as dark as winter night. Something about him was familiar. The man stared back.

"Miss Chamberlaine? Sorry to disturb you so early on a Sunday morning. I'm Sergeant Windspirit, Maine Marine Patrol. We need a statement from you regarding the body found yesterday in Saco Bay."

Clare cinched the belt on her bathrobe and opened the door wider. "I was expecting someone about that, but not this early. If you don't mind waiting a few minutes till I get dressed, please come in." Clare led him into the kitchen, motioned to a chair, then cat-walked on bare feet back to her room.

She grabbed a sweatshirt from a dresser drawer, didn't bother with a bra, and pulled on jeans, all the while thinking about the guy in the uniform. She rinsed her mouth and finger combed her hair, hoping it wasn't sticking up all over. A look in the dresser mirror brought a reflection on the opposite wall into view—an old school banner draped over her high school graduation picture. Memory suddenly kicked in. BHS champion hockey team . . . 2002. His face was plastered all over the newspapers that year

The sergeant was tapping a pen on the kitchen table, staring into the sugar bowl when Clare barefooted it into the kitchen.

"Remi Windspirit?" she asked.

His head whipped up. "Yes." His eyes narrowed. "Uh . . . have we met?"

"Not officially, but when I was in high school you were captain of the champion hockey team, the best one Biddeford had in a decade. You graduated and—" Clare hunched her shoulders and shot him a quizzical look. "I thought you became a big league hockey star somewhere."

His mouth started to turn up in a smile, crinkling those big dark eyes fringed with incredibly long lashes. *Man, I could get lost in those eyes.* Suddenly he cleared his throat, the smile disappeared and he was all business.

"Nope. Didn't take that route." He methodically withdrew a notebook and tucked his sunglasses into his shirt pocket. "So, if you're ready to answer some questions, Miss Chamberlaine, we'll get on with this.

"Clare. My name's Clare. What kind of a cop are you, Remi Windspirit," she asked with fake formality.

Remi stared icily at her. "It's Sergeant, and I'm an officer with Maine Marine Patrol, established to promote and protect coastal fishing industries. We cooperate with all local, state and federal agencies and work with retrieval and investigations into incidents in area water. Now, Miss—Clare, do you recall the time of day when you discovered the body?"

"I guess it was about five o'clock when we sailed in to the mooring."

"You were sailing with Paul Fontaine? Just the two of you?"

He's making it sound like a rendezvous.

"Yes."

"What's the name of the sail boat?"

"*Julie's Dream.* That's important?"

"Just verifying for the record, Miss Chamberlaine."

"Clare."

"Clare," he demurred, his measured gaze traveling down from her chin to her bare toes. "What were the weather conditions?"

"Sunny, with a light breeze."

"Can you give the location where your boat first encountered the body?"

"Gee, Sarge, we were in Wood Island harbor, but more than that, I couldn't say. I'm a nurse, not a sailor—just learning to crew on Fontaine's boat."

Remi sat back, covered his mouth with one hand, then straightened and looked Clare in the eye.

"If you will tell me, nice and slow, Miss Chamberlaine, how the discovery happened, I'll try to get it down on paper."

"Clare."

"Clare." He said, picking up his pen. He wrote fast as she spoke. When she got to the part where Paul confirmed that he could see a body, Remi stopped writing.

"Can you describe the body, Clare?"

"I couldn't see much, with it being face down in the water. Kind of a shadowy torso was visible, and it bobbed with the waves and looked like it could be caught up somehow on the marker buoy. The head looked bloated and grotesque with long hair streaming out. I thought it was a woman."

Sergeant Windspirit was bent over the table, writing in his notebook. Straight black hair fell over his forehead. Clare's fingers itched to push it back. She folded her hands under the table and curled her toes around the rungs of the chair.

"Tell me, Sergeant, why is my description of the body necessary, anyway? The coroner will be giving you stats on the body."

His head jerked up. He grimaced and shot her a steely look. "I'm sure you understand, Miss Chamberlaine, that when a

23

body is recovered from the water, two questions need to be answered. One, was he or she alive or dead when he or she entered the water? And two, was the cause of death drowning and if not, what was the cause of death? These are questions for investigation, and the first step is identification of the victim. Any impressions or descriptions from involved citizens are procedural and vital to that investigation."

"Involved citizens! We happened to see a body from a boat. It was a one-minute glance at the most, Sergeant Windspirit. We immediately reported it, so how in God's name are we involved?"

"Easily. You called it in."

She could see it did no good to get riled. This guy was one cool cucumber, and she didn't think he liked females challenging him.

"Are we done here, Sergeant?"

He scowled and shoved his notebook and pen across the table. "If you will read this, please, and sign it, yes, we're done. For now."

His glower deepened as Clare slowly read his notes, purposefully feigning indecision. He had it down, though, word for word, like an instant recording of what she'd said. She signed the statement.

"Thank you for your time, Miss Chamberlaine. We will be in touch. He rose, his eyes raking over her body before he left the kitchen.

Clare followed him to the door. He was wide shouldered and narrow hipped. Olive green uniform pants fit snugly over his muscled calves and thighs. Her eyes were pleasuring their way up to a trim butt when he suddenly turned.

"Sorry to have disturbed you so early in the morning, Miss . . . Clare. I trust you'll be here if we need anything further?"

24

She stood there, mouth open for a second, while he put his hat on. *Good God, but he's a tall drink of water.* "Uh, either here or at the medical center. I work in ER."

He nodded. She thought she detected a warm glint in those dark eyes before the door closed on Sergeant Windspirit. Maybe it was because she wanted it to be so.

Clare rang the bell and pushed open the door to Maddy and Patrick's apartment. She was halfway down their hall when Maddy's voice called out.

"Come on back, Clare, I'm in the kitchen."

The long hallway held a gallery of paintings interspersed with framed family photos of Jacques Fontaine, Maddy's mom, Julie, and Maddy and Clae, all taken in front of Francois's Fancy. There was a great photo of Paul at the wheel of *Julie's Dream*. The last picture on the wall was Maddy and Patrick's wedding portrait. Clare had seen it a dozen times, but could never pass it without pausing. Maddy was a head-turning beauty, and Patrick brought a smile to your lips, just looking at his gorgeous face. Eyes so blue, Maddy always called them pure cobalt.

"We've got twenty minutes before we have to leave for church, CeCe. Come have a blueberry scone or some cake." Maddy pulled out a chair for her at their round oak table and poured coffee. "My mother-in-law sent the scones home with us last night along with huge slices of Rosemary's birthday cake."

"You know me, babe. Never refuse homemade. So, Patrick's sister had a birthday. Seems like yesterday she was your eighth grade student. How old is Rosie?"

"Fifteen, but she's not like your typical teenager. She's a shy, soft-spoken beauty, and Patrick still looks out for her more than his other sisters."

"Where is Patrick? He's not coming to church?"

"He left on a fishing trip down the Saco River with a buddy

of his. They left very early this morning, and I'm kind of glad. Patrick hardly takes any time for himself. He spends countless hours on this place. Work, work, work."

"Paul told me he tried to get Patrick to sail with him last month when *Julie's Dream* was ready for the water."

Maddy pursed her lips and nodded with a sigh. "I know. But I think it will be some time before Patrick is comfortable with the yacht club set. Paul is certainly not typical of the racers at the club either."

"Well, hell, neither am I, but I guess I was Paul's next best choice. So, tell me about your brother. He's been home since the end of June, and all I know is he's consumed with that boat."

"That was Papa's idea. Paul was so depressed over losing his job that he began drinking too much. My father suggested overhauling the sailboat to give him something to focus on. The boat had been in dry dock since my mother died. You're the best result of the boat project, Clare." Maddy smiled as Clare finished the last bite of her scone.

"Ayuh. He talked me into sailing lessons and things were going really well, until yesterday. It was the first time I saw an uptight Paul. I don't think it was all about the dead body, either. Mainly, it seemed to be about your father."

"Well, there was a little incident with Kathleen just before Paul was ready to launch *Julie's Dream*."

"Don't tell me there's still friction between your stepmother and Paul. I thought that disappeared after Fiona was found."

"Well, let's say things got better after we found Fiona, but I don't think Paul will ever be comfortable living at the house with Kathleen. Any more than I could before I moved in to your apartment with you. It's just a temporary solution for him until he finds a new job. Papa wanted him to enjoy what's left of the summer before he started job hunting."

"That sounds like Papa Jacques. So then, what happened with Kathleen?"

"When the boat's restoration was complete, they all had a few drinks to celebrate. Paul suggested they launch the boat and give her a test sail. Papa and Kathleen went along to the boat launch, but she balked when she saw the boat. My father thought it was because she's not a swimmer and isn't too keen about boats. I got this story second hand, but according to Paul, Kathleen said something like, 'No, I think I'll pass. You two go along and sail. The boat looks nice, Paul, but she's Julie's dream. You two enjoy, okay?'

"Paul picked up on it and put his foot in his mouth. 'Dammed right she's Julie's dream, and nobody is ever going to change that,' he said. My father paled, got real short of breath and panicky, and had to be taken back to the house. It's all blown over now, but Papa still hasn't been out on the boat."

"Geez, no wonder Paul is walking on eggs." Clare rose and checked her watch. We should leave now, Maddy, if we're going to be on time for mass."

"Okay, but go peek in the living room at Patrick's latest project while I get my purse."

Clare was driving out of St. Joseph's parking lot when Maddy asked if she minded a little change of plans.

"Instead of coming back to my place, let's drive out to the Pool and take Paul out to lunch," she suggested. "I haven't seen my brother in over a week."

"I'll go for that. Maybe I can ease Paul's mind a little about my visit from the Marine Patrol sergeant. Driving out Pool Road should give us time to talk. I didn't take time to tell you how impressed I am with your condo. I really liked your new work center and book shelves. Every time I come out to Factory Complex, Patrick has created something new. He must be a workaholic."

"He volunteered from the get-go when they started turning the factories into condos. Patrick was a natural, seeing as his was one of the first craftsmen shops in the converted buildings. He drew up plans that helped the clerk of the works and the construction crew divide up space in those cavernous old buildings."

"Lucky duck. You've got a talented artist for a brother and a cabinetmaker extraordinaire for a husband. I'll bet Patrick would have made a helluvan architect if he had studied for it."

"He's very content with what he's doing, Clare. This summer he picked up a lot of what he calls the carriage trade—summer people from the Pool all the way down past Fortunes Rocks. Word of mouth, you know. He's really become quite successful. I only wish the same was true of Paul."

Clare drove up Mile Stretch Road to the side drive at Francois's Fancy. "Speaking of the man, I don't see his car here. Maybe Paul's not home."

Clare slid out of the car, hooding her eyes with one hand to stare at the sun-bright beach stretched out in front them. "Someone's down on the beach, Maddy," Clare said, pointing up-shore along the edge of the rocks. "Got a peaked cap on and it kinda looks like Paul."

Shoes in hand, they barefooted it across the lawn toward the rocks. Suddenly, Maddy's face lit up in a smile, and she paused with a hand on Clare's arm, "Halleluiah! Look Cec, Paul is painting."

Paul's profile was cast in golden sunlight, facing northeast, his shoulders forward, an arm stretched out to an easel anchored in the sand.

"We gave him a Julian easel for Christmas, and this is the first I've seen him use it," Maddy said.

"Hey, Cap," Clare called out. "You're wearing a different hat today."

Paul looked their way and waved a paint brush.

When they reached him, Maddy leaned from behind his camp stool to hug him and get a look at his canvas. "Plein air, huh? I like that, Paul. Birds flying into the Sanctuary from the sea. Nice composition. Streaks of amber and orange in a red sky. Must be sunrise, and no sailing today."

"You got it. I should get you to write copy for my paintings. Maybe I could sell a few."

Clare stood to his side looking at the painting. "I don't know what this plein air business means, but what you've done is beautiful, skipper."

Paul quirked his mouth at her. "Plein air means painting from life," he said. "When you are outdoors, you concentrate every sensory nerve on what's in front of you. You channel things in your head and re-create them on canvas." He dipped his brush into a small pot of water in the easel tray. "I used to trail around the Bird Sanctuary with Pa when I was young, and some of those sights were committed to memory, but being out here this morning is the best."

"How long did this take?" Clare asked.

Paul rubbed his eyes and started to clean his brushes. "I started sketching from memory inside the house about five o'clock this morning. Then I brought my camp stool and gear out here around seven, I guess."

"Cripes," Clare said. "The sky has cleared already, and it's near high noon. That's almost seven hours. How about a lunch break with Mad and me?"

He looked up at Clare, poker-faced and with tired eyes. "Who's buying?"

"Us." Maddy and Clare chimed in chorus, giving each other a high sign behind him.

29

Paul rose from his camp stool, laughing. "You two are something else. Okay, team, if you'll help carry my stuff up to the house and wait while I clean up, then I'm your man."

Kathleen greeted them at the front door as soon as they climbed the porch steps.

"So there you are, Paul. Your father didn't know where you went off to early this morning. We've been to church and back."

Kathleen gave her cheek to Maddy. "So have we," Maddy said. "Good morning, Kathleen. We found Paul down on the beach."

The last one in through the door, Clare echoed Maddy. "Hi, Mrs. Fontaine. Lucky for us, we got to see Paul's painting."

Paul didn't pause in his stride. He was climbing the stairs in seconds, canvas in hand, calling back over his shoulder. "You can put my easel and the camp stool in Pa's study, babe. I'll be down in ten minutes."

Maddy grabbed the stool from Clare and started down the hall, leaving them standing at the parlor door.

"Well," Kathleen said, pouting her lips and trailing Paul with her eyes, "I didn't even get a peek. What was he painting?"

"A seascape," Clare said as though she was familiar with artist's lingo. "Is Professor Fontaine home?"

"Yes, Clare. Come with me to the kitchen. We just returned from church, and I was checking the front porch for any sign of Paul."

Maddy joined them at the study door and followed Kathleen into the kitchen.

"Look who's here, darling. They just arrived and found Paul at the beach."

"Madelaine!" Jacques said. "And Clare. What a nice surprise."

"Hi, Papa. Patrick's off fishing today, so Clare came with me to see if Paul would come out to lunch with us. He's upstairs getting presentable."

Jacques looked from Maddy to Clare. "You're looking ﹅ pretty, both of you." He said, slipping his arms around theiɪ shoulders. "Went to St. Joseph's, did you?"

"Thanks, Professor," Clare said. "Yes, we just came from mass."

"Ah, then maybe you'd like to have some refreshment here with us first. Kathleen, what do we have for my ladies? Clare deserves something special after that ordeal she went through yesterday. I'm sure you've heard about it by now, Madelaine?"

"Yes, I did, Papa, and that's one of the reasons we'd like Paul to go to lunch with us. Clare is curious to know if there's any scuttlebutt at the village."

Jacques frowned. "Paul and I planned to bring the boat back out to its mooring this afternoon. I thought he'd do his nosing around then."

"Maybe then, too, but this is Clare's last day off, and . . ." Maddy shrugged.

"I can open a bottle of Pinot Grigio," Kathleen said. "Will that do?"

"Not this time, thanks." Heads spun around to see Paul sauntering into the kitchen. "I'm buying drinks down at the Yardarm. All set, ladies?"

"Wow. That was a quick change. You look pretty sharp, Paul," Kathleen said.

Paul's white linen pants and navy crew shirt were a far cry from the baggy sweats and faded jersey he wore on the beach. Clare almost gave him a whistle but caught herself when she looked at Papa Jacques's frown.

"Thank you," Paul said, with a brisk nod to Kathleen. "I didn't take time to shave, but I'm not out to win hearts—already have these two," he said, throwing his arm around his sister and giving a smooch to Clare's cheek.

Jacques was still frowning.

"Not to worry Pa, I'll be back early to bring you down to the boat."

CHAPTER THREE

Paul listened from the back seat of the car while Clare told him about Sergeant Windspirit's interrogation.

"Was it the same guy, and did he ask you the same kind of questions?" Clare asked.

"Ayuh, but I asked some questions of my own about the body."

"And?"

"Well, I took a good look at the corpse before they zipped it into a body bag. The Coast Guard had what they called a Stokes litter, which is a flotation device that looks like chicken wire. When the body was finally retrieved and placed on the litter, you could tell it was a woman, all right. The officers from Marine Patrol and the Coast Guard were doing a thorough look-see, trying to find identification on the body, so I couldn't get too close a look. I asked if there was any identification." He shook his head. *"Nada."*

"Could you see how the body got tangled with the buoy?"

"Not exactly. But there was some kind of a silver belt on her torso with links trailing down. Maybe that's what tangled in the marker rope. One thing I won't forget though, CeCe, was her skin. It looked like goose skin—all swollen. One of her eyes was picked clean—"

"Ugh. Gross, Paul. Enough!" Maddy said, shuddering. "I'll have nightmares."

"Sorry, babe. I thought CeCe knows about this stuff and

33

could fill me in."

"Well, of course. We've had drowning victims in ER, but it's best you wait for the coroner's report, Paul." Clare gave him the eye in the rearview mirror. "Definitely not lunch talk," she said, shaking her head. She pulled into the only parking spot near the restaurant. "We may hear some gossip in here. As your dad said, 'It's bound to stir up the locals.' "

They sat at a small table near the bar, and Paul ordered mimosas. "We need a little jazz in our life after yesterday, huh, Cec?"

"Uh . . . yeah." She said, rolling her eyes. Maddy and Paul faced the restaurant's front entrance from their seats, but Clare could see down the length of the restaurant to a large round table at the back where four men were eating lunch. Smack in the middle was Claude Duval.

"I hate to dredge up bad memories, guys, but this may not be the best place to hear any news about yesterday. But then again, maybe it is."

"What do you mean?" Maddy asked.

"There's a gathering of men in the back that includes Claude Duval."

"Damn," Paul said, draining his glass like it was a shot of whiskey. "He's all over the place. I saw him at the yacht club with some tony chick last week. She was definitely one of the summer sailing crowd, but the phony bastard doesn't even own a boat."

Maddy pursed her lips and nodded. "Patrick saw him at a planning commission meeting at Factory Square recently, too, but Claude had sense enough to avoid Patrick, and, of course, Patrick gives him a wide berth. Fiona wouldn't have it any other way."

"Geez, we all know Duval's past all too well, but I don't get it about the present. What are you saying, guys?" Clare asked.

Paul shot her a puzzled look. "Don't you read the papers? Duval has big ideas ever since his father was elected District Attorney. Rumor is Claude's looking for a seat in state government next year, coasting on his father's coat tails. You might say he's putting feelers out on the campaign trail by sucking up to all the power people."

"I must be out of the loop," Clare said. "Working crazy shifts doesn't leave much time for schmoozing or local stuff. I didn't even know his father was DA."

"All work and no play. You know what they say, Cec." Paul wagged his finger at her.

The waitress came to take their order. She was a skinny blonde wearing a Hills Beach t-shirt and a soiled white apron over thigh-hugging jeans.

"Hey, JP, ready to order?" she asked.

Paul gave her a wink and pretended to look at the menu for all of a second. "Shall we make it easy for Patty, ladies? How 'bout lobster rolls all around?"

They agreed. Paul flashed a smile at the waitress. Maddy whispered to CeCe, "A lot of his old high school crowd used to call him JP. Only *Tante* Margaret uses his full name, Jacques Paul."

Paul tugged at Patty's apron when she put her order pad into the pocket. "Have you heard anything going around about the excitement out in the harbor?"

"I saw Marine Patrol and Biddeford police coming in and out of here last night, asking the boss if anything suspicious happened during the last couple of days or was anyone lookin' for a missing person. The boss said, 'No, nothing like that he knew of.' "

The waitress put her hands on her hips. "I'm workin' double shift today, guys, and it's same old, same old. Fishermen coming in and out of here early this morning, summer visitors up

35

the wazoo, and a few locals, all gabbing about the body." She lowered her voice and dipped her head. "I think that's the harbormaster from the yacht club in the back booth with those lawyers, but he don't come in here that much. That's all I know, JP."

She left to put their orders in the kitchen, and Paul made a face and shook his head. "Be right back," he said as he rose to walk to the bar.

"I see there's still animosity toward Claude," Clare said to Maddy.

"Yes, at least where Paul's concerned. No one in Patrick's family even breathes Duval's name because that's what Fiona prefers. Patrick says Fiona is trying to change her life and wants no reminders of him. I feel the same, but of course, I have Patrick."

"Doesn't Claude's name come up in your papa's conversation with Kathleen?"

"Yeah, Claude is still Kathleen's lawyer—" Maddy broke off abruptly and jutted her head toward the bar. "He's coming back to the table."

Paul threw his open palms in the air. "I asked the bartender for the scoop, but he hasn't heard anything either." Paul laughed. "He was touting the last of the Saco Spirit summer concerts coming up next weekend. Said he plays sax in a jazz group. Seems everybody is a goer and doer with jobs around here. Except me."

"It's the season, Paul," Maddy said, "and there isn't that much left of it."

The waitress brought their plates, and before anyone had eaten a bite, Paul's hand closed over Clare's. "I'd like to do something to make up for the debacle you went through yesterday, CeCe. How about taking in that Saco concert with me Saturday night? I haven't been to a local gig since God knows when, and you just said you haven't either."

Clare shot a look to Maddy. The mission today was to try and raise Paul's spirit. Maddy returned her gaze with smiling, hopeful eyes.

"Sounds good, Cap," Clare said. "Barring any emergencies, you can count me in."

Tante Margaret pointed at the headline in the newspaper, slapping the paper down on Clare's kitchen table. " 'Body Found In Bay' What's this, *Chérie?* You didn't tell me about this. *Mon Dieu!* What happened? It says here that the professor's boat discovered the body. You had to be in the boat, *non?*"

"Yes I was, but Paul and I only called the discovery in to the authorities. I guess we didn't think ahead that it would be reported in the paper. I didn't want to upset you by telling you about it Saturday night because—"

One hand posed on her hip, *Tante* clamped the other on Clare's shoulders, her big brown eyes snapping.

"Not telling me is what is upsetting. All that you do has been part of my life for so long, your bruises and pains are my pains. Don't take that away from me, my love."

Clare hugged her close. "Not to worry, Mom. I will keep you informed if anything comes of our reporting the incident, but I'm almost certain it won't." She stepped back from their embrace and tucked a strand of *Tante*'s glossy black hair into the chignon she always wore. Pointing to a chair, Clare asked her to sit. "Besides, the officer who took our statements was one of your compatriots."

"My compatriots? What do you mean?"

"Sergeant Remi Windspirit, the officer from Maine Marine Patrol who came to question me. He's half French and half Native American Indian."

"Abenaki?"

"No." Clare chuckled. "He's not from here originally. I think his father belonged to one of the Southeast tribes, maybe Cherokee."

"How do you know this, Clare?"

"Well, at first I recognized him from high school. When I was a freshman, he was captain of the most successful hockey team Biddeford had in a decade. He's a big hunk, *Tante*. Fearsome but awesome."

Tante raised an eyebrow and smiled, seemingly more at ease.

"Remi's family came to Maine when he was young. At least that's what the yearbook said about him. I looked him up in my yearbook last night. They had profiles on all the seniors. He was years ahead of me, but one of those unforgettable faces, you know, and talents."

"I hear you, Clare, but that doesn't tell me what he said about the dead body or why he questioned you."

"He gave no details about the body. He wanted my statement about *finding the body*. You know, what I saw and where we were . . . that kind of stuff. They have to investigate to find out who she is and how this woman ended up in the harbor. They'll know more when the autopsy reports come back. Paul knows more about it than I do because he had to stay at the docks until the Coast Guard brought the corpse to shore."

"Mother of God." *Tante* shook her head. "Jacques Paul seems to find trouble without ever looking for it. His papa is probably upset, *non?*"

"Papa Jacques wasn't too upset, no. Surprised and shocked, 'course, but he took it pretty well."

"Jacques Fontaine is a remarkable man. Since his stroke, he seems to be more . . . gentle, *non?* Takes his ease more, eh?"

"Mmm. A near death experience does make you think about your mortality," Clare waggled her head back and forth sing-song fashion, "but, *Je ne sais pas, Tante*. Jacques is more compliant now, and certainly he misses Maddy's presence out at the Pool, but . . . him and Paul? That's a tough one. There have always been bumps in the road between those two, ya know, and I don't think Kathleen makes it any easier."

"*Oui*, sometimes life seems too wrinkled to iron out, but the Fontaines can work things out. Blood ties are strong in that family, and remember, *chérie*, triumph follows tragedy. So true, eh? With the search for Patrick's sister Fiona, it was true, for sure. That was unforgettable, *non?*"

"Ayuh. Strange that you bring that up because Maddy and I were just talking about that today. Maddy was a woman possessed until Fiona was found, and it did forge a strong love between her and Patrick. I guess you'd call that a triumph. But, heh, blood ties or no, there may not have been a search for Fiona Donovan if you hadn't had a vision, *Tante.*"

"Uh-uh. The hurricane came to Biddeford. That was nature's force, not spirits. Let's put that aside, okay, Clare? I want no more talk about visions." She rose, patting Clare's shoulder, her big brown eyes sending her a piercing gaze.

Clare's iron-bound conscience wouldn't let her do anything except nod her head in agreement.

Tante pointed at the newspaper. "I promised to help at Star of The Sea Retreat House today, and I'm sure the good sisters will ask about this. From now on, I want to be the first to know if you have any worries about this corpse you found."

Clare took *Tante*'s arm and walked with her to the door. "Look, *Tante*, Saco Bay is pretty big, and the nuns may not have even read the papers or know anything about this at all. It will all blow over as soon as the body is identified. Stop worrying about me and the Fontaines, okay?"

Clare looked around after Margaret left. The open door to the spare bedroom always brought Maddy to mind. It reminded her of the few happy months when Maddy had occupied that room and shared the apartment with her. It was such a small room . . . probably meant to be a den or maybe a nursery. *I sure don't need either of those, but I haven't got the heart for another roomie, either.*

She walked into her bedroom and stared at the bed. She'd had a dream last night, better called a nightmare. She was standing in the morgue, watching the coroner perform an autopsy on the corpse from the bay. The body suddenly sat up on the slab, moaning and groaning about a dory ride and spitting small fish from her mouth. Clare shuddered at the memory and went back into the kitchen and poured herself a glass of wine. *Gotta call Maddy and see if she can meet me for lunch tomorrow.*

Clare smiled at the man making sandwiches behind the deli counter at the Blue Elephant Café and Catering.

"I'm glad you suggested this place," Maddy said "It's late to have lunch, but that was a delicious salad."

"Yeah, Reuben and I are on pretty good terms. I met him when he catered the wedding of one of the nurses from the medical center. Reuben is co-owner of the café. I'm surprised you and Patrick haven't been here. It's just around the corner from the condo."

"You know Patrick. He's such a traditionalist. He doesn't stray often from the café over on Main. His mom still works part time there, you know."

"Well, the Blue Elephant is a good bet for me, especially when I finish a night shift and get here early in the morning. It beats making breakfast."

"Don't you still love to cook? You're so good at it, CeCe."

"Ayuh, I do, but I'm beginning to rely a little more on places like this. It's not much fun eating alone or cooking for one. These guys have really great stuff with a little more flair and creativity than most of the restaurants. Not that I need fancy, mind you. I'm still watching my weight." She stole a sheepish grin at Maddy, but Maddy just laughed knowingly and nodded her head. "Thick and thin we used to call each other, and that hasn't changed."

"I brought *Tante* here a couple of weeks ago. She loved their chowder, and she raved about Pepperell Square, especially the gorgeous flowers out front of the gift shop and the deli. She's amazed at all the changes taking place on Factory Island."

"Talk about changes, were you really surprised about Claude Duval getting into politics?"

"Well, of course! You'd think he would have stayed in a hidey hole after he abandoned Fiona. Conceit and deceit gotta be his middle names. You know that first hand, babe."

Maddy lowered her head and nodded. "It seems like ages ago. His name hasn't come up in any talks with my father lately, but there was no mistaking Paul's attitude when we saw Claude at the Yardarm, Sunday."

"Speaking of Paul, how about you two joining us at that concert tonight?"

Maddy raised an eyebrow at Clare. "Paul invited you, CeCe, not me or Patrick."

"I know. I just thought it might be more fun if . . ." Her words drifted off.

"If you weren't alone with my brother? I'm sensing something here, Cec, and I'm not sure I understand. Care to enlighten me?"

Clare sat back and covered her mouth with her napkin. Silence hung there for a minute until she put the napkin down. "I'm at sixes and sevens, babe. It seems like your brother has changed. At least around me, anyway. He's not the teasing, playful guy who used to be like my big brother. He's become, well . . . sexy—up close and personal like, and I don't know what to do about it."

41

"Hmm, maybe he really is attracted to you. Wouldn't you find that flattering?"

"Flattering, yeah, but frustrating. Don't get me wrong. I think of Paul as a really, really good friend, but I don't want anything more than that. Just friends is the way I want to keep things."

"Is there someone else you want to be more than friends with? Someone I don't know about?"

Clare raised her eyebrows and quirked her mouth. "There could be," she said, her head bobbing back and forth as though she was considering the question.

"Well in that case, I guess you have to somehow let Paul know how you feel."

"Geez, that's not so easy to do. Paul is vulnerable right now. I don't want to give him another blow to his ego. On the other hand, maybe I'm sensing more here than is intended. I thought maybe you could feel him out. Could you do that for me?"

"I can try. He's coming to Sunday dinner at our apartment. Why don't you just go along to the concert tonight and have a little fun. Nothing serious can happen at a public event like that."

Chapter Four

Paul set up the lawn chairs while Clare spread big, checkered napkins between them. He poked into a picnic basket she brought. "Wine, two glasses, *paté,* and a candle. Hmm, for someone who doesn't do the social circuit, you sure came prepared, CeCe."

"Hey, it's what I see happening on TV and in the movies. Open the wine, Paul, and we'll be 'the beautiful people' for the evening."

Clare sat in the lawn chair and threw her head back to scan the darkening sky. Paul shot her an amused glance while he opened the wine.

"The music is supposed to start at seven-thirty and that should be any minute now, but you are looking up instead of at the bandstand. Whatcha lookin' for?"

"Just checking out the stars. I'm looking for early entertainment in the night sky. I see a pale moon rising, but what I really hope to see later is Sagittarius. Some people see a teapot or a milk dipper, but Sagittarius is really an archer, half man and half animal."

"How do you know when to look for him?"

"August, around nine P.M. is the best time to see it."

"Whoa," he said handing her a glass, "I didn't know you were into constellations."

"I've been star gazing since I was a kid. Back then, I thought the Milky Way was a candy bar, but my uncle Jèan taught me most of what I know about the heavens. He knew a lot about navigating with the stars, like the old sailors, you know. 'Course, I have a reason for looking for Sagittarius. I was born under that sign, November 23rd."

"I never remember birthdays, Cec, and I never thought much about astrology," he clinked her wine glass with his, "but here's to the twenty-third—in case I'm not around to celebrate your birthday. *La joie de la vie.*"

"Amen to that. Everyone needs a little joy in his life." As Clare reached into the basket, she heard someone loudly clearing his throat behind their chairs. She turned just as a tall, muscular man stopped behind Paul and stared. He was wearing a Red Wings sweatshirt and jeans. Clare looked down. His feet were clad in boat moccasins, no socks, and no yellow rubber boots.

"Sergeant! I almost didn't recognize you out of uniform," Clare said.

Paul's head whipped around, and he stood, extending a hand. "Hey, everybody likes a little music, right, Sarge?"

Remi Windspirit shook Paul's hand and glanced down at Clare.

"Clare," he said, nodding with a knee-melting smile.

It was hard not to warm to his smile, but the only words that would come out of her mouth were, "Hey, Remi."

"You're right, Paul, I'm a jazz fan and lucky to be off this weekend. I didn't want to miss this concert." He patted a small blanket on his shoulder and pointed to the left. "I'm going to move up a little closer if I can find a spot near the sax player. He's really good."

Clare watched him step carefully around the people sitting in chairs and on blankets. Tight jeans clung to his thighs and trim butt. *Oh my.* She craned her neck to watch as he spread his blanket at the foot of a tree. *I wouldn't mind snuggling next to him on that blanket* . . . but there was no point in wishing. Bad habit, wanting things to be different.

The musicians were warming up, and Paul filled his glass again. "First name basis, huh?" he said in a less than curious tone.

"Well, yeah. I recognized him from a high school yearbook after he came to get my statement. He was just a couple years ahead of me."

"That would make him a year behind me. Funny, I don't remember him."

"Probably cuz he was a jock, and he came over to BHS from Ocean Park because of the sports program. You were into art and theater, as I recall."

"You found out a lot about him in short order, Cec. Who was interrogating who, anyway?"

A loud shushing sound came from behind them, and Clare poked Paul. She pointed to the bandstand where someone was introducing the jazz band. "Later," she whispered.

Remi was right. The tenor sax was good. He took the lead with "How High the Moon," which Clare had never heard, and he played it to perfection. Next the group swung into "Hey Jude." She knew that one and swayed with the music while she spread crackers with paté. Mumbled remarks came from behind them, but CeCe tuned them out. Paul seemed absorbed with the music, and that was good. Clare sipped her wine and settled back for some serious listening.

Sets of smooth jazz followed, and Dixie Land tunes kept her toes tapping and her head bobbing to the music. Candles began to flicker across the park grounds as the sky darkened. Clare lit her candle, setting it on a small plastic plate at their feet.

Halfway through the concert, she noticed that Paul had finished off the bottle of wine without ever refilling her glass. *So much for "beautiful people" . . . a real Romeo would be trying to get me mellow.*

Almost as though he was reading her thoughts, Paul reached for her hand. She wanted to pull her hand away, but her conscience wouldn't let her. Instead, she closed her eyes, listening.

The band leader introduced each selection with a bit of history. Clare concentrated on the music titles and the jazz artists who had made them famous. A little knowledge like this might come in handy. She was picturing a conversation with Remi in her mind, so she only half-heard the band leader's announcement of the closing selection of Oldies: "Our version of a Coleman Hawkins's sweet sax rendition of 'Stardust.' " It wasn't until the melody was half finished that the lyrics clicked in her mind. Stars. Sagittarius! She jerked her hand from Paul's fingers, circled her eyes with her hands like a pair of binoculars, and looked heavenward. There it was. Clare poked Paul and pointed to the sky. "Look, Paul! He's there. The archer. Can you see it?" She clutched his sleeve and drew Sagittarius's bow with her finger in the air. "OhmyGod, it's clear as day."

A distinctive voice behind them yelled "Stuff it, lady. We came to hear the music."

Clare paid no mind. Truly excited with her find, she couldn't take her eyes from the constellation. Suddenly, everyone was on their feet, applauding the band's finale. The concert was over, but Clare never saw Paul get up and turn away. She was too busy dousing the candle he'd knocked over when he bolted from his chair. People were folding their chairs and exiting the grounds. She looked right and left for Paul. No Paul, but she couldn't miss Remi Windspirit, head and shoulders above the crowd, striding toward a small knot of people behind her.

Something was wrong. Lights from the bandstand helped Clare see a person on the ground, and Sergeant Remi was suddenly bending over that person. She grabbed the napkins and pushed through the crowd. Paul stood off to the side, glowering and rubbing his hand. A frightened young woman, nervously dancing from one foot to the other, was watching Paul.

Clare did a double take from the man down to Paul and gasped. The man on the ground, sprawled across a broken lawn chair, was trying to get to his feet with Remi's help. It was Claude Duval.

Her gray eyes darkened with concern. She turned her back on the others, clutched Paul's shoulder and whispered in a raspy voice, "What did you do?"

Paul did not whisper back. His voice was loud and menacing. "Something I've wanted to do for over a year. He just gave me a new reason. I punched the bastard in the mouth. Duval's the guy who told you to shut up."

Remi's "sergeant voice" was suddenly loud and effective. He was steering gawkers away from the scene and out of the park. "Move on, folks. Move it out. Show's over."

Claude seemed dazed and not too steady on his feet. He held a blood-stained handkerchief to his nose, trying to focus on the guy who was trying to help him. "Who are you?" Claude asked.

"Just a concerned bystander," Remi answered, taking a firm hold of Claude's arm.

Whether he did it to steady him or restrain him from coming back at Paul, Clare wasn't sure, but she wasn't taking any chances. She tugged on Paul's arm. "Come with me, Paul. We need to pick up our things before all the lights go out."

Paul hesitated. Either his anger wasn't spent or the wine had taken its toll. He pulled away from Clare and swore. "You stand right here. I'll get our stuff. This isn't over," he yelled over his shoulder as he stalked away.

Clare couldn't stop herself. Claude's nosebleed was out of control, and she couldn't just stand there. She reached out, grabbed his soaked handkerchief and threw it to the ground. She clamped her napkins over his nose and pinched his nostrils, replacing her hand with his. "Squeeze tight, and tilt your head back," she said. Clare dragged a lone chair past the frightened woman and pushed Claude into it.

Remi stood back, hands on hips and stared, an incredulous look spreading over his face. Clare matched him stare for stare. He was about to speak, but Paul was back, carrying the chairs in one hand and the picnic basket in the other.

Paul shot a look at Clare's checkered napkins covering half of Duval's face. He dropped everything on the ground and glared at her. "What the hell?"

"I acted from pure instinct," Clare said. "I'm a nurse, and he was bleeding badly."

The silent woman next to Remi squeezed Claude's shoulder and took two timid steps toward Paul. "You've got this all wrong, mister," she said. "Claude wasn't the one who yelled at your friend. It was a weird guy sitting next to us. He was trying to impress his girlfriend with stupid comments all through the concert." She pointed to Clare. "When he hollered at her to stuff it, his girlfriend stood up and left the park. The weirdo chased after her, and they were gone before the music ended."

It took a minute for that to sink in. Silence hung there.

"Jesus," Paul said, swiping his hand through his hair. "That's hard to believe. I saw you standing there applauding, and I was sure it was you, Duval. Convince me I'm wrong. Convince me this isn't another of your devious maneuvers to avoid responsibility."

Claude rose slowly from the chair. He handed the napkins to Clare and shot Paul a flinty look. "She told you the truth. I'd take you to court for assault and prove you're wrong, but it wouldn't be worth my time." He took the girl's arm, grabbed a chair, and was gone before Clare found her voice.

"Helluva way to end a concert, Paul. You really blew it this time."

Remi picked up the broken chair. "You okay to drive, Fontaine?"

Clare picked up her picnic basket and shook her head. "He's not driving. I am."

The bandstand lights went out, and the park was suddenly in darkness but for pale moonlight and a star-studded sky. The three walked in silence toward the parking lot, Paul, smoldering; Clare, embarrassed and upset, and Remi Windspirit, totally confused.

They reached a big, black pickup first. Remi tossed the broken chair in the bed of the truck and turned to Paul.

"Seems like you run into trouble without even trying, man. Are you okay?"

"Yeah, well, this trouble goes way back, and it has nothing to do with finding a corpse in the bay."

"I didn't say it did. I just thought you might want to talk about what happened back there. I only witnessed the tail end."

Paul scowled, first at Clare, then at Remi. "In case you don't know it, that guy I slugged is a lawyer. You sure you want to hear about it?"

"Yeah, I do. I know who Duval is. Known him since last year, and I think I know why you took a swing at him." Remi shot a quick look at Clare. She chewed her lip and looked away. Remi shrugged. "Hey, I've got time off tomorrow. Strictly off the record, if you want to do a little talking and fishing, I keep a boat at Charlie's Marina. Give me a call, Fontaine."

Clare watched as Remi opened the truck door, threw in his blanket and climbed in. "Take it easy, Clare," he called from the cab's open window. There it was again, that infectious smile. "Drive carefully."

After following the disappearing tail lights, Clare couldn't help but look up at the star-studded sky. Sagittarius was still aiming his bow.

Sagittarians have a good and a dark side. Dark side: Sometimes outspoken; could be tactless, restless, and impulsively angry. The last two fit. Good side: honest, usually jovial, ardent and straightforward in love. Geez, no chance for the last one. *Sagittarius . . . where were you when I needed you?*

CHAPTER FIVE

Sleep was slow to come. Prayer didn't help. Clare thought about the music she'd heard at the concert . . . Remi sitting under the tree . . . Paul planting a fist in Claude Duval's face. Duval deceived Maddy, and then Fiona, but that was over and done with long ago. It should be Patrick's concern more than Paul's. Why did Paul Fontaine have to be everybody's defender? It was a stupid, embarrassing thing he did.

She reached to the nightstand for her eye shades. They blotted out everything whenever she worked a late shift and needed to sleep in the daytime. This wasn't daytime, but she desperately needed to sleep. Sunday was the start of a new shift, three to eleven.

Clare donned her uniform with little enthusiasm. Sleeping late meant she didn't get to church. Three cups of coffee later, she picked at leftover pasta salad for lunch and searched through the Sunday paper for some local news. Nothing about the dead body. The autopsy should have been completed by now. A last-minute check in the mirror held bad news. Dark shadows under her eyes, and she really needed to do something about her hair.

As she grabbed her car keys and collected her bottled water from the refrigerator, her answering machine clicked on. "Two-thirty P.M., Sunday," the machine intoned. "Hi Clare. Remi Windspirit here. Guess you're unavailable, so I'll—" Clare slammed the bottle down and grabbed the phone.

"Hey, Remi. You caught me. I was just about to leave the house."

He continued without a hitch. "Your friend Paul had to be back in town for a dinner date, so we cut our fishing short this morning. I took a chance that maybe the dinner was not with you."

"You're right. It's not. Paul's having dinner with his sister and brother-in-law."

"In that case, are you free, Clare? Could I take some of your time?"

Suspicion took its wary turn. "Is this to be 'off the record' about last night?"

There was a few seconds' silence. "I have another reason for wanting to talk with you, Clare."

She drew in a breath. "Oh. Well, uh . . . I'd like to talk, but I have to be at work in fifteen minutes." She bit her lip and scowled. "I'm afraid I'll have to pass."

"What hours do you work?"

"I'm on from three to eleven this week."

"Can I buy you lunch tomorrow before you go to work?"

Her scowl dissolved into a smile. "I'd like that, Remi." *I'd love it!*

"Let me work on where to go after I get a look at tomorrow's schedule. Can I leave you a message later?"

"Sure. Leave me a message. Gotta run, now. See yuh."

She blew out a breath as she hung up the phone. "Whooeee! Thank you, Lord."

Clare did a little happy dance as she stepped out the door, chanting her mom's favorite saying, " 'When need is greatest, God is nearest.' That's what *Tante* would say."

Tante Margaret had an aphorism for almost every occasion. This time she'd be right on target. Clare had been praying for someone to come into her life ever since her best friend Maddy got married. Maybe, just maybe, Mr. Right had come along!

Clare tuned the car radio to a smooth jazz station. A vocalist was singing the last strains of "Love's Divine." That was followed by "No Rhyme, No Reason." By the time she pulled into the hospital parking lot, an instrumental was playing. She counted out the minutes until the announcer named the tune, "I Can't Help Myself." Clare slapped a palm against her forehead. "Oh man—talk about serendipity." She tapped a finger on her forehead getting out of the car. "Have to store these tunes up for tomorrow's conversation."

Clare pushed the play button on the answering machine as soon as she got home from work. True to his word, Remi had left a message.

"Clare, I've managed to juggle my schedule to be on call late tomorrow by taking a longer than usual lunch hour. I'd like to pick you up at twelve and have you back at two o'clock. Will that work? No need to call, unless you have to cancel. Later— Remi."

She set her alarm for eight A.M., determined to get a facial and hair appointment for early morning. No need for eye shades tonight. She curled up in her sheets and in moments was asleep.

Remi was prompt as clockwork. His brows shot upward when Clare opened the door at noon. He wasn't prepared for the transformation. His wide eyes roamed up from her black Capri pants to a strappy white top that clung to her body. A lovely tourmaline necklace rested in the curve of her full breasts. The necklace caught his eye, but his gaze only paused briefly, making his way up over Clare's full lips and creamy cheeks to rest on her hair. He sucked in a breath, and had to still the temptation to reach and touch her formerly spiky black hair. Short, feathery curls framed her face, shimmering with silvery white highlights that made her eyes sparkle.

"Hey, Ms. Chamberlaine. Do you have a twin I don't know about?"

She laughed and slung her purse over her shoulder. "I needed a little change, Sarge. Ready to go?"

"Yes ma'am." He grinned, nodding his head. "We're going to take a little drive. I have a place in mind for lunch. Okay with you?"

"Okay with me." She said, following Remi out to the big black truck parked in front of the apartment.

Inside the truck, the first thing she noticed was the police radio equipment. It reminded her of the incident that landed Sergeant Remi Windspirit at her door a week ago. "Wow, Sarge, four wheel drive and all the latest equipment. Is this yours?"

Remi chuckled. "It was issued to me after I made sergeant. Technically it belongs to MMP."

"Have you had an autopsy report on the drowning, yet?" she asked, trying to maintain a serious look.

"Not that I can speak about. The woman's still a Jane Doe."

"I haven't seen anything in the paper. Off the record, can't you tell me anything?"

"I'll get to that later," he said, giving her a sideways glance. "Pleasure first. We're going to Ocean Park. There's a new little restaurant there called the Sea Urchin. I think you'll like it."

Heaven forbid he should know I checked up on him and know all about Ocean Park.

"I never knew there was a quiet side to Old Orchard Beach. You've been there, I take it?" she asked.

"Oh, yeah. Actually the park is a separate little community right around the corner from our place. We're pretty proud of the village, you know."

Our Place? We're pretty proud? "Who's we?"

"My family and just about everybody in the village. My folks run a B and B in the grove along Temple Avenue. It's called Lord's Castle Inn."

Clare heaved a small sigh of relief. "Interesting name. It seems to fit in with a Chautauqua community."

Remi cast a surprised glance. "Didn't know you knew anything about Ocean Park."

"Well, I've not had much occasion to go there, but I know it's nothing like the Pier at Old Orchard. It's kind of Victorian isn't it . . . old timey?"

"It is that. A classic village, settled in a seaside grove of pines. There are still some of the original buildings, a lot of little cottages, and of course, the Temple."

"Temple? You mean, like, synagogue?"

Remi grinned, then burst into laughter. "No. The Temple is where the original folks gathered for religious services. Still do, in season. They say the visiting preachers there are incredible."

Clare was about to comment, but Remi was easing his truck into a tight parking space in front of a quaint little house. A hand-painted sign in the yard read "Sea Urchin House." First thing in her view was a flower garden below a bay window. The flowers gave a riot of color to the small gray cottage.

Remi had to duck under the lintel to enter. His presence suddenly seemed to fill the room. All tables were occupied, but he steered Clare nonchalantly to an alcove where a wing-backed, upholstered booth fit into a bay window, snug as a harbor. The window looked out at a garden profuse with summer blooms. It seemed a very private and special space.

He gestured for Clare to slide in the booth, then lowered his long, lean body across from her. They no sooner had seated themselves than a waitress came directly to them.

"Hey, Remi. Glad you made it. I was a little nervous when the place began to fill up." She gave his shoulder a friendly squeeze when she handed out the menus. He gave her his breath-taking smile.

"You know me, Judy—steady as they go."

"Seeing as you're in uniform today, I'll be back in a jiff to take your order."

He put a staying hand on her arm. "No need to hurry. Not this time, anyway. Just bring us some iced tea, for now, okay?"

Clare couldn't miss the appraising glance she got before the waitress left their booth. *Don't go there,* something told her. "So, tell me more about what's happening in Ocean Park, Remi."

"Well they had a jazz pianist and his bride together in concert at the Temple a month ago. It was a record breaking attendance. Let's see, there's a brass quintet scheduled that I'd recommend on the twenty-seventh. They're supposed to be one of the best in New England. Then there's a Highland band coming with pipers and drummers that my mother swears is heavenly music to her ears. Interested in any of those?"

"I might be."

Don't be too eager drummed in her mind, along with other dos and don'ts she and Maddy had written on their "How to hook a guy" list, eons ago. "I do like music, and you obviously do, too." She smiled and looked down at the menu. "Do you have a recommendation from the menu?"

"The seafood salad is good. The chowder is excellent. Have whatever you'd like, Clare. I'm going to have chowder and a burger."

She sipped the iced tea the waitress brought. Ever conscious of her weight, she looked down, sucked in her belly and sat back against the plaid upholstered booth. Trying her best to act the "perfect guest," and let him order for her, Clare handed Remi her menu, "I'll try the seafood salad."

She kept her eyes glued on him while he ordered. He looked as good in uniform as he did in casual clothes—in a way, even better.

"So, Sergeant Windspirit, did you get all the info you wanted yesterday from my friend Paul Fontaine?"

"Ahh. I was waiting for that. Is that why you think I invited you to lunch? To find out more about what happened at the concert?"

"Well, isn't it?" *Those deep, dark eyes seem to read my mind.*

"Not entirely. I knew Claude Duval as an attorney. He represented a family involved in a boating death that we investigated earlier this year. Paul filled me in on Duval's relationship with his sister Maddy and Fiona Donovan."

Clare's voice held a slight edge of wariness. "That covers everybody but me. I suppose he gave you the skinny on me, too."

An amused grin turned up the corners of Remi's mouth. "Not really. Only that you and his sister Maddy were best friends, and your aunt Margaret helped you and Maddy find Fiona Donovan."

"Didn't leave much out, then, did he?"

The smile left his eyes. He sat back against the booth, toying absently with the silverware as he spoke. "Paul attempted to explain why he had it in for Claude Duval. I knew about the Donovan girl's disappearance back when it happened. Patrick Donovan contacted state police early on, and they pulled us in to see if anything suspicious happened in the harbor at the time of her disappearance. There wasn't any evidence. End of story, Clare."

The waitress brought lunch, wished them *bon appétit* and quickly disappeared again.

It seemed Paul and Claude Duval were not what Remi was concerned with. Not what he appeared anxious to talk about, anyway. *If he didn't ask me here to talk about last night, or the Duval-Fiona scenario, then maybe he has a hidden agenda . . . maybe—*

"How do you like the salad, Clare?"

"It's really good. Did you know I'm a seafood nut?"

"I guessed as much. Paul told me that you and your aunt were really good cooks. Any other siblings in your family with talent like that?"

"No. I was orphaned when I was three, and my aunt Margaret has been my surrogate mother ever since."

"Paul said he's known you since you were five years old."

"That's true. Paul Fontaine is kind of like a big brother, you know. His father and my *Tante* go way back. Both French, you know." Clare glanced up from her salad bowl. "How about you, Remi, any brothers or sisters?"

"Only a younger half-sister. She married a year ago and moved back to North Carolina."

"North Carolina? Is that where you're from originally?"

"Sort of. It's a little complicated. My father was born in North Carolina but was working in Florida when he married his first wife, a French woman. She died when I was born. My Dad is Cherokee. Cherokee Tribal lands overlapped Georgia, Tennessee and North Carolina, so eventually he went back to his roots. Moved back to North Carolina, with me in tow, married again, and eventually he and my step-mom Mary decided to locate in this area. We came here when I was eight."

"Now I understand your name. Remi is French, but"—she paused, smiling into his eyes—"I don't think you could ever deny your Native American heritage."

"I know. Everyone says I look like my dad."

The waitress was back with the check. "Can't deny his step-mom, either," she said. "She is a stunning Scot, and Remi's got her wondrous ways." She rolled her eyes and patted his hand as she left.

Remi threw back his head and laughed. He unfolded his long frame from the booth, extending a hand to Clare. She shot him a puzzled look. Still laughing, Remi took her hand, tugged her out of the booth, then tossed a twenty-dollar bill on the table.

He angled his head in the waitress's direction. "Judy's my cousin—on my mother's side, of course."

Outside, Clare looked up at a darkening sky. Thunderclouds were moving in from the sea, blotting out the sun. She shivered at the sight. Beyond the Sea Urchin, set back in a park-like corner, stood a big house with stone foundation, fanciful turrets and gables. She ventured a guess. "Is that your parents' B and B?"

"Yeah, it is." He opened the truck door. "Hop in and we'll drive past for a better look."

Clare checked her watch. "Okay, but looks like a storm coming. Do we have time?"

"We have a half hour before I need to get you back."

Clare tried to focus on the house as they drove slowly past it, but the threatening storm was vying for her attention. "Do you live here?" she asked.

"Same address, but I have an apartment over the building in the back. It used to be a stable."

"The house does look a little like a castle. Is that how it got its name?"

"Nope. It's Lord's Castle Inn, like in the Lord. My step-mom is a faith-filled person. That's why she chose to live in Ocean Park. The Temple, you know."

"I get it. My *tante* is religious, too, only a different faith."

"Tell me about your aunt. She's French, huh?"

Clare looked quizzically at him. "Ayuh. I bet Paul told you. He was half right. *Tante*'s really three quarters French. Her grandmother was part Indian. Actually Abenaki, from the St. Francis tribe in Canada. Truth be known, I'm pretty proud of Margaret. She's been my mother in every way that mattered."

Remi paused and gave her a thumbs-up. "Hey, seems we

have something in common, Clare. Kind of kindred spirits, you know?"

"I don't know about that," she said, coyly. "Kindred spirits don't keep secrets."

"Who's got secrets?"

"Well, you've talked about everything except the corpse we found. If the woman's identity has been established, why haven't you told me about it?"

Remi turned the car toward Saco Avenue. Wind driven rain was beginning to blow across the windshield, making it hard to see. Clare waited for an answer. She thought she detected reluctance in his usually "in control" manner, but decided maybe it was the weather.

"Remi?" she prompted.

"I've not told you because the case is still under investigation." He glanced sideways at her serious face. "I doubt you'll be spreading this around until the findings go to press, so, off the record, I'll tell you one fact. The woman identifies as a Native American Indian."

Realization was slow, but sure. *Oh, God, this isn't about me . . . It's about* Tante *Margaret. I'm not a lunch date. I'm a pawn in Remi's detective game.* She battled an angry irritation. She knew he was investigating, but the romantic in her didn't want to accept that maybe he was baiting her for information.

Honest and outspoken, Clare was sensitive. She huffed out an annoyed breath, attempting to rid herself of her resentment. She used her down-east voice, flattening her vowels for emphasis. "Well," she said, her eyes smoldering as she raised an eyebrow and gave him a sidelong glance, "so much for kindred spirits, keeping secrets and all that jazz. I guess I'm just a pawn *heah* in your investigating *gayem.*"

Remi hadn't bargained for that. His throat went dry, but he managed to keep an even expression. He shot her another look

60

as he slowed for a traffic light. Her mouth was wide and pouty. Not a beautiful face, but very interesting. Deep-set eyes were her best feature. Intensity flared now in those big gray eyes. They revealed none of the jovial mood from lunch.

"Investigation at any level is not always easy. Despite what you might think, Clare, I didn't set out to ferret information about your aunt's heritage. All we have is scraps of clothing, an Indian-crafted belt from the body and an abandoned dory found near Wood Island Lighthouse. Sometimes obstacles we meet present ways for us to improve things. Paul told me your aunt Margaret was a psychic, and I thought maybe she'd be willing to help with the investigation."

"And you want me to make that happen."

"No, I'd like that to happen, but only if—" Thunder roared, punctuating his words as a slash of lightning revealed downed branches in the road ahead. Remi swung the car to the right shoulder of the road.

Clare bucked and gasped as Remi braked to a stop. The hitch in her breathing was panic, her face a mask of fear. She pushed her feet into the floor mat, and took short, panting breaths. She didn't want him to know she was deathly afraid of thunder storms, but her body was betraying her.

Remi's eyes flashed to hers, and he instinctively pulled her into his arms. His fingers ran over her silky curls, then he tucked her head under his chin.

Clare's heart hammered staccato against his chest, like the rain pelting the windows.

"It's okay, Clare. It's okay. It'll be over in a few minutes."

His manly scent washed over her, sending shivers skittering down her spine.

His fingers ran back and forth, soothing her shoulders. The fear that numbed her began to fall away and new feelings took over. Warm, cosseted feelings.

As her body relaxed, Remi held her at arm's length. His eyes were dark, deep and full of feeling. "You all right now?" he asked.

Clare couldn't find her voice. She nodded.

"I really did want to take you to lunch today, and I'm sorry if you think you're a pawn in a game." Remi shook his head. "You're not. I admired what you did at the concert the other night. I wanted to see you again, and I took this chance to get to know you a little better."

He flashed a heart-stopping smile. "At least I found out that underneath your 'nurse in charge' attitude is a woman afraid of thunder storms."

Clare winced and humbly took the proffered olive branch.

te, while I make coffee."

t yesterday?"

er when I told you about the investigating offi-
lian, like you? Well, he's the one who told me
's report. Part of it, anyway."

er back to *Tante,* Clare measured coffee and
ffeemaker, speaking as nonchalantly as pos-
e took me to lunch." She could not see *Tante*
in the air, but she heard her murmur, *"Une*

gs from the cupboard, placed them on the
. "Let's see what Sergeant Windspirit has to
short article aloud.

a woman found in Saco Bay is still not identi-
sy analysis from the medical examiner
by drowning. An examination of circum-
the death and circumstances in the recovery
be compared to determine if findings are
autopsy analysis.' "

in the chair, eyebrows raised in surprise.
Gotta think how to proceed here."

s in the recovery.' Does that mean you are
on because you found this woman?" *Tante*

to worry. Remi doesn't even know who the
he did tell me stuff that's not in this paper.
y was found anchored in the bay near Wood
They have to examine everything relative to
t boat, as well as something found on the
be investigated."

ean, something from the body?"

l poured coffee. "It was a belt. A hammered

CHAPTER SIX

Yankee sensibility came to Remi early as a marine patrolman. He did his job well, worked long shifts, but the money was good. Getting promoted after only two years allowed him to give a little back to the Lord's Castle Inn during long winter seasons when guests were scarce.

Remi's family was on the edge of poor until they moved to Maine. His father, Jamie Windspirit, was a hard-working man, proud of his heritage and his family, and he never let his children know they were poor. He crewed eight years on a lobster boat until he had enough saved to buy the B&B.

By then, his son was a teenager. An ace at basketball, Remi's real love was hockey. He reveled in winter sports, spent his spare time practicing with pucks when the ice firmed up in winter. It was Jamie who insisted he transfer to BHS for the sports program.

It stuck in Remi's craw that the corpse Clare found was suspected to be Native American. He hadn't told his father yet, only that a dory was found. If he knew one thing about fishermen, it was that they were a tight-knit community, fiercely supportive of each other.

Something should break soon about the dory.

He wished he hadn't told Clare that the woman was suspected Native American Indian. The belt from the body fit the mold, but it could have been a gift or a purchase she made. Shops all along the pier sold pieces like that. A clairvoyant could help, but not as long as Clare thought she was a pawn.

Clare Chamberlaine crowded his thoughts. *I've never been attracted so suddenly to a woman. Got to go slowly with this. Being attracted to Clare is illogical in a lot of ways . . . especially when a pawn could lose me the investigation. I can't risk that. Damn, but she felt good in my arms.*

Clare only had time to re-do her lipstick, slip out of street clothes and into her uniform if she were to get to the hospital on time. Not enough time to remove mascara; maybe later, on her break.

She got along well with nurses and doctors alike, and she loved her job. When Clare came into the ER at five minutes before three, the ER team, one nurse and two interns were gathering for duty, waiting for the resident doctor. One by one they took a second look. Her nurse friend, Mary, raised an eyebrow.

"Man, Clare. When did you qualify for 'Extreme Makeover'? Why didn't you tell us, so we could have watched?"

Clare hooted. "Hey, guys, no way would I be on TV. Just made a little change, that's all."

"Must be a man in the picture," Mary said.

Before Clare could comment, Dr. Harry Stone (known to the nurses as Horny Harry) pushed through the swinging doors, stopping suddenly in front of Clare.

"Ooo hah! Miss Chamberlaine." He squeezed her shoulder and whispered in her ear. "I always thought you were a sexy lookin' babe, but now you're absolutely crème de la crème!"

Clare had dated Harry once last year, and once was too much. She met his gaze with a smile that never reached the steel in her gray eyes and shrugged away from the hand on her shoulder. "Compliments are nice, Dr. Stone, but I think your steady, strong hands could be better used on the patients."

silver, jeweled belt."

"A hand crafted belt?"

"Yes. They think it's a Native American piece."

"*Mon Dieu.* Was it an old piece?"

"Oh, I dunno, *Tante.* That's what the investigation needs to find out."

"This Sergeant Remi, do you think he's a good investigator?"

"I guess so. Why do you ask?"

"I'm wondering why he took you to lunch."

Clare didn't like where this was leading, but there was no avoiding it now. "I wondered that myself. Paul and I met him at a concert, and the next day Paul went fishing with him. Paul told the guy about you and me. Especially about you . . . uh, being a psychic."

"Jacques Paul should not have told him that."

"He spoke the truth."

"*Oui,* but I would rather it not be true."

Clare leaned over to stroke *Tante*'s shoulder. "You were incredible last year when you helped Maddy get clues to find Fiona. No one has forgotten that."

"That was different. The vision I had of my *grandmére* was unplanned. It is she, the *quérisseur,* which makes things happen. She is the seer. I don't think that power will come to me again."

"But you have her genes, the clairvoyance. Wouldn't you be willing to try if you thought it would help?"

"Is that what this Sergeant Remi wants, or is it you that wants me to help?"

Clare tugged at her lower lip. "At first I thought Remi was trying to get to you through me and maybe that was why he took me to lunch. But then I found out that he really wanted to see me, so I'd say it's both of us needing your help, Mom."

"I have to think about this, Clare. I'll pray about it, eh?"

Maddy Fontaine Donovan dipped a taper into the glass cup of a lighted candle, transferring the flame to a new candle. Slanted rays of sunlight streamed through the church's stained glass windows, firing Maddy's chestnut hair with glints of gold when she bowed her head in prayer. She rose from the sanctuary rail when she heard footsteps and a rustle of skirts.

Seeing Clare's aunt Margaret behind her shouldn't have been a surprise. She knew that *Tante* made daily visits to Holy Redeemer, but the church had been empty when Maddy stopped in on her way home from St. David's School.

Margaret kissed Maddy's cheek, whispering to her, "Wait for me, *ma chérie*. I'll only be a minute."

Maddy walked slowly to the vestibule, waiting for *Tante* to catch up.

"It is so good to see you, Madelaine. Is your papa all right?"

Maddy smiled and nodded. "Yes, Papa's fine. I was lighting a candle for Paul—and for me."

"I haven't seen much of Jacques Paul all summer, but of course, my Clare fills me in from time to time. I know all about the terrible happening on your papa's boat, and I lit a candle to pray for that to get resolved. You, too?"

"Well, yes, but that doesn't worry me as much as Paul himself. His drinking is getting out of hand, *Tante*. We've always been close, and I'm usually able to reason with him, but lately Paul doesn't listen to reason."

"But you have faith, *ma petite*. Faith is at the heart of what we pray for, eh? I will add Jacques Paul to my list."

They were leaving the church, going down the steps in front, when Maddy slowed her steps. "Would you like to come home with me, *Tante*? Have a cup of tea, maybe? Patrick is working on a special order, and he'll be late today."

"*Oui,* I would like that, Madelaine. Clare tells me what

beautiful things Patrick has made for your apartment. I would like to see for myself."

Margaret studied Maddy's face as they drove the short distance to Factory Square. Something seemed amiss with Madelaine, and she didn't think it had to do with Paul. She watched Maddy carefully as they entered the kitchen.

"Go have a look around the living room. I'll be right in with tea," Maddy said.

Margaret was remembering something her grandmother used to say: "When you have no words that you can sing, hum. God will supply the words." Margaret strolled around, humming a nameless tune, concentrating on Madelaine and Patrick, admiring the built-in shelves and corner cabinets adorning the spacious room.

She sat on a love seat and ran her fingers along the top of a cherry wood coffee table in front of her just as Maddy came in to set a tea tray on the table. "Beautiful, Madelaine. Such talent God gave your husband. This room looks like a picture from a magazine."

"Thank you, *Tante*. I'll tell Patrick what you said. I apologize for these store cookies. Usually we have scones on hand from Mrs. Donovan, but Patrick has gobbled them up. Guess I should learn to make them myself."

"Ah, Madelaine, no apologies. Working all week doesn't leave much time for baking, eh?"

Maddy shook her head, sipped her tea, aware that Margaret's measuring gaze seemed relentless.

Margaret suddenly reached for Maddy's hands. "I think something else is on your mind, *chérie.*"

Maddy's face flushed. "What do you mean?"

Margaret squeezed her hand. "I think you are with child, Madelaine."

Maddy stared, unbelieving. "*Tante!* How on earth . . . what

69

makes you say that?"

Margaret gently rubbed a thumb over Maddy's wedding ring, cocking her head to gaze into Maddy's eyes. "It came to me when you lit the candle in church, then on the drive here, and now as I hold your hand, I am sure—*un bébé vient, non?*"

"Oh, *Tante.* I've only missed one period, and we're hoping it's true, but we haven't told anyone, yet. At least not until I get one of those pregnancy tests to be sure. I can't believe that you know! How can you know?"

Tante sipped her tea, smiled and shrugged. "Must be my genes. That's what Clare says when I predict things that come true." She pulled Maddy into a gentle hug. "Don't worry, *ma petite,* you will be just fine, and I will keep your secret until you tell me otherwise."

Maddy's eyes filled with tears. "Times like this I really miss my mother, but in your arms, *Tante,* I feel especially close to her."

"I am glad, *chèrie.* Julie is smiling down on you, Madelaine. Of that I'm sure. She would be so proud and happy for you." *Tante* held Maddy at arm's length. "But about your brother, Jacques Paul, she would not be smiling. I think a little intervention, eh? Maybe God will supply the words and *Tante* Margaret will say them."

CHAPTER SEVEN

Dammed if my soul isn't connected to the rhythm of the sea. Paul sat on the beach, mesmerized by the blue-green waves growing bigger and closer. Gulls swooped and dove, screeching in a cerulean sky laced with puffy white clouds.

He'd been sitting for over an hour, sketching sailboats that skimmed the water far out in the bay. He drained the last can of a six pack of beer, stuck pencils in his pocket, and tucked his sketch pad under his arm. *Tide must run in my blood.* "I've got to get away from here, got to move on," he said aloud. Brushing sand from the seat of his shorts, he grabbed the mini cooler and climbed over the rocks.

Halfway up the dune path to Francois's Fancy, he heard a car engine. It looked like a female driver easing into the side drive of the house, but a few steps closer and there was no mistaking the woman. CeCe's aunt Margaret.

Margaret got out of the car and waved her purse in an arc over her head. "Hallo Jacques Paul."

"Hey, there Auntie Mame. You're a stranger out here. Are you here to see Pa?"

"I came to see you, *mon cher.* I called first, but no one answered, so I took a chance and came anyway."

Paul kissed her cheek. "I'm flattered. Did I goof up again? Maybe forgot something with Clare?"

Margaret's eyes, narrowed and flinty, stared at the empty cans in the cooler. "No, no. It's just that I have some questions that maybe only you have the answers to."

Paul took her arm to lead her up the porch steps. "Let's sit on the porch, okay? Pa's not home. He teaches a late class on Wednesdays. Maybe you'd like a cold drink or something from the kitchen? God knows where Kathleen is, but I can probably rouse up some iced tea or a glass of wine if you'd like."

"*Merci,* nothing to drink for me." She sat in a porch rocker. "Just some answers from you, Jacques Paul."

"Fire away, Auntie Mame."

"Did you read the morning paper today?"

"Ah, so that's what this is about. The body. Yes, *Tante.* I read the article. Didn't surprise me."

"No? Then, what do you think of Investigator Windspirit?"

Paul raised his eyebrows, pushing his lower lip up in surprise. "Remi? He's a stand-up guy. I like him."

"You must have liked him pretty good to tell him that I'm a psychic, eh?"

"You mean I shouldn't have told him?" Paul shook his head. "*Tante,* it came up innocently during a conversation about Fiona Donovan. Is there a problem?"

Margaret eyed him thoughtfully. "Maybe yes, maybe no. Did you know he took Clare to lunch and mentioned me being a psychic?"

Paul looked more surprised than ever. "Jesus! Er, uh . . . sorry, *Tante.* When was this?"

"Yesterday. Now Clare says he wants me to help with the investigation. He thinks I can find out things about the dead person." She raised her brows quizzically and threw up her hands. "I think I smell a fish, Jacques Paul. What do you think?"

Paul threw his head back and laughed. "No. Not Remi. He's a really nice guy. In a way, I'm not surprised he took Clare out. He told me he was impressed with her at the concert, but I'm not getting into the whys and wherefores of that scenario.

Honestly, Auntie Mame, Remi did ask me about Clare, and you just logically came into the conversation."

"I don't want my Clare getting hurt, you know? She seems to trust this Sergeant Remi, but maybe he is just using her to get to me, huh, *chérie?*"

"Let me get this straight. Remi seems to think you could help identify something from the body, something that will clear up circumstances about the death. So he mentions it to Clare, and Clare tells you. Right?"

"Oui."

"I think the guy is just doing his job, *Tante*. He doesn't think Clare and I are suspects."

"You sure about that?"

"Yes. Remi made that clear to me at the get-go. Off the record, of course. The newspaper listed his name as investigator for Maine Marine Patrol, but it didn't reveal a hell of a lot about the autopsy. It did say death was by drowning. So now they need to investigate everything relative to the dead person's life—or to the crime, if it was a crime. I guess if you want to find out how someone died, you find out how they lived, right?"

"Oui, but I'm not sure I can help with that, or even if I want to. Clare wants me to try and help, but I don't want her mixed up in this investigation any more than I wanted her to go sailing with you in the first place."

Paul arched a brow. "Sailing with me? That's bad? I don't understand."

"Oh, Jacques Paul, it's not you. It's boats and the sea, or anything to do with either one. I stay away as much as I can, but I never forget my Jean. He lost his life to the sea, you know, and I don't need these reminders."

Paul reached to take her hand. "I'm sorry, *Tante*. You know I would never put Clare in danger. No one in our family would. I guess we're just drawn to life on the water and everything connected with it. My mom and pa chose to live here year round after Grandpa Frank died. I was thinking about him just before you arrived. How he loved boats and the sea. I sketched a few sailboats off shore, but I ended up just watching the tide and thinking about why I'm here."

Tante eyed the empty beer cans. "You don't plan to stay here, though, do you?"

"No. I'm going up to Portland soon. Put some feelers out. I might even try farther north. Augusta, maybe." Paul stood and picked up the beer cooler. "I'm going to the kitchen. You sure you won't have a drink with me? A glass of wine, *Tante?*"

Tante shook her head. "No. I have to leave you now." She took the cooler from Paul's hand and set it firmly on the floor. "Jacques Paul, you've given me some straight answers and good advice, so I'm going to talk to you now like your momma, Julie, would." She pointed at the empty beer cans. "I think you must slow down your drinking. Your family worries about you!"

Paul grunted. "Uh-oh. Sounds like my sister's been talking. Not to worry, Auntie Mame." He took *Tante*'s hands in his. "I just need some smooth sailing and a lot of luck."

Margaret met his gaze with a raised brow.

"Just remember, *mon ami,* that the deck under your feet is more often preferable to the view from the crow's nest."

Paul's mouth dropped open, but no words came. Margaret released her hands from his, descended the porch steps, leaving Paul staring after her. "Bye bye," she called as she climbed into her car.

Clare sat in the nurses' lounge flipping notebook pages until she came to a page entitled "Lecture Notes on Forensic Medicine." Not her notes, but a borrowed notebook from her friend Mary. Clare had no luck getting information from the hospital coroner, so she was trying to dig up research on her own. Mary had dropped out of med school and caught up with Clare's RN class the year before graduation from UM. Mary's notes were thorough and clear.

Some pathological changes that indicate a victim was alive on entering the water are: a fine white froth in the airways, over inflated lungs heavy with fluid, large quantities of water and debris in the stomach, and hemorrhages in the bony middle ear. However, most of these changes could be attributed to death by other causes. There are no autopsy findings pathognomonic of drowning. Consequently, obtaining proof that a victim was alive on entering the water, excluding the presence of natural, traumatic and toxicological causes of death, is critically important. These deaths remain a challenge because the mechanism in death by drowning is neither simple nor uniform. The question for examination remains: Why did the victim enter the water and why was the victim unable to survive in the water?

Clare closed the notebook. "That didn't tell me jack. It's mostly stuff I've learned on duty."

She dumped her cold coffee in the sink, checked her watch and decided to call Paul to see if he'd learned anything more about the investigation. That meant stepping outside to use her cell phone, but she didn't mind that one bit. There were ten minutes left of her break, and the cool night air felt good.

"Hey, Cap," she said, when Paul picked up on the first ring. "You must have been right beside the phone. What's going on?"

"Just passing through the kitchen on my way out of here. Aren't you working nights this week?"

"Yep, but I'm on a break. I'm curious about that article that was in the newspaper. It was pretty sketchy. Have you heard anything more about the case from Remi?"

"No, but I would have thought you did since you were out

with him yesterday."

Clare caught her breath. She couldn't miss the slight edge in his voice. She hated that their friendship might vanish because she wasn't returning romantic feelings—but then, she wasn't even sure Paul had romantic feelings for her. "How did you know about that?"

"From a source who's probably the most honest person I know. Auntie Mame. Sorry, Cec, but I'm on the run. Gotta go. Catch you later."

When Clare heard the click, she snapped her phone shut, staring at it with a scowl. "Good bye to you, too, Paul. Guess I'll have to go to the source—tomorrow morning, for sure."

Clare stifled a yawn, sat up and glanced at the clock on her night stand. Eight-thirty. Twenty minutes to shower and dress. Ten minutes to get to *Tante's* and let her feed me breakfast. "Okay, haul your buns out of bed," she chided herself.

She was close to being on schedule until she opened her apartment door to leave. Remi Windspirit stood there with his hand outstretched toward the bell. As the door snicked shut, Remi stepped back and flashed a smile that made her toes curl.

"Good morning, Clare." His crow black hair was neatly combed, and his uniform looked crisp as a new dollar bill. "I was worried I was calling too early, and here you are up and out already."

Man, I could get used to these early morning greetings. "Up and starting out, you're right. I'm on my way to my *tante's* house. Is there something I can do for you?"

Remi twisted his hat in his hands. "Actually, that's the reason for my call this morning. I'm here to see if you've spoken to your mother about the investigation?"

Clare had trouble meeting his gaze. "Well, yes . . . uh, I did . . ." Clare covered her mouth, thinking how to answer him.

"*Tante* would like it . . . you calling her my mom." When she looked up to his eyes, she knew at once that there was no point stalling. "She told me she needed to pray about it."

His words were smooth as cream. "I respect that. Prayer is a good thing. I'd like to meet Mrs. Chamberlaine. Do you think she'd object to my coming along with you?"

Clare drew in a breath. "She might, but she would be very polite and try not to let you know her true feelings." Gray eyes dancing, Clare's mouth turned up in a grin. "She might not have reached a decision about the investigation, but at the least, *Tante* will serve you coffee and try to feed you. Come on, and you can follow my car, okay?"

They parked down the street at the end of a neat row of small new homes all painted alike, a soft butter yellow. "These look like fairly new town houses. How long has your aunt been living here?"

"Actually, since they were built, seven years ago. We moved in just before my uncle Jean died. This was intended to be their dream home." Clare looked up at him with sad eyes. "We lived in mill houses before that."

"Mill houses? I thought your uncle was a fisherman."

"He was, but first he was a mill worker . . . for many years, until he was injured on the job. That's when he became a lobsterman."

"Hmm, we do have things in common," he said. "My Dad was a lobsterman before he became an innkeeper."

As soon as Clare took her hand from the doorbell, the door was pulled open. *Tante* angled her head to look up at the uniformed man standing beside Clare. Her eyes widened, heightening a look of panic on her face. "*Sacre bleu*," she whispered.

"Good morning, *Tante*." Clare said, taking a step inside the foyer. "I brought Sergeant Remi Windspirit to meet you. Remi, this is my mom, Margaret Chamberlaine."

Remi stood straight and still, hat in hand, just inside the threshold. *Tante* looked from one to the other, then poked her head out the door to look up and down the street. After an agonizing, speechless moment, she gestured to Remi to enter.

"*S'il vous plait*," she said, mumbling, "I'm forgetting my manners." Remi followed as *Tante* brushed past Clare, rolled her eyes, and stepped into her comfortably furnished living room. "Please sit down while I get coffee." She said, motioning for them to sit at the table in the dining area before she disappeared into the kitchen.

Remi stood, uncomfortably looking at the round table set for one.

"It's okay." Clare whispered. "I called just before, so she knew I was coming for breakfast. She's just surprised to see you." Clare pulled out a chair opposite the one set for her. "Please sit down."

Margaret came from the kitchen with mugs of coffee and a covered plate. "I had your omelet ready, Clare. Shall I make another for you, uh . . . Sergeant Windspirit?"

"Oh, no thank you, Mrs. Chamberlaine. I had breakfast earlier. I probably shouldn't have dropped in on you this way, but when I stopped at your daughter's to inquire about you, she agreed to bring me with her to your home."

"You inquired about me?"

"Yes ma'am. I believe our investigation could use your help. Clare indicated that you might be willing to assist us, and the truth is we could use someone with clairvoyant perception." He glanced at Clare, who had started to eat her omelet, but he couldn't read anything in her cool gray eyes. "You see, very little is known about the drowning victim discovered in Saco Bay. There was no blunt trauma to the head, and no obvious wounds to suggest she was a crime victim, and neither do we have direct evidence that it was a planned suicide."

Remi paused, trying to read Margaret's reaction.

Tante Margaret cocked her head and narrowed her eyes but said nothing.

"We do have articles of clothing and a belt that was on the body. If we knew more about the victim, we could rule out coercion, or at the least begin to understand why she went into the water in the first place. Would you be willing to work with us on the evidence items, Mrs. Chamberlaine?"

Margaret's emotions were conflicted. She took a deep breath, gazed at the sergeant, then paused to look sideways at Clare. Clare stopped chewing long enough to nod to her. "The knowledge about me being a clairvoyant is from my dear friend, Professor Fontaine's son, Jacques Paul. *Oui?*"

Remi shifted in the chair. "Yes, that's correct."

"Then, let me tell you something about me, Sergeant. I do not practice clairvoyance. On very rare occasions I have received spiritual messages in a vision. That happened to me last year when I prayed for safety during the hurricane. I could see my *grandmère* and the professor's deceased wife Julie. When my *grandmère* was alive, she had healing energy, and she could see into the future. I received a message from her, here." She placed her hand over her chest. "In my heart, and in my head. I tried to give Madelaine Fontaine the message, but instead, my vision started a chain of events that I take no responsibility for."

Clare placed her fork on the plate and reached out to cover *Tante's* hand with her own. "*Tante,* you are too modest. Maddy got the clues she needed to start a search for Patrick's sister Fiona, and before the search ended, you found the information needed to find her. Everything got resolved."

"But this is different, *chérie*. I didn't plan that vision."

Remi finished his coffee and cleared his throat. "I do not wish to pressure you, Mrs. Chamberlaine. I think I understand your hesitancy, but I can assure you that all procedures will be handled confidentially and professionally if you choose to help us. I can bring the evidence whenever and wherever you wish."

He rose and bowed his head to Clare before turning back to Margaret. "I have to leave you now, but if you should decide, Clare knows how to get in touch," he said, backing away from the table. Remi flashed a big smile. "It was my pleasure to meet Clare's mom."

Clare left her place, and Margaret rose, moving quickly to Clare's side to walk the officer to the door. She angled her head to watch him, holding his hat as he ducked under the lintel. "Thank you for your courtesy, Sergeant Remi. Your momma raised you well," Margaret said.

Clare covered her mouth to stifle a laugh, and Margaret threw her hands in the air when the door closed on Remi.

"*Mon Dieu.* He is so tall from cap to toe, and such a nice man, too."

"If you think so, why is it you didn't tell him you are willing to help?"

"It is not so easy a decision, Clare. I know nothing about this clairvoyance business. I wouldn't even know what to do."

"Listen up, *Tante.* I did some checking on the internet about clairvoyance, and it seems pretty straightforward to me. Clairvoyance is the psychic ability to receive messages from other realms. You've had messages from your *grandmére,* right?"

"*Oui.* But she is the seer."

"Then you should be able to channel her energy, ask for her help to receive information about another person in the spirit world."

"Clare, I'm getting a headache just thinking about it. If my Jean thought I was doing such things, he would roll over in his grave."

Clare rose to clear the table. "No, I think he would be proud of you, Mom. Helping others was something Uncle Jean always did, and you, too, for heaven's sake. Papa Jacques and Maddy and Paul would vouch for that. Think about it, okay? I've got errands to do, but I'll check back later."

Clare bent to kiss Margaret's cheek. "Breakfast was great." She wiggled her eyebrows, Groucho Marx style. I'm glad you like Sergeant Remi, *Tante*."

CHAPTER EIGHT

Patrick swept wood shavings into a pile in the back room of his wood-working shop. Patrick was anxious to get home to Maddy. If her "surprise" was what he suspected, then a big celebration was in order, but Paul Fontaine came through the door just before he decided to close shop early.

He tried to be patient with Paul's story about clobbering Duval at the concert, but he couldn't help but remind him that Fiona wouldn't want anyone taking revenge—for any reason.

While he cleaned and put away his tools, Patrick listened to his brother-in-law's misgivings about finding work in Biddeford or Saco, when a thought struck.

"You know about the Art Guild, right, Paul? Well, they just moved into the next building in the mill complex, and I've been helping them set up display areas. I heard the director talking yesterday about some involvement he has with a new gallery in Portland. It's worth checking out, but that's about all I can come up with."

"I'll follow up on that as soon as I get my portfolio together, but they more than likely know me, anyway. Everybody in town knows my life is one damn screw-up after another. Coming back to Biddeford Pool was probably my biggest mistake. All the guys I went to school with are either married, successful in business, or they've moved the hell away from here. Christ, I'm like a fiddle without a bow. No job, no money and no woman in my life."

"I thought you and Clare had a thing going."

"Nah. I think she's interested in somebody else."

Patrick stopped emptying sweepings into a big trash bin and raised an eyebrow at Paul. "Maddy thought you got kinda close to Clare when you were sailing."

"Well, yeah, but that was mostly me, flirting." He grinned at Patrick. "Old habits die hard. Clare is one hell of a woman, don't get me wrong. But I could never really come on to her seriously. She's like a kid sister, you know?"

Patrick nodded in agreement. "I know all about sisters," he said rolling his eyes. "If you're ready to go, I'm going to lock up here, make one delivery in Saco, and then I'll take you home with me, to *your* sister. She took the day off, called me earlier and said come home early."

Remi pulled in at the garage behind Lord's Castle Inn. A short, stocky woman carrying a basket of dirty laundry and cleaning supplies was leaving the private door that led upstairs to his studio apartment. "Mrs. Boudreau! Good morning. Looks like my mother sent you up to my place for a reason. Am I booted out again?"

The woman slowed her pace only to nod and smile. "Yes, Remi. She got a reservation last night."

Remi followed the hired woman through the back door of the Inn. "Do you know for how long?"

"Your mama is in the laundry room. She will tell you all about it."

Mary Windspirit was folding sheets on a table next to the dryer. She tucked wisps of honey-red hair behind her ears and wiped her face with a small towel. "Gonna be a scorcher today," she said, turning as the two entered the room. "Remi! You surprised me. I was hoping you would stop in for lunch so I could tell you—"

"I know about it, Mom. I stopped by to pick up something at the apartment, and Mrs. Boudreau was leaving with my dirty linen. What's with the reservation?"

"A single man. He wanted a suite for a week, but of course we don't have suites, and all the rooms are filled through Sunday, so I told him about your apartment. Perfect, he said. He'll be here by one o'clock."

"A single guy wants a suite? Why didn't he check out the hotels at Old Orchard?"

"He said he was looking for something quiet, away from the hustle and bustle, needed to relax. Someone referred him to us. There's no way to tell age on the phone, but I'm guessing maybe he's an older gentleman."

Mary's blue eyes glinted when she reached to give Remi a hug. She was a tall woman, long legged and shapely, but she barely came to Remi's shoulder. "You know we love having you here in the house with us." She reached to kiss her son's cheek. "Sorry that you don't have much time to gather up your personal stuff, love. I've got some rare roast beef to make you a sandwich, and Mrs. Boudreau brought us a blueberry pie, today."

"How can I resist that?"

"You can't, and neither can I." The deep voice had both their heads turning. Jamie Windspirit stood in the doorway, grinning. He held a large bucket in one hand, newspapers and mail under his arm. "I think you'll relish these, Remi, when your mother steams them tonight," he said holding the pail up. "Eddie hauled traps with some big beauties yesterday."

"Hey, Dad. Captain Ed must be getting generous, or you were down at the docks for another reason."

"Actually, both are true. I called him last night just nosing around to see if anyone he knew was missing that dory in your investigation. Eddie hadn't heard of any, but he asked me to stop by this morning and pick up something. I was there at the crack of dawn, and it sure brought back the old life when I worked for him. All the guys at the docks, standing with their coffee, getting ready to shove off and haul lines."

"Get on with it, Jamie," Mary said, giving her attention to the linen she folded. "What did he have for you?"

"Why, the lobsters, of course!" he said, holding them up. "He sent his regards to Mary."

Mary turned to face them and claimed the pail. "He must have had a record catch. I've never known Ed to be giving much away."

Remi traded looks with his father. "So there's still no one claiming a missing dory, huh, Dad?" Jamie pushed up his bottom lip and shook his head. Remi shrugged. "I'm not getting very far with this drowning, Dad."

Mary gave her husband a little shove, shooing them both ahead of her, out of the laundry room. "Sorry, guys, move it on. I've no time for dallying, even with my gorgeous men. In the kitchen with you, Jamie, and Remi already knows what he has to do."

Mary Macgregor, aptly named for Mary, Queen of Scots, left no doubt that she was in control. In fact, Remi and his father referred to her, privately, as the "queen." Strangely enough, neither man gave the slightest objection to her orders. She was the force behind everything that went well at Lord's Castle Inn.

The men moved side by side into the kitchen, their strides and their shoulders in rhythm. Remi could never deny his father's blood. Except for a little graying at the temple and the start of a paunch, Jamie had the same unruly black hair, dark eyes, and prominent nose. Both had a gentle manner, which didn't seem to fit their tall, muscled frames.

Remi exited the back door and climbed the stairs to his apartment. He packed casual clothes in a duffle bag, put personal stuff from the bathroom into a kit and grabbed his extra uniform and dress shirts that hung in the small closet. The two bottom drawers of the dresser were locked with a small key, so the bulk of his personal stuff would not be disturbed whenever he had to move to the Inn. Having done this a number of times before, Remi had the transfer from apartment to Inn down to a science.

Back in the laundry room he hung his clothes on a rack beside the ironing board and stashed most of his gear on shelves amidst sheets and towels.

Up the stairs to his apartment one last time, he headed straight to a small desk he'd had since he was in high school. He checked his laptop and spotted a message from Clare Chamberlaine. The simple two line message produced a smile. "Don't give up on my *tante*. I think she's softening. Call you tomorrow, CeCe."

Remi poked through writing materials and postcards of the B&B that filled the desk's center drawer. Next, he checked the file drawer that held his books and manuals from the police academy. At the bottom was the item he needed to take out of the apartment. A large clear plastic bag containing evidence.

Withdrawing the bag, he held it in his hands and stared at the jeweled belt. *None of the shops on the beach sell this belt or know its maker. Time to lock this in my truck with the laptop.*

Downstairs he opened the door and glanced out at the parking spaces behind the Inn. A half hour ago there had only been a Ford mini-van with a New York license plate. Now a late model, silver Mercedes with Miami plates stood next to it. *Strange,* he thought. *Most guests at the Inn drive conservative cars. If it's the new reservation, he's early.*

Remi pulled open the screen door, bolted past the laundry room and entered the kitchen. His father was reading the paper at the kitchen table. "Your lunch is covered on the counter.

Bring it here and rest yourself, son."

"I'd like to, but I have to run with the sandwich. Got to go to division headquarters." He slipped the sandwich into a baggie and grabbed a paper napkin. "I've taken too much of the Patrol's time already, today. Where's Mom?"

"She's out front registering the new guest. You're not having any of the pie?"

"Save mine for tonight, will you? Looks like I cleared out just in time. Did you see the fancy wheels this guy came in?"

"No. Didn't even see the man. Expect he's probably just another tourist."

"Maybe so. Gotta run, Dad. Tell the queen I'll be here for supper, okay?"

CHAPTER NINE

Five-thirty was usually supper break for Clare. The floor nurses and aides were busy with meds and patients' trays, and the nurse's lounge was quiet. She sipped coffee, her thoughts jumbled, picturing Remi sitting at *Tante*'s table, attentively listening to *Tante* explain why she couldn't help. His sincerity had impressed them both.

She closed her eyes and jumped to another scene . . . the feel of Remi's fingers soothing knotted muscles in her shoulders. *He has nice long fingers . . . and such a gentle touch . . .* The vibration of her cell phone ended her reverie. Because the lounge was empty, she chanced clicking the phone open. It was a voice mail message.

"Paul, here. Call Maddy when you get home tonight, no matter how late."

Right after Clare's supper break a major accident on I-95 brought four injured into ER, and the hours until eleven flew by with little chance for her to ponder what Paul's message meant. Bone weary when she finished her shift, Clare got ready for bed, settled in and dialed Maddy's number.

"Hi, babe. Paul left me a message to call you. What's happening?"

"Oh, CeCe, I've got wonderful news. I called *Tante* first, and she told me your schedule. Paul was here, so I let him give you a head's up. I wanted you and *Tante* to be the first to know. Hold on to your hat, girlfriend. I'm pregnant."

"OhmyGod. Maddy! You're sure?"

"Yes, as far as I can tell. I think it will be a March baby, but I haven't seen a doctor yet. I took one of those pregnancy tests today, but the amazing thing is Aunt Margaret stopped here for tea and she predicted I was pregnant before I knew it myself! Somehow *Tante* knew, so that's why Paul called you. I told her she'd be the first to know if she was right."

"Geez. *Tante* knew? I've got to talk turkey with her tomorrow. Not about you, 'course. I'm super happy for you, babe. And for Patrick!"

"He's walking on air right now—even thinking about how he can partition some space here for a nursery."

"I can just picture his smiling eyes. I'm so glad you called, Mad. It is wonderful news! Wish I could talk longer, but it's been a really long day, and I'll have to catch you up later on the details."

"That's okay, Cec, just couldn't wait to tell you."

"Sweet dreams, tonight, babe. Guaranteed. Love you to bits."

Clare tossed and turned in bed, images running before her eyes. Remi sitting at *Tante*'s table. *Tante* predicting Maddy's pregnancy. The accident victims parading one by one as they came into the emergency room, bodies bleeding and broken. She reached for her eye shades. *I have to think of pleasant things . . . sailing . . . blue skies, warm summer wind . . . Paul teaching me to reef the sails on* Julie's Dream. That was her last conscious thought before she fell into a fitful sleep.

In a dream, Paul Fontaine carried an unconscious woman into the ER. It wasn't the dead body she found on the buoy. The body looked exactly like *Tante* Margaret if she'd had a twin. Clare awoke with a start, sweaty and tangled in twisted sheets. She shuddered, tore off her eye mask and sat up in bed, staring at the clock. "Oh, God," she mumbled. "Seven A.M."

89

She reached for the phone and dialed. *Tante* was always up at the crack of dawn.

When Margaret answered, it was a relief to hear her voice. "Mornin', Mom." *She likes it when I call her Mom.* "I'm not sure how good the morning really is, 'cause I've had a really bad night. Any chance of getting a repeat on breakfast today?"

"*Mais naturellement.* I'm making apple pancakes, and I'll wait to eat with you if you come right away."

"I'll be there in twenty minutes, and I'll need strong coffee."

Clare rolled out of bed, made short work out of bathroom preparations, dressed in sweats and a t-shirt, and was in her car in twenty minutes. Fog from the river hung over the street. Dark clouds shrouding the sun didn't help her spirits, but the aroma of coffee drifting through *Tante*'s screen door was like manna from heaven.

"Mornin', Mom. There's no denying that food from your kitchen restores my soul. Good thing you're only a stone's throw away."

Tante was flipping pancakes on an iron griddle. "You know you can come anytime without asking. God gave us each other, eh? So, pour the coffee, Clare, and I'll bring our plates to the table in a minute."

Clare eyed the chair where Remi sat yesterday, his presence still strong in her mind. Maple syrup, brown sugar and butter were on a lazy Susan in the center of the table set for two. *All those lovely calories I can't resist,* she thought. *And a man I can't get out of my mind.*

"Here we are," *Tante* said, handing Clare a plate stacked with pancakes. Margaret took her place across the table. "So tell me why it was such a bad night."

Clare poured syrup over the hotcakes. "Bad dreams after a really hectic shift at work. When the adrenalin is pumping, you don't realize what a toll it takes, working in that hospital. I tried to wind down back in the apartment, and I couldn't. There was one bright spot, though. I know you got the same call I did from Maddy last night, yes?"

"*Oui.* I am very happy for Madelaine and Patrick. Maybe they'll make you godmother, eh?"

Clare was savoring each bite of her breakfast, fixing her gaze on *Tante*'s warm brown eyes. She sat back and sighed. "I don't know about that, what with all of Patrick's sisters. The more important question right now is how did you know Maddy was pregnant before she was sure of it herself?"

Tante put down her fork. Although surprised for a second, she answered without hesitation. "It just came to me when I looked at Madelaine. Something I felt, here." She placed a hand over her heart.

Clare nodded, lips pursed. "Call it intuition, sixth sense, or even Jacques Fontaine's word for it, 'prescience.' You can't deny it, Mom. You've got your grandmother Henriette's genes."

Tante put her coffee cup down. "I think I know where this is going, Clare. You want me to try and help your friend, Sergeant Remi."

"See? You are even reading my mind! I really do want you to help, but it has to be because you want to."

"I have thought about it. If that poor woman took her own life, I worry mostly about her tormented soul. That, more than anything else, gives me a reason to try."

Clare pushed back her chair and threw her hands in the air. "That's the best reason yet, and I know you won't regret it." Sunlight streamed through the windows as Clare bent to clear Margaret's plate. "You just made the sun shine, Mom. Now I know it's going to be a better day, and I can go back to the apartment and get some sleep."

"An anonymous call came in to Marine Patrol Division: The

91

report of a missing tenant, a missing Native American woman like the body found in Saco Bay. When asked for ID, the caller gave one word—Mariner. Zip. That was it. The call cut off without time to trace it. Can you believe it, Dad?"

Jamie shook his head. "That's a hell of a note," he said, watching his son run down the rentals in the yellow pages.

"Mariner. There's no listing for such a place," Remi said. He sat at the Inn's kitchen table, surrounded by directories from Biddeford, Saco and Scarborough.

"Maybe it's too new to be in those directories. The name sounds familiar, though. There used to be a big old shipbuilder's barn down on Harbor Road, just before the marina. Somebody was converting it last time I went by there. Seems to me the name on the permit sign was Mariner Construction. It's near the harbor, anyway. Do you think that might be what you're looking for?"

"It's worth a try. Want to ride down with me?"

"Can't leave right now, Remi. I'd like to, but I promised your mother I'd stay put in case the guests needed anything. She's over at the hall, and she's only supposed to be there for a half hour."

"What's going on there?"

"Just a planning committee meeting. The Highland Band is coming to the Temple in a couple of weeks, and Mary wants to make sure the band leader gets an invitation to have lunch with us at the Inn."

Remi smiled and shook his head. "Always one step ahead. Did she say anything about the guy who is in my apartment?"

"Just that he looked about my age." Jamie threw back his head and wiggled his eyebrows. "But he wasn't nearly as handsome as me."

Remi laughed. He stacked the directories on the shelf next to his mother's cookbooks. "I hope your memory's as good as your looks, Dad. I'm going down Harbor Road and have a look around before it gets dark."

Remi's cell phone rang as soon as he walked outside. He stopped beside the silver Mercedes and flipped open the phone.

"Hi, Remi. It's Clare. Did you get my E-mail yesterday?"

"Yes, but I didn't think you expected an answer."

"I didn't, but I have good news to tell you. My *tante* has agreed to try and help with the evidence."

"Wow. She had me convinced she couldn't do it. How did you manage that?"

"I'll tell you all about it, but right now I'm on break using my cell phone, so I have to make this short. Today's my last three to eleven shift, and if you have no problem waiting till morning, you can come for coffee tomorrow. Just don't make it seven-thirty A.M."

"I'm on duty tomorrow, too, but whatever you say, I'll be there, and Clare . . . something tells me I owe you, big time." He clicked the phone shut, pocketing it with a smile.

Remi glanced through the tinted glass of the Mercedes parked beside his truck. An oversized briefcase occupied the passenger seat. It was the solitary item visible in the car. No maps, no coffee mug, no newspapers, nothing personal. *Almost looks too perfect. Wonder what the guy does. He's a long way from Miami if he drove.*

He swung out of the driveway onto Saco Road, slid a Kenny G disk into the player and tried to let his mind run free with the music. Halfway down Harbor Road he began to look for the building his father told him about. An old wooden schooner on blocks sat on the side of the road after a bait shop. It almost hid a dirt road leading from it, but the ship didn't conceal a tall frame structure at the end of the dirt road. The building looked big enough to be an airplane hangar.

Remi slowed, pulled the turn signal, and checked his side-view mirror. A silver car sped past him on the narrow road, but he was into the turn before he could check the plate. For some reason, that car gave him an uneasy feeling, but the building in front of him took all his attention.

It was a compelling puzzle. Circular painted steps led to an entrance wide enough for a boat to go through. The entrance was re-fitted with a triple-paneled doorway, making it look like the entrance to a fancy carriage house. Crescent windows rested over each paneled section. Raised vertical trim resembling wainscoting dressed the bottom of two side panels, while horizontal bars decorated a center door. Fitted with a lock and massive brass knob, the center door appeared to be an entry. Recessed over it in red and gold letters was what he was looking for: Mariner's Lofts.

Remi stood on the step. He was tall enough to peer into the half-moon window over the locked door. The dark, vast interior was dimly relieved by two narrow, vertical windows, one on each side at the back of the cavernous space. The windows looked to be eight feet long. Slanted sun rays cast eerie light onto circular stairways beneath each window.

Remi whistled under his breath. Somebody sank a pile of money into this place. *Wonder what the space is for—garages . . . boats?*

They both started at the sound of the apartment door opening and closing.

"Hallo, *chèrie*. Anybody home?" In seconds Margaret appeared in the kitchen doorway. "Oh," she said, surprise widening her eyes. "I should have rung the bell."

"No, no, that's okay, Mom," Clare said, rising quickly. "We actually just telephoned your house.

Remi stood. "Good morning, Mrs. Chamberlaine."

"Whatcha got here?" Clare asked, relieving Margaret of two bags she held in her arms.

Margaret looked from Clare to Remi. "Good morning Sergeant Remi. I brought beautiful tomatoes from my neighbor's garden and a loaf of fresh bread from the bakery. Good for lunch, eh?"

"Later, for sure, Mom," Clare said, "but right now I have something else in mind. I called you on the phone to see if you would like to take a look at the evidence from the drowning victim. Are you up to that this morning?"

Surprise and apprehension mingled on her face. A note of fear worked its way into her voice. *"Bon Seigneur!"* she said. Brushing past the counter, she collapsed into the nearest chair.

Clare traded looks with Remi.

"It's okay, Mrs. Chamberlaine," Remi said. "I happen to know the French words for 'Good Lord.' Mrs. Boudreau, a lady who works for my Mom,—she says that all the time." He smiled reassuringly. "If you aren't comfortable working with the evidence today, we can go any place you wish another time."

Tante seemed to struggle for composure. She folded her hands under her chin and closed her eyes for a second, before meeting Remi's gaze. "It isn't the place, or the time, Sergeant Remi. It's me. I don't have confidence in my ability."

Clare moved quickly to her mom and squeezed her shoulder. "I have confidence in you, Mom. Remember what I told you

CHAPTER TEN

Clare chose her clothes carefully for a rainy morning. New jeans and a turquoise short-sleeved cotton sweater. "Keep it simple. Don't gild the lily," *Tante* would say. *'Course she's the only one who thinks I'm a lily.*

She wielded a wire brush and hair dryer, trying to achieve the do the hairdresser gave her a week ago. Looking closely in her magnifying mirror she took care to apply eyeliner lightly and evenly. She fluttered thick lashes in the mirror. *Maddy's right,* she thought. *I don't need mascara. Just a touch of blush, and I'm ready.*

Twenty minutes later she checked the clock in the kitchen. Nine-fifteen. "Geez, I didn't mean for him to come this late," she muttered. Lining up the coffee mugs again, she checked the covered blueberry muffins one more time. She pictured him out there maybe stuck in rainy day traffic, or maybe he got called somewhere on an emergency.

She chided herself . . . how had she gone so quickly from a confident person being interrogated by a Marine Patrol cop, to a frenzied, fussing person wanting to charm the cop's socks off? The doorbell saved her further frustration.

"Mornin' Clare. It's a wet one out there."

"Mornin'. Just my luck, though. I worked through all the sunny days, and it rains when I get a weekend off. Come in the kitchen, Remi. Coffee's ready."

"You're looking pretty nice for early in the morning. Two

days off, huh? We'll have to do something about that."

Clare popped the muffins to warm in the microwave and poured coffee. "Let me ask you something, Sarge. Have you ever worked with a medium before—on other cases, I mean."

"Nope. But some of the guys in the division have."

Clare placed a plate of warm muffins in front of him. "Have you given any thought to where a session would take place? I mean . . . when my *tante* could actually take a look at the evidence?"

"Any place she's comfortable with. Could be her own house, a restaurant, or right here, if she'd prefer."

"She probably thinks she has to go down to your division headquarters. That may be partly why she's been resistant. That and her history with clairvoyance."

"History?"

"You probably heard about *Tante*'s vision that sent my friend Maddy back in time a year ago?"

Remi nodded. "Yeah, Paul told me about it, but was that the only incident she's had?"

"Just about. I should explain things about my *tante*. She was educated by French nuns, and the good sisters knew all about her grandmother being a seer. If *Tante* ever showed any inclination in her early life to be like her grandmother, it was squelched, pronto, by the sisters. They put the fear of God in her. Much, much later on, before Fiona's disappearance, she did try to get help from the spirits—help for Maddy and Paul's mom, Julie Fontaine."

Clare shook her head. "Mrs. Fontaine had cancer. Maddy and I weren't told much about it because we were away at college, but Jacques swears that my mom's prayers for mercy were heard. There was no cure, but Julie had a swift and peaceful death. Jacques always says 'From Margaret's lips to God's ears.' "

Remi sipped his coffee thoughtfully. "I'm not a Catholic, but my step-mom raised me with a strong faith in God. I think your Aunt Margaret is going to be awesome."

His words created a fuzzy warm feeling in her chest. Was it the message or the messenger?

"Well, there's only one way to find out how awesome she will be." She refilled their cups. "Have a muffin, Remi, and I'll give her a call."

Clare stood behind Remi's chair to dial *Tante*'s number. Margaret Chamberlaine had a standard land line, no answering machine, so Clare gave up on the fifth ring. "No answer. She must be out on errands, or maybe at church." She reached past Remi's shoulder for his coffee mug, and he covered her finger with his hand.

"It can wait, Clare. Sit and talk to me. Tell me about you. How long have you had this apartment and how long have you worked at the hospital?"

She withdrew her hand and sat opposite him. "Four months for both. As soon as I graduated college I got the job at the medical center and my mom helped me find this place."

"And you don't mind working the late shifts?"

"I don't like three to eleven because that shoots the whole evening. I'd rather work all night on the dark shift, eleven to seven A.M., but hey, you don't always get what you want, you know."

His eyebrows shot up without raising his head. Deep, long-lashed brown eyes locked with hers. "Are you seeing anyone, Clare?"

The question was a surprise. She lowered her eyes, struggling for an answer. "No one special."

"Good," he said, grinning, as he reached again for her hand. "There's a concert at the Temple Sunday night. Will you go with me?"

about channeling energy? All you have to do is channel *Grand-mère's* energy. Let Remi bring the evidence in, okay? Maybe you'll feel different when you see it."

Margaret stared straight ahead, folded her hands on the table top and nodded. Clare signaled with a jerk of her head, and Remi left the kitchen. "Whatever happens, you're only trying to free this person's spirit. You felt bad about that, so think of it as helping to accomplish that, okay?"

"*Oui,* but my vision last year was of people I know, and it happened while I was praying. You surprised me with this today, Clare. I don't know if I'm ready."

"I didn't mean to surprise you. I invited Remi for coffee this morning to tell him that you're willing to help and maybe plan a place for that to happen. After he arrived, I phoned you to ask about a place, but you weren't home. You arrived right after my phone call, so the opportunity just seemed to come together without planning."

Clare began clearing things from the table. "Remi is just looking for accurate information about this woman. I know it's a strain, but I think you can do it. You just need to relax, Mom, and let it happen."

Margaret held her head in her hands. "Let me be for a few minutes, Clare. I need to be quiet and think about this. I hear Sergeant Remi at the door. Go to him, eh? I want to pray and see if I can clear my mind."

Clare shuffled out to the foyer where Remi was removing his wet boots. She put a finger to her lips and pointed over her shoulder with her thumb. "She's getting relaxed," she said in a low voice.

Remi pulled the large plastic bag from inside his poncho and shrugged out of his wet coat. "It's raining harder than ever. Good thing I had this rain gear in the truck."

Clare opened the hall closet and hung his wet hat and coat

on a door hook. She motioned him into the living room. "Let's sit for a minute. I try not to let her know it," she whispered, "but this clairvoyance stuff has got me unnerved, too."

Remi settled beside her on the sofa. Her gaze flew to the evidence bag resting on the coffee table. She shuddered. "God forbid that my mom dredges up something we aren't prepared for."

"You needn't worry about that. That's my job. I'm thankful you're making this happen, Clare, but . . ." He crooked a finger under her chin, tilting it up to meet his gaze. "This is awkward for me, too. I try not to mix work and pleasure. My invitation to come to the concert is not the pay-back I owe you. I asked you because I want to be with you. Not in this uniform, and not in a séance with your mom. Do you understand?"

Clare gulped. "Yes. I still feel guilty about Mom, though. Maybe I shouldn't have urged her."

"I thought you said she is willing."

"Yeah, but I was trying to be upbeat and positive, and that's really pushing, you know?"

Remi suddenly stood. "Then let me be the fall guy. This is my investigation, Clare, so let me try something my way." He grabbed the evidence bag.

Totally surprised, Clare jumped up to follow him when he strode back into the kitchen.

Margaret opened her eyes when Remi cleared his throat. "Mrs. Chamberlaine, this is not a favorite part of my job. I don't like it when people are uncomfortable with procedures or interrogations. I sense that is the situation here, and I want you to know you're under no obligation to cooperate. Not to Clare and not to me." He held up the evidence bag. "I'll leave with this right now if you're not totally ready. You can make a decision in your own time, okay?"

Tante Margaret's mouth opened, but no sound came out.

Clare blinked in surprise. *Tante* closed her eyes, and whispered French words that sounded like a prayer. She drew a deep breath, looked from Clare to Remi and patted the table in front of her. "I am ready now, Sergeant Windspirit. Please sit down and put your things on the table."

Remi moved without hesitation. First the silver belt, then the tattered remnants of a long skirt and a tunic-like shirt from the body. Clare sat facing Margaret, staring at the items on the table. The only sound was the rain, pelting against the living room windows.

Tante closed her eyes, willing her mind to be blank, willing images to come. Slowly, she traced her fingers lightly over the clothing. She bunched the fabric in her hands and held it to her face as though she were trying to breathe life into the folds. Sweat sheened on her forehead. She held the clothes for what seemed like long minutes. Then, slowly, she put them back on the table.

Her fingers skimmed over the topaz jewel that formed the center closure of the belt. The jewel sparkled in its raised silver setting. Margaret turned the belt this way and that. The links clattering on the table top shattered the silence of the room. *Tante* raised the belt in both hands, closing her fingers around it as tenderly as one would hold a child. Her face was a study in concentration. Minutes of silence passed.

As she pressed her fingertips against the jewel, something from another place filled her senses. She held one hand to her ear and the belt against her heart and sat perfectly still for what seemed like an eternity. Suddenly her eyes flew open. Her fingers closed tightly around the belt, and her mouth turned up in a weak smile.

Remi and Clare both spoke at once. "What?"

Margaret's eyes blurred as she stared at the belt in her hands and a tear rolled down her cheek.

101

"What is it? Mom, are you okay?"

"*Oui.* The gift of tears cleanses the soul, Clare," Margaret said, trying to smile through her tears.

"Did you make a connection?" Clare asked.

"*Oui.*" *Tante* held the belt out to Remi. "This belt is a symbol, but in a way it is a real chain. It traps a soul in a dark building . . . a very big building near the sea. The woman who wore it is a woman without hope. She is called Awinita."

CHAPTER ELEVEN

"Your mom is a godsend. She shed light on new evidence in this case."

Clare frowned. "New evidence? Why didn't you tell her that? It might have stopped her from rushing off in the rain."

"Clare," he said, flashing a scolding look. "You couldn't convince her to take a ride home in my truck, so how could *I* do anything different? Your mom seemed anxious to get to her house on her own two feet, and she probably wanted to be away from us."

"Maybe so. Still, this had to be an intense experience for her, and I thought you'd talk more with her about the drowning victim."

Remi shook his head. "I can't reveal details about this case. Not yet. All the pieces aren't in place. As soon as they are, your *tante* will be with me on this, trust me."

Clare trailed close behind him as he strode to the hall closet. "I do trust you, Remi Windspirit. Your uniform makes it difficult not to."

Remi shrugged into his rain gear and faced her. He cocked his head and sought her eyes with a tender look. Slowly, he traced the back of his fingers down her cheek. "It makes things difficult for me, too. Can't really do what I'd like to, in uniform. Tomorrow, Clare. I'll pick you up at seven."

Remi drove down Harbor Road more slowly than usual, headlights piercing the gray murk, wipers slashing rapid fire

103

against the driving rain. *Maybe. Just maybe, somebody is at Mariner's on a rainy day.* The sagging old schooner looked even more doomed for the wood pile in the relentless rain. Rounding the turn onto the dirt road, he caught sight of a red pickup parked near the front of Mariner's Lofts. Bingo! Remi radioed the plate number, make and model while his headlights beamed straight on it. He pushed his wide-brimmed hat down firmly, shoved a flashlight in his pocket and sloshed across the muddy drive to the truck. His eyes skimmed over W JENSEN CON-STRUCTION lettered on the side of the truck before he shined the light inside.

"You got a problem with my truck?" A lanky young guy in jeans and a nylon jacket was sloshing his way from the back of the building, splashing muddy water with each step.

Remi moved to block the red truck's door. "Not yet." He motioned to the building with his flashlight before stuffing it in his pocket. "Are you a tenant here?"

"No, sir."

"Manager of the building?"

The guy snorted. "You kiddin' me? Hell, no."

Remi tipped his head toward the entrance. "Are the lofts oc-cupied?"

"Wouldn't know that. I was just checkin' out something for a friend."

Remi glared at him. "Checking out the back of the building?" *Up close this guy doesn't look more than eighteen. He's trying to be cocky, but there's something more here than bluff.*

"Let's see your license and registration, please."

The young man swiped a shock of wet blond hair out of his eyes and pulled a wallet from his back pocket. "Registration's in the truck," he said, handing his ID over. He rubbed at his scrubby beard and pulled a baseball cap further over his eyes. "Man, it's wetter 'n hell out here. Got to get in my truck."

Remi looked back and forth from the ID to the man, registering information in his mind.

"Look, if there's something wrong with parking here, you need to talk with my father." He shifted back and forth in muddy work boots, pointing with his thumb at the sign on his truck. "He's the 'W' in Jensen Construction."

Remi handed back the license. "Jensen do the work on this place, William?"

"It's Billy, and yeah, we worked here. What's this about, anyway?"

Remi stepped away from the door of the red truck. "That's what I'm about to find out. Maine Marine Patrol is conducting an investigation here. You can be on your way for now, Billy, but don't plan on leaving the area. Biddeford PD may need you for questioning."

He watched Billy Jensen jump in his truck, pull the door shut and throw his head back against the seat. There was no mistaking the words Billy's lips formed before he started the engine: "Holy shit!"

Remi pulled his truck as close as possible to the building and radioed information about Jensen Construction to headquarters.

Following muddy footprints around the side of the building, he hoped to find what drew Billy Jensen to the back of Mariner's Lofts. He passed by the long vertical window at the back; the rain made it next to impossible to see through them. The surprise came when he turned the corner.

Centered on a high back wall was another entrance, reached by the same kind of painted steps and covered by a semicircular cedar shake roof. Not nearly as grand as the front entrance; black metal mailboxes flanked either side of a locked door. No surprise that both boxes were empty. High above the entrance, two picture windows marked what seemed to be two separate lofts.

Remi ran down the details in his mind on the drive back to Ocean Park. The location and the isolation fit *Tante's* description. The dead woman could have been trapped there. With a name like Awinita she could be the missing Native American tenant someone called in. *Not a lot to go on, but things are beginning to fit together. Time to check in with Dad.*

Jamie Windspirit whistled softly to himself as he riffled the pages of a weather-beaten old manual. He held up the small leather-bound book. "This book would have the name, if it's a Cherokee name. Did you know that thousands of my people in North Carolina can speak the Tsalagi language?"

Remi shook his head. "I was probably too young to know much about the language when we left North Carolina. I do remember your telling me about your great-grandfather and the Trail of Tears, though."

Jamie sat back and nodded. "A lot of that history is preserved in museums in Oklahoma, but I have it up here," he said, pointing to his head. "Your mother is tied into that history, too, in a sentimental way. My great-grandfather was only ten when his family was forced to leave his land and go on the trail west. Before long, he was too sick to walk and his father left him with a Scottish farm family in the foothills of the Alleghenies." Jamie smiled and raised his eyebrows. "Not Mary's family, of course, but it was a Scot in North Carolina who raised him and gave him his given name. James. The boy kept his own surname, and three generations later that Scot's given name came down to me."

"You've told me about the Trail of Tears, Dad, but I don't remember that part about your name. You really ought to write this stuff down or dictate it into a tape machine so it can be preserved." Remi stared at the book his father held. He really didn't want to spoil his father's mood, but excitement about the case was building. "Can we get back to my name problem,

Dad? I've got to tie together some details I got today. See if you can find the word I just gave you in your book."

"Okay, let's see. Awinita . . ." Jamie ran his finger down a page. "It's here, Remi, right after Amadahy. Awinita means fawn. It's Cherokee all right." Jamie closed the book, tapping the table with it. "Now, tell me what you can do with that."

"For starters I can get a search warrant for Mariner's Lofts. If the dead girl lived there, there's probably something there to identify her or maybe give us a clue as to why she took her own life."

Clare was bursting to talk about all that happened. She especially needed Maddy's take on Remi and what happened with *Tante* and the evidence. If anybody could relate to that kind of an experience, it would be Maddy. She was a little surprised at her best friend's reaction. *Maybe this pregnancy has her a little moody or uptight . . . better go slow with this . . .*

"What's got you traveling down memory lane, Cec? Why the questions about Hetty?" asked Maddy, sipping her tea.

"Well, the Hetty in your trip back in time was my *tante*'s grandmother, Henriette, right?"

"Yes, but where is this leading?"

"It's leading back to my *tante*. She agreed to help Remi investigate some evidence from the dead woman we found, and to do that she had to call on Henriette."

"You mean Aunt Margaret had another vision?"

"Kind of. It was a séance. *Tante* called on her *grandmère*'s spirit, and by channeling Hetty's energy, *Tante* could contact the aura of the dead woman's spirit."

"I can't believe this is you, Clare, talking to me. You, who barely believed that I traveled in time last year. Now you're talking séances and psychic channeling as though you were a medium yourself. What's going on?"

"I know, I know. It's not my usual lingo. But it's not same old, same old with me anymore, babe. I had to look all that stuff up and learn about clairvoyance in order to convince *Tante.*"

"And you did all this for the investigation?"

Clare shrugged her shoulders. "What can I say? Talk about mediums, I'm beginning to think I'm the one possessed. It's like Sergeant Remi Windspirit has taken up residence in my mind. I think about him at night and I wake up with his name on my lips. It's a longing I've never felt before. I really need your sage advice, Mad."

Maddy smiled at last and nodded at Clare. "It sounds like *more* than an attraction to me." She poured more tea in their cups. "Do you think the feelings are mutual?"

"Well, he asked me out tonight," Clare's dimples deepened in a smile. With a questioning glance, she hunched her shoulders. "He said he wants to be with me."

"Hey, there you go. That's great CeCe!"

Maddy's words were punctuated by the ring of the doorbell, and a male voice called out, "Anybody home?"

"That has to be my brother. We're in the kitchen, Paul. Come on in."

"*Bon se bon.* Luck is with me," he said, kissing each of them on the cheek. "Two lovely ladies to share my good fortune with."

"Good news?" Maddy asked.

"Couldn't be better. Patrick's not here?"

"No. He's building custom bookshelves at a big house down in Fortunes Rocks."

"Well, I especially wanted to thank him for the tip he gave me. He suggested I speak to the director of the Art Guild, and I've just returned from there. They have new space near Patrick's shop in Factory Complex, but the director there is also involved in opening new digs in Old Town, Portland." Paul stood between them at the side of the table and put a hand on each of their shoulders.

"Some philanthropist left a big trust to finance a gallery in Portland with one stipulation. It must showcase Maine artists first, before it acquires other paintings."

"Let me guess," Maddy said. "You showed them your portfolio, and they want to exhibit your paintings."

"You got it, babe." Paul gave her a high five. "They looked at my seascapes and the watercolors I did of East Point Sanctuary. If I can get two more big ones together in the next couple of weeks, I'll be the featured artist for the fall opening of the gallery in November."

Maddy stood and threw her arms wide to draw him in. "Oh, Paul. I'm so proud of you. That's wonderful news. Does Dad know?"

"He will tonight. That's another reason I stopped here, to invite you guys over later tonight when I break the news."

Paul turned to Clare. "You too, Cec. I already invited *Tante* Margaret. She happened to be leaving the bakery when I stopped at the wine shop to buy champagne. She said she'd love to come out to the Pool."

"Ooh, I would, too, Paul, but I can't make it tonight. Sorry." Clare stood and smiled at Paul. "Doesn't mean I'm not super happy for you, though. I gotta run, Mad. Thanks for the tea and sympathy. Whoops!" Clare chuckled at her unplanned figure of speech.

Maddy clapped her hands. "That was a good one, CeCe. You know you're welcome here any time. Oh, and if it will help, we can bring *Tante* with us to Papa's house tonight. I know she doesn't like to drive after dark. What time would you want us there, Paul?"

"Seven-thirty would be fine. Dinner will be over by then."

"That would be great, babe, if you don't mind bringing

109

Tante," Clare said. "I'll call her to tell her you're coming, and I'll call you tomorrow for sure, Mad."

Before she turned to leave, Clare squeezed Paul's shoulder. "Congratulations, again, Cap."

Paul nodded and sat in Clare's place, staring at her as she walked jauntily down the hall. "Tea and sympathy? Is CeCe working tonight?" he asked Maddy.

"No. She's got a date."

Clare did all the things she rarely did. She ate a plain green salad with strawberries for her dinner, painted her toenails hot pink, then gave herself a facial with lemon juice and yogurt. Her dilemma was what to wear. The Temple was kind of a conservative place, so she couldn't go sexy. She poked through the few dressy things in her closet and chose a long sleeved soft pink Henley shirt trimmed with navy. It would match the navy cotton skirt that she hardly ever wore. Toeless espadrilles with a high wedge would bring her nearly up to Remi's shoulder.

Perfume that Maddy gave her for Christmas sat on the dresser. *That should do it,* she thought, dabbing perfume below her ears and at her temple. Clare checked herself in the mirror one last time.

The door bell rang promptly at seven. A smile crinkled Remi's eyes in devastating attraction when Clare opened the door. "You're looking mighty pretty, Miss Chamberlaine."

It was so good to be able to look into his incredible eyes without craning her neck that Clare was lost in awe for a second. She nodded her thanks and cast her eyes down. No L.L.Bean boots tonight. From loafers and gray linen slacks to a black silk shirt, Remi was no longer Sergeant Windspirit. She put one hand on her hip and swept her eyes up and down again. "I liked the uniform, but you look terrific without it—I mean in casual clothes, of course." Clare blushed and laughed at herself. Remi laughed with her.

He took her hand. "Ready to go?"

She nodded, grinning like a cat in cream.

"I hope you'll be okay riding in my truck," he said as they left the apartment. "You'll dress it up, for sure." He leaned down to nuzzle her cheek before he helped her up to the bench seat. "Mmm, you smell good."

She closed her eyes and drank in the compliment. Her mind was in a whirl as they started the drive to Ocean Park. She didn't want to talk about the séance or the investigation. *This has to be a night for us.*

Luckily, Remi's thoughts were on the same track.

"You're going to hear really good music tonight, Clare. The Blue Hill Brass will mix classical with a little contemporary. That's what they usually do, anyway."

"Uh-oh. You'll have to be my mentor when it comes to classical. The only thing I ever recognize is the trumpet part of the 'William Tell Overture.' "

"Not to worry. My mom raised me to appreciate all kinds of music, so I'll be happy to oblige whenever I can. You'll hear some music you've probably heard before. The Temple is a pretty neat place, so I think you will like it no matter what music is played." He squeezed her hand as he pulled the truck to a stop.

Remi helped Clare down from the truck. She looked up and drew in her breath. Pale moonshine above the trees sent blue-white light on an evergreen grove. A full moon chased the sun, shadowing tall pine trees surrounding a white octagonal building with green-shuttered windows on all sides. It was like stepping back in time to a church a hundred years ago.

Musicians were tuning up somewhere unseen. Clare looked up and around in awe. Old fashioned dome lamps hung from a high post and beam ceiling, reflecting light off the honey-toned

111

natural wood interior walls. People sat on folding chairs and shaker benches in groupings around a stage standing opposite the entrance. *Kind of like theater in the round,* she thought.

Remi nodded to a volunteer at the door. "Evening, Mabel."

She nodded back and checked his name off the ticket list. "Remi. Follow me, please." She led them to the left front of the hall. Two folding chairs had fliers left on them. "Enjoy the program," she said.

"Do you know everybody in Ocean Park?"

Remi grinned. "Small place, and it's my mom who knows everybody." He pointed to the message at the bottom of the flier. *Please turn off your cell phones.* "Do you have yours with you, Clare?"

"Yes. I guessed as much, 'cause they ask that you turn cell phones off in church now, too." She patted her purse, grinning at him. "All taken care of, Sarge."

Seconds after being introduced by the Ocean Park Association Director, the Blue Hill Quintet paraded in playing "Bill Bailey, Won't You Please Come Home." Remi took Clare's hand. "See? I know you've heard that one."

She smiled and nodded. The trombone player stepped up to the microphone. "We're thrilled and honored to be back at the Temple once again, folks. What a nice warm place to play tonight. It's like being in the shower with a whole bunch of people." Clare seemed to relax more when laughter mingled with heads nodding. It was a very warm night. "We're going to play a variety of music tonight, folks. Our first piece is composer anonymous; 'Sangra Sangralita.' "

Clare raised her eyebrows and quirked her mouth in question. Remi grinned and squeezed her hand. She was surprised how fascinating it was to watch and listen to the individual instruments. How beautiful it sounded.

She glanced sideways at Remi when the second selection was

Not a stroke or a heart attack . . . He went directly to Clare's friend, Madelaine.

"Clare asks that you wait until she knows more and can talk with you. It shouldn't be too long."

"That's it? Can't anyone see her?" Paul interrupted.

Remi calmly placed a hand on Paul's shoulder. "They've taken her for a CAT scan. The nurse said it was a severe concussion."

Maddy drew in a breath. "She must have hit her head pretty hard when she fell. I remember the blood, but as soon as Patrick found a pulse, he sent me back to the car to phone nine-one-one."

Remi nodded. "Calling emergency was the right thing to do, but her head injury wasn't from a fall. The nurse said she sustained a blow to the head."

Maddy's face turned ashen. She covered her mouth with one hand and reached for Patrick. He ushered her to the only vacant chair nearby. Paul followed, and people shifted from chair to chair so that Patrick and Paul could sit on either side of Maddy.

Remi brought her a cup of water from the cooler. "Are you all right, Madelaine?" he asked.

Maddy nodded, sipping the water. "Thank you. This helps."

"She'll be okay once we get out of here," Patrick said with a sheepish grin. "She really doesn't like hospitals, and right now she's more than a little sensitive."

"Who does like hospitals?" Paul said. "We had enough of this place last year, huh, babe?" He stood and motioned to the door with his head. "Step outside with me for a minute, okay, Remi? We'll be right back, sis."

Outside, Paul blew out a breath and raked his fingers through his hair. "This place gives me bad vibes since my father's stroke. But what you probably don't know is that my sister is pregnant and not handling things very well. Finding *Tante* like that has

announced. "Our next piece features Scott on the French Horn playing the Rondo movement from Mozart's Concerto."

Remi caught her questioning look. "I'll explain later," he whispered.

Halfway through the selection, Clare noticed a small light shining on the floor beside Remi. Mabel was whispering in Remi's ear. Clare caught the puzzled look on his face. Mabel stood back, waiting.

Remi lowered his mouth to Clare's ear. "We have to leave now." Without another word, he tugged her out in the aisle to follow Mabel's flashlight to the nearest exit. There was no chance to ask why or what was wrong.

A tall, regal-looking woman with beautiful red-gold hair stood outside the entrance, clutching her hands together. Remi rushed to her. "Mom?" he said with a worried look.

"I'm so sorry, darling. There's an emergency." She looked from Remi to Clare. "This must be the lovely friend you told us about." She took Clare's hands in her own as though she'd known her forever. "I'm so sorry, my dear, to interrupt like this, but we just got a call from someone named Madelaine. She said she couldn't reach either of you, but she knew you were with our son. We are the only Windspirits she found in the directory."

Clare paled. "My friend Maddy called?"

Remi instinctively put his arm around Clare. "What is it Mom?"

Mary Windspirit stepped closer. "Your mother's been taken to the hospital, dear, and that's all I know." She looked worriedly up at Remi. "Take her to the medical center right away, love, and God go with you."

CHAPTER TWELVE

Maddy, Patrick and Paul stood together in a corner of the crowded ER waiting room at the Medical Center. Heart racing and body tensing, Clare broke from Remi's grasp and ran straight to Maddy. She grasped her shoulders. "What happened?"

Maddy's startled eyes blinked. She opened her mouth, but no sound came out. Patrick stepped between them and drew Clare to his side. "Cec, hold on. Maddy's upset and scared because she couldn't reach you earlier. She's the one who found *Tante* when we went to pick her up. She was lying on the floor near the open door. We called nine-one-one and the medics—"

Clare grabbed his arms and shook them. "Just tell me. Was she breathing? Conscious?"

"Yes. No," Patrick stammered. "The medics brought her here immediately."

Remi and Paul closed a circle around Maddy, Clare and Patrick. Clare's eyes blazed wildly from Paul to Remi as Remi extended his hand toward her. She pushed away from the circle, ran past the triage nurse and bolted through the door to the ER examining rooms.

"Jaysus," Patrick said. "I've never seen CeCe like that."

"I have," Paul said. "She's terrified."

"Hasn't anyone told you what's happening in there?" Remi asked Paul. "What her mother's condition is?"

"Hey," Paul answered. "You can see how crowded it is in here. It's not like we could barge right up and say we're Margaret's family because they know different. Clare is on staff here, and they know that *Tante* Margaret is all the family Clare has."

Patrick shook his head. "We arrived right after the ambulance, but the nurse said someone would come out and speak to us. Nobody has yet."

"You must be Remi," Maddy said. "I'm Madelaine Donovan, and this is my husband Patrick." Patrick shook Remi's hand. "I'm sorry to meet you this way, but it's lucky I knew you were with Clare tonight. She told me about your date, and when we couldn't reach her cell phone, we called Paul. He found your name in the directory for us."

"Let me see what I can find out." Remi said. He approached the triage nurse. "Could you please tell me if you have anything yet on Margaret Chamberlaine's condition?"

The nurse looked him up and down. "Are you related?"

He drew his Patrol ID from his pocket and showed it to her. "I'm off duty, ma'am, but I was with Clare before her mom was brought in by the emergency team. Her friends called in the nine-one-one, and they're pretty anxious to know what's happened."

She shuffled the papers in front of her, choosing the second one from the top. "I'll check," she said, leaving her small desk to push through the ER door.

Remi checked his watch. Two minutes later she was back. The nurse's eyes never left his as she spoke.

"Mrs. Chamberlaine has a severe concussion from a blow sustained to the side of the head. She's dazed and very confused, but they are about to take her to radiology for a CT scan. She most likely will be kept overnight for observation. Clare asks you to wait a little longer until she can come talk with Maddy."

Remi thanked her, his mind whirling. A blow to the head?

really got her jumpy. Clare and *Tante* are like family, you know?"

"I didn't know about your sister's pregnancy, but Clare told me they are very close, so I can understand how she feels."

"I'm spooked about *Tante* myself. Especially what the nurse told you. A blow to the head?" Paul scowled, "Who in God's name would want to hit *Tante* Margaret? I mean, my sister just told me about *Tante* helping you scope out the evidence from the dead woman. You don't think this has anything to do with that, do you?"

Remi wished the nurse hadn't said a blow to the head. He wished the question Paul just asked hadn't popped into his own mind. He was the kind of guy who hardly ever let his feelings show, but now things were different. A muscle in his jaw tightened. "It's a possibility, but it could have been a totally different scenario. Something is missing, and it will be up to BPD to investigate."

Patrick cut their conversation short by poking his head out the hospital door and motioning them in, but as soon as he held the door open, Clare appeared with Maddy in tow. Clare took Patrick's arm and pulled him with her out the door.

"It's a zoo in that waiting room. We need some privacy." Clare shuddered. "Weekends are usually bad, but this one has turned into a nightmare." There was an underlying sadness in her words. Tears filled her eyes as she looked up at Remi. "I just apologized to Maddy, and I owe one to you. I don't usually react like a wild woman. Let's all sit for a minute on the benches under that maple tree."

"No apologies necessary, Clare," Remi said as they walked to the bench. "You acted like any daughter would." They moved as one to the tree, Clare managing to hold on to Maddy's hand.

"What did the doctor say?" Paul asked.

"*Tante* was in and out and very dazed when I got there. They had cleaned up the head wound and asked all the routine questions for a concussion, but she wasn't answering much, or she couldn't remember. Her vision wasn't clear, and I don't think she really knew me. Because of her age and the symptoms, the doctor ordered a CAT scan. That determines if there's serious bleeding in the brain." Clare choked back a sob and closed her eyes for a heartbeat.

"There were so many other serious cases needing attention in there that I took time to come out while I wait for the results. They're going to observe her overnight, anyway, so I'm staying."

Paul stood and squeezed Clare's shoulder. "She'll rally, Cec. Auntie Mame is a tough lady. Got a lot of grit like another Chamberlaine I know." He smiled and kissed her cheek. "I'm going to go back to the Pool and let Pa know what happened. When Maddy called us, we only knew she was trying to find you because something happened to *Tante*. Pa will be getting anxious, so don't hesitate to call us if you need anything, okay?"

"I will, Paul," Clare said.

"Tell Papa I'll call him first thing tomorrow," Maddy said. "Hopefully CeCe will know more by then."

Clare turned to Patrick as soon as Paul left. "Maddy said the screen door was closed, but the main door was half open and Mom was on the floor face down, as though she was headed for the living room. Did you look around to see if anything was unusual in the house?"

"No. We didn't even go into the living room. We stayed with her in the foyer until the medics arrived. We were so shocked. We didn't think of anything except finding you and getting help. Maddy made all the calls from her cell phone."

Clare shook her head. "I don't understand it. Her head had a nasty laceration. It had to be an attack . . . some unknown person followed her or came to her door. No one who knows

Mom could have done this. She didn't have an enemy in the world."

"Did she remember anything at all?" Remi asked.

"Doc says no. My friend Mary was on duty. She questioned her, too, but all Mom said was a few French words." The pain in Clare's voice was almost palpable. "I've got to talk to her!"

Clare started to rise. Remi quickly stood, took her hands and pulled her gently toward him. He spoke softly. "Let me help you, Clare. Maybe the local PD should be called in, and—"

"No!" she said in a loud whisper, a whisper that startled like a scream. Fear and regret mingled in her eyes. "I pushed *Tante* into this investigation of yours, and if what happened to her tonight is any way connected to that, I'll never forgive myself." Clare shot a helpless look to Maddy. "I've got to go back in. I'll call," she said before bolting toward the ER door.

Maddy and Patrick tried to reassure Remi that Clare was too upset to make rational decisions. "She's panicked," they said, "not herself." Remi tried not to show any emotion, but he left the hospital deeply troubled.

For the first time in a long time there's a woman in my life I admire. A woman I want to please. Remi groaned and felt his loins tighten at the thought of her. Clare Chamberlaine would be an easy woman to love . . . got to focus on what to do next . . . Proceed methodically, and leave no stone unturned. His mind was churning out possibilities as he drove.

He was almost to Lord's Castle Inn before he noticed a car following closely in his side view mirror. He kept it in view as he turned away from Temple Square and pulled into the parking lot behind the Inn. He parked in his old space in front of the garage apartment, but before he got out of his truck, the silver Mercedes pulled in and parked two cars away.

Remi let his truck idle until the man got out of his car and headed for the garage apartment door. Bright moonlight augmented the truck's headlights, providing a good view of a short, slim man with a full head of pepper and salt hair. His profile was not unusual. Short dark hair, a trim mustache and dark complexion. He was stylishly dressed in a sport shirt and tailored slacks, not the usual tourist's garb. The man's step did not falter, nor did he look around before he put the key into the lock and disappeared inside Remi's apartment.

Remi pushed through the Inn's screen door, left open to let sea breezes flow from the front of the house for cross ventilation. He could hear Chopin's "Etude" playing softly as he walked the long, wide hall into the living room. Mary Windspirit was curled up in a big easy chair. She laid her book aside on an end table.

"Sit, love. Your father's gone up to bed with a headache. I'm so sorry I had to take you from the concert and even sorrier to deliver that message to your lovely friend. Is her mother all right?"

"They don't have results from tests they did, but she's holding her own, I guess."

"That must be a relief to her daughter. Clare, isn't it?"

Remi nodded, a frown furrowing his brow.

"But not to you? You look worried, darling. What is it?"

How can I tell her it isn't just Margaret Chamberlaine's injury, but it's Clare who has me in knots? "Clare's mother was helping me with evidence in the investigation. Something suspicious happened to her tonight that's got everybody in turmoil."

"Then why did you leave the hospital, Remi? Shouldn't you be there helping the poor girl?"

The muscle in his jaw tightened. "I wanted to, Mom, but Clare's refusing my help. It's complicated, and I don't want to get into details about the investigation right now."

"You asked your father's help about the missing dory, so why am I out of bounds?"

He slipped her a sideways glance, trying to marshal his defenses, but under her gaze he found it impossible. "It isn't just the investigation, Mom. It's me. I've got feelings for Clare, and it's so complicated now, that I don't know what to do about it."

Mary could hear despair in his words. She blinked in astonishment. Remi always went to his father first with problems, big or small, but things often ended up in her lap eventually. This was the first time Remi expressed anything so personal to her alone.

"Oh, Remi, love. Matters of the heart are often complicated. The Lord steadies my heart when I am troubled. He blesses me with patience when I need it. You must be patient and always gentle with Clare, and if you are, she will come round."

Remi nodded silently and rose, unsure of anything except the knotty complexity of his feelings. "Guess I'll turn in early. Something tells me tomorrow is going to be a tough day." He got as far as the doorway when he suddenly turned. "I forgot to ask. The guy who is staying in my apartment. What's his name?"

"Name? Why . . . I think it's Smith or Jones. A plain name like that, with just an initial. That's how he signed the register. He paid cash for the week, so there is no credit card information. Why do you ask, Remi?"

"Just an uneasy feeling I have about him, that's all. I'll talk to you in the morning. Good night, Mom."

Maddy had called Paul with the news of *Tante's* release as soon as she heard from Clare, but Jacques had insisted on being the one to bring Margaret home. Jacques and Paul drove together to the medical center.

Clare pushed the wheelchair out to Jacques's waiting car. *Tante* Margaret's eyes filled with tears when Jacques Fontaine hurried to take her hand. "This is silly, Jacques; me in a wheelchair and you coming all the way into town to see me? It's only a scratch on my head, eh?"

"Not silly to offer a dear friend a hand. No, Margaret. We're here to make sure you get home safe and sound." He took over the wheelchair from Clare.

Paul opened the passenger door. "You needed some transportation, Auntie Mame, and Pa's car will be a comfortable ride," he said, helping to ease her into the front seat. Although she loved it when Paul called her Auntie Mame, the corners of her mouth turned down suddenly. She turned her head slowly, seeking Clare. "Where is your car, *chèrie?* Didn't you drive it to work?"

Clare glanced from Paul to Jacques. "It's back at my apartment for now, Mom." Clare walked around the car whispering to Paul. "She's really confused. She thinks it's still yesterday."

Not until they had her propped up with pillows on the sofa at home did Clare heave a sigh of relief. It was her first chance to check the house. Nothing in the living room looked out of place. *Tante's* purse sat undisturbed on the kitchen counter next to a box from the bakery.

"Someone is pounding like a drummer. Up here, Clare," *Tante* said, pointing to her temple. *"Mes maux de tête."*

"Of course your head hurts, Mom. You've got a nasty wound. Try to relax, okay, and I'll fix a cool compress for your head."

"First, be kind to our friends, *s'il te plait.* Make coffee for them, Clare. There should be something in the kitchen from the bakery. Forgive me, Jacques. It is too hot to bake, lately."

"I should say so. But really, Margaret, Clare shouldn't bother. I'd like to stay, but I have a class in an hour. Summer session, you know. I'm afraid I must leave, but Paul will stay, won't you son?"

"You bet, and if it's the pastry you bought when I met you

outside the bakery, I'll have some of that."

"*Oui*, it is cheese pastry. They looked good enough to eat when I came home, but I was very tired. I took a nap to rest up for your celebration, Jacques Paul."

Clare looked at Paul and rolled her eyes as Jacques bent to Margaret and squeezed her hand.

"Rest well, Margaret. I'll check in on you later."

"*Merci*, Jacques, for caring about me."

"Always," he said.

Clare walked Jacques to the door, stepping outside with him for a minute. She looked at him with mournful eyes shadowed with dark circles. "I'm getting worried about her. That business just now, about her taking a nap after coming from the bakery . . . that was the first thing she's said that makes sense. She has no memory of what really happened to her after that. She's missing the whole night."

"Margaret probably just needs time. I'll keep her in prayer, but you, my dear, need to get some rest. Let Paul help you, and please call me for anything at all. I think you know that, to us, your mother is a very special lady."

CHAPTER THIRTEEN

A wooden sign, JENSEN CONSTRUCTION, hung over the door of a weathered cedar shake house, setting it apart from other fishing cottages near the marina. There was a huge storage barn sitting in the middle of a fenced-in back lot behind the cottage.

They were expecting him. Remi had done his homework. He found building permits and land deeds for Mariner's Lofts, originally filed under the name W. Jensen Construction, the owner being Jensen/Mariner Corp. A police detective from Biddeford had requested state police assistance. Officer Meloche was a good man for the job, particularly because he was a local, knew the Jensen family, and was willing to call ahead to arrange the meeting after Remi filled him in on the details.

State Police Lieutenant Frank Meloche parked his cruiser beside Remi's truck in the driveway. He didn't hesitate or knock, so Remi followed him through the open door. The lieutenant was a balding giant of a man whose presence filled the small room. He nodded toward the elder of two men. "Will," he said, and then glanced at the younger one. "Billy, this is Sergeant Windspirit."

Billy Jensen sat in a worn easy chair to the right of the desk, his wary blue eyes watching his father. A deeply tanned, barrel-chested man, Will Jensen spread big, calloused hands on top of a cluttered desk. Muscles rippled in his forearms. "Frank. Long time no see."

124

He walked around the desk, lifted a delivery of light fixture boxes from the only other chair in the small room and deposited them on the floor. He motioned with his thumb to his son. "Get a stool from the back, Billy." Then he gestured with his hand to the chairs. "Have a seat, gentlemen, and tell me what this meeting is all about."

Meloche shot a look at Remi, and Remi answered. "Maine Marine Patrol started a retrieval and investigation in the death of an unidentified young woman found in the waters of Wood Island Harbor. A call came in last week reporting a missing tenant, a Native American woman. The caller gave the name Mariner and hung up."

Will Jensen froze, jaw dropped open, eyes wide. Billy entered the room carrying the stool. Will turned to him with a glare that was a mix of disgust and despair. "Christ Almighty, Billy! Tell me it wasn't you doin' a stupid ass thing like that."

Remi struggled to stay still and let the scene play out.

Billy's face reddened. He dropped the stool and stood defiantly beside it. "You wouldn't understand, Dad. I made the call because of Nita. I didn't want to believe it was her that might be dead." His words hung there.

Will's face tightened with anger. He swiped his hands through his hair. "Jesus, I can't believe this! That dick of yours has gotten you into deep shit this time."

"No!" Billy said, his hands tightening into fists at his side. "I knew you'd think that. It wasn't like that at all."

"Hold on now," Remi said, raising a restraining hand flat out toward Billy. "Let's back up here. You recall I confronted you in the driveway of Mariner's Lofts a couple of days ago, Billy. You remember that?"

Billy's head dropped, and without looking up he muttered, "Yeah."

"You said you were checking on something for a friend. What

were you really doing there?"

Billy's eyes flicked from Remi to Lieutenant Meloche. He dropped his head again, averting his gaze from his father's. "I was going to search the loft for anything that might tell me she was still alive."

"Who was still alive?" Lieutenant Meloche asked.

"The Indian girl who lived in one of the lofts."

And?"

"The key was gone. She used to leave the key in the mailbox, but the bastard probably took it."

Will shot out of his chair. His lower lip pushed out and his eyes narrowed. "That's it, Billy. Bad enough you've smeared the Mariner name once already. I'm not going to sit here and let you shoot off your mouth about my tenants and my business."

Frank Meloche cleared his throat. "Calm down, Will. Nobody's trying to question your business. I've known you for twenty years, and you've built yourself an honest reputation. You built my brother's house, for criminy sakes. What's goin' on here that's got you so riled?"

Will Jensen sat down and shifted in his chair. He stared out the west window of the room, a vista that rolled across wooded land to Mariner's Loft. He heaved a sigh before he spoke. "My mother's maiden name was Mariner. She left this cottage and all the land that stretches from here to beyond the lofts to me. It was her family's old ship-building business that folded here when I was a kid. I was trying to resurrect the old building, turn it into apartments upstairs, maybe have a little boat-lending business downstairs." He shook his head. "But with the market the way it is, and business bein' down, I didn't get much done." He shot a piercing look at his son.

"A guy came along who was willing to back me with seed money, but the whole thing had to be a private deal. There were strings. I had to build the lofts to his design and lease it

126

exclusively to him. I took his money and did what he wanted. End of story."

Pictures of the lofts' high-end features—custom windows, circular stairs, fancy front and back entrances flashed through Remi's mind. "We need more than that, Mr. Jensen. We need to get into the lofts, talk to your renter. We could easily get a search warrant, but I think it would be simpler if you just identify the tenant and give us a key to the building."

Will shook his head, looking menacingly at his son. "The first is not possible. The leaser is not available."

Billy snorted, and Officer Meloche suddenly stood. He put his hands on his hips. "Sounds like you have nothing to hide, Will. So let's have the keys to the building, and we'll take Junior here for a little ride."

Will Jensen's eyes blazed. He pursed his lips and stared at his son for a long moment before he reached in a drawer for keys. "I'll be over at the Johnston site, waitin' on you, Billy. I've lost enough time this morning. Frank, I'll be obliged if you'll bring him to Dock Street when you're done. We're working on new construction there." He nodded at Remi, squaring his broad shoulders behind his desk. "Sergeant, I believe we're done here?"

Remi nodded. "Yes, sir. For now."

Officer Meloche shoved his hat on and shuffled toward the door. "Take it easy, Will. I'll see that the boy gets back."

Remi followed Billy and Meloche outside. As soon as they were in the cruiser, Remi sat back and played Billy Jensen's words in his mind. "I did it because of Nita . . ." Nita . . . Awinita . . . It was beginning to make sense.

He dialed Clare's number on his cell phone. She had been racing in and out of his mind since seven this morning when he made the first attempt to call her. No answer again. This time he left a voice message. "It's Remi, Clare. I'm worried about you. Please call me."

Clare was trying to wake up. In the foggy reaches of her mind Remi was speaking softly . . . "Let me help you, Clare."

"No more nightmares, thank you," she mumbled. Squeezing her eyes shut, she daydreamed about Temple Square, the music and Remi's big hand squeezing hers. Suddenly she jolted to the ring tone of her cell phone. She was sprawled on the bed in her old room at *Tante's* house. *No need to hurry,* she thought, reaching for her cell phone on the night stand. The phone had been on voice mail since dawn—right after the doctor released *Tante* on his early morning rounds.

Propped up on one elbow, Clare listened to Remi's message then clicked the phone shut.

Paul tapped lightly on her bedroom door. She felt guilty leaving Paul to tend to *Tante* while she slept, but God knew she needed it. "Coming," she said.

"Sorry to wake you, Cec, but you've had two phone calls, and your mom is hungry. That's a good sign, huh?"

"Yes it is, but who were the calls from?"

"Maddy and your friend Mary from the hospital."

"I spoke to Maddy very early this morning." Clare paused outside her room, rubbing her eyes.

"Yeah, well it's four-thirty, now, kiddo. You slept all afternoon."

Clare motioned toward the living room and tapped her forehead. "Any better?"

Paul turned up his palms and shrugged. "A little, I think. I've convinced her she didn't miss my celebration. I told her I put it off until she's feeling better. I didn't mention anything about the hospital, but I think she's beginning to wonder about you, your work schedule and how long you're here in her house. She's getting a little antsy. Maybe that's good, too?"

"Did Mary leave a message?"

"Ayuh. She said the nursing supervisor is giving you three more days. You can come in Friday if all is well."

Clare clasped her hands as though she were praying and lowered her voice to a whisper. "Thank you, God, for tender mercies. Still, if *Tante*'s not straight about things by then, I'm taking her somewhere for an evaluation." She made a zipping her lips motion, and they walked together into the living room.

Tante was trying to use the remote. "Hey, Mom, you must be feeling better if you want to watch TV. Paul says you're hungry. Me too. Anything in the freezer?"

"There's a chicken pot pie you could defrost and heat in the microwave. It's too hot this week to cook much else. I'd like to sit at my table, but I'm a little dizzy when I move around. What do you think, my *chèrie?*"

"I think you should definitely stay put for a while longer. After we eat something, I'll help you into the shower." Clare peered at Margaret's wound, gently titling her head to the light. "Got to find a shower cap to cover that," she said. Clare raised an arm and took a whiff of her armpit. "Phew. I might jump in with you, Mom."

Paul watched *Tante* and Clare laugh together as CeCe adjusted her pillows. "My sister said she was bringing a salad over. I don't think there's much left for me to do here, is there, Clare?"

"Well, there is one small thing that would help both of us out. If you wouldn't mind driving *Tante*'s car to my apartment, you could bring me some clean clothes, and then you'd have *Tante*'s wheels to go home or anywhere else within reason, if that's what you want to do." She looked into her mother's eyes. "You won't be driving for a while, *Tante,* so I'm sure you wouldn't mind if Paul used your car, huh?"

"No, I don't mind. You said you have paintings to make, eh,

Jacques Paul? Just remember what I said to you at your father's house. Remember about the deck under your feet. Especially remember that it will be my car under your feet."

Paul laughed at Clare's puzzled look. "Now I know you're feeling better when you spout those gems of yours, Mom, but I haven't a clue what you're talking about," Clare said.

"That's an inside joke." Paul winked at *Tante*. "I'd love to drive your car, Auntie Mame, and I promise I'll be sober at the wheel. Are there keys someplace?"

Clare headed to the kitchen. "I'll look in the kitchen drawer after I put the chicken in. That's where keys usually are, but you can't leave, Cap, until I make a list of stuff I want from my bedroom."

Hearing voices inside the screen door, Maddy knocked softly and entered the house. "Hi, everybody," she called. She hesitated only a second in the foyer, then went directly to the sofa and reached for Margaret's hand. "Feeling better, *Tante?*"

"Oh, Madelaine. *Oui*, God is good to me. He sends all my dear ones to help, eh?"

"Small help I am. I only had time to throw this salad together after I got home from the doctor."

"You are all right, Madelaine?"

Madelaine squeezed her hand. "I'm fine," she said.

"I'm in the kitchen," Clare called. "Bring the salad in here, okay?" She looked up from a list she was making and smiled when Maddy set the bowl on the counter. "Tell me, babe. Did you get a date from the doctor?"

Maddy grinned and nodded. "He thinks mid-April. Maybe an Easter baby." Maddy pointed her thumb toward the living room and whispered, "Does she remember anything?"

Clare shook her head. "Only old stuff."

"Paul said you are going to stay here with her for a few days. Have you called Remi about *Tante?*" Clare looked away, but not before Maddy noticed a shadow of sadness in her eyes.

"No. He's called me twice, but I can't talk to him yet." She looked up, her eyes filled with regret. "I want to, but I can't."

Paul walked into the kitchen. "List ready?" he asked.

Clare handed him the car keys and her list. "There's a duffle bag in my hall closet, and you'll find most of these things in the bedroom dresser drawers and in the bathroom. Put the air on in the apartment because it's been off since yesterday, and it'll be hotter than Hades in there. You've been an ace, Cap. You sure you don't want to stay and eat something before you go?"

Paul shook his head. "No, I might want to wind down at your place for a little while, though. I'll make sure the air cools the apartment off and make a few calls before I bring your stuff back."

He put an arm around each of them. "Okay, my ladies. It's been a long day. Later," he said, kissing their cheeks. "Got to say so long to Auntie Mame."

CHAPTER FOURTEEN

Remi propped his elbows on the kitchen table, holding his head in his hands. "How's the investigation going?" his father asked.

"Complicated. We're running down leads."

Jamie raised his eyebrows silently and sent a questioning look his wife's way. Worry pinched her face.

"Remi, you look frazzled," Mary said. "You picked at your supper, and you've been less than civil to your father. Is it because you can't get into your apartment?"

"No. I'm used to the rollaway. How much longer is that guy going to be here, anyway?"

"Actually, he just paid for extra days. He said he was finding a lot more to see and do than he expected."

Remi grunted.

"I can put you in room two. That couple checked out this morning. You'll sleep much better, Remi. It has a queen bed."

Remi rose and flexed his shoulders. "Nah, I don't want to be shuffling around. I can handle the rollaway for a weekend. I've got something I have to take care of tonight, and I may not be back until late, anyway. Maybe very late."

Remi slid the tape into the player and backed his truck out of the Inn's driveway. Much of what he'd seen at the loft was catalogued in his notebook. The important stuff was on this tape. Except the painting. The painting in the loft was a watercolor of a fawn. Awinita meant fawn. Remi couldn't get the painting out of his mind.

Billy's voice came through pretty clear on the tape. "I got to know her pretty good. When I was working in here, putting on molding and baseboard, you know . . . finishing work. Nita had already moved in. She'd be working on her stuff at the workbench, and we'd talk."

"You're saying she talked to you about her personal life while you were working in the loft?"

"Yeah. Sometimes she told me things I really didn't want to hear, you know? I guess she trusted me because I wasn't like my old man."

"How old was she?"

"She said she was seventeen."

"How old are you, Billy."

"Almost twenty."

"What about the painting of the fawn? She do that?"

"Yep. Nita painted it . . . said that was her initials at the bottom."

"The initials are AY, but you call her Nita. How do you figure that?"

"That's what she called herself. I didn't question it. She didn't tell me any other name. Told me she brought that painting to a Native American Museum gift shop, and a customer bought it. From then on, for about a year, the same guy bought all her stuff. Nita didn't just paint, you know. She was a talented metal smith and jewelry maker."

"She probably had a parent that taught her, right?"

"Nope. Said she was orphaned when she was five, grew up in a trailer in the Everglades with a grandmother. The grandmother died, and, eventually, the SOB who bought her stuff brought her to live with him." Billy shook his head. "He's forty years old, for Christ's sake. Told her he wanted to set her up in a shop eventually. In her words, he lived in a mansion compared to her grandmother's little place."

"How did you win her confidence to tell you all this? Were you intimate with her, Billy?"

"Hell no, man. By the time the bastard brought her here from Florida, he owned her, body and soul, if you get my meaning. A lot of the time she acted kind of paranoid, you know? Wouldn't let anybody close to her. I think the man was feeding her dope. She was always scared that he would appear. I felt sorry for her."

Remi stopped the tape when he pulled into a parking space in front of Clare's apartment building. He slipped the tape into his notebook case and locked the truck.

He paused to muster his courage before ringing her doorbell. Then his head jerked up at the sound of a male voice bellowing. "It's unlocked. Come on in."

Puzzled, Remi walked into the foyer cautiously, staring straight ahead into the living room. He hadn't recognized the voice, but he had no problem recognizing Paul Fontaine lounging on the sofa, his feet propped up on the coffee table. The small table lamp didn't throw much light on Paul's face, but his bare chest glistened with sweat. Remi stared at him for a second, then walked toward him, looking into the kitchen as he passed it. The kitchen was dark.

"Hey, Remi. If you can stand the heat, come join me." He held up a glass of iced tea. "Only thing available, though, is tea."

Remi couldn't tell if it was Paul's half-dressed presence, in Clare's apartment, or his familiar tone that set him off, but resentment rankled. "Aren't you taking a chance, inviting trouble with an unlocked door?" Remi asked.

"Spoken like a true cop, Sarge. Actually, I left the door open because I thought you were the building superintendent arriving. I had to call management because CeCe's air conditioning's not working. She turned it off yesterday, and I couldn't get it

134

started today. Wouldn't you know it happened on the hottest day? We probably get two days of ninety-degree weather all summer when we have to use an air conditioner." Paul shook his head and drank some tea. "I've got all the windows open, but it's still too dammed hot in here."

Remi looked at the duffle bag at Paul's feet and shot him a steely look. "You staying here?"

Paul couldn't help a smug grin. "Uh-uh. It's not what you're thinking. That's not my duffle. It's Clare's. I drove over here in *Tante*'s old Chevy. CeCe asked me to pick up her things and bring them back to *Tante*'s house. Didn't you know Clare's staying with her mom?"

"No, she didn't tell me." Remi drew in a breath and blew it out. He felt sweat trickle down his back. Frustrated with feelings he was unwilling to admit, he reached a handkerchief to the back of his neck. He was not only hot, he was boiling with emotion that he couldn't express.

"Geez, Sarge, I thought you two were in sync. Talk to me, and I'll tell Cec you stopped by."

Remi shook his head and started back toward the door. "I'm not staying. I'll tell her myself. Good luck with the AC." He was out the door before Paul could get to his feet.

Remi drove faster than he should have and reached Margaret Chamberlaine's house in less than five minutes. He was another few minutes in the truck with the fan blasting cool air at him before he calmed down enough to go to the door. *This is not like me at all,* he told himself.

Clare answered within seconds of the bell. Surprise registered on her face when she opened the door. She immediately pulled the door closed behind her and stepped outside to face him.

"Can't we talk inside, Clare? I wanted to share some information with you and your mom."

"I'm not sure that's a good idea, and it's not possible right

135

now, anyway. She's sleeping."

Clare was standing barefoot on the doorstep, the top of her head barely coming to Remi's chest. He tilted her chin up with one finger, forcing her to meet his gaze. "I especially want to talk with you. You didn't return my calls, and I've been worried." His dark eyes were intense. "Not just about your mom. I stopped at your apartment to tell you that I'm sorry if I said anything last night to hurt you."

Clare shook her head. "You didn't."

"I want to tell you about what's happened today. It's kind of a breakthrough that your mom—"

She pressed her fingers over his mouth. "Not the investigation, please, Remi. I'm just not ready to talk about it or hear about it." Clare fought tears that burned her eyes. "*Tante* still doesn't remember being hit or much about the hospital." She turned her head away and adopted a veiled expression just as she did in the ER when families held their dying loved ones.

Remi suddenly pulled her to him, pressed her face against his chest. His hand gently caressed her head. "There is more I'd like to say to you, Clare." He swallowed hard, not wanting to let her go. "I'll wait, though, until you're ready." Remi kissed the top of her head, backed up and took her hands in his, squeezing her fingers before he turned away.

He couldn't remember ever feeling such frustration, regret, and passion all boiled together. It was torture to get in his truck and drive away. As he neared Clare's apartment, he noticed the old Chevy that Paul mentioned was still parked in front of the building. Realization jolted him. *It's stupid to be mad at Paul Fontaine. He never admitted any feelings for Clare. If I'm honest with myself, I've been wasting emotion on Paul . . . It's that old green eyed monster . . .*

Remi rang the bell but walked in without hesitation. Paul was in the kitchen packing supplies into a paper bag.

"Hey, Remi, glad you're back. It's finally cooling off in here. The super came and had that baby working in nothing flat." He flashed a grin at Remi. "It's humiliating not to have any skills in that department."

Remi leaned on the kitchen bar. "It does feel cooler in here, but it wasn't the heat that made me leave in a huff. Sorry about that, Paul. I had to see Clare."

"I figured that. Everything okay over there?"

"Can we sit down for a minute? You've been involved since the beginning of this investigation of mine, and I'd like to get your reaction to something, if you don't mind."

"Sure. Sit right here at the table. I'm just packing some supplies CeCe had on her list. The kitchen is as cool as it gets."

Remi sat uneasily. *This is where it started, at this table.* "Clare's mom gave me a lead after she viewed the evidence from the dead woman. You knew that, right?"

"Well, I knew she looked at the evidence, but I wasn't privy to anything else."

"Margaret came up with a Native American Indian name. She connected to the belt the woman wore, and she gave a vague description of a place that we already had under suspicion. The location is outside Biddeford limits, so the state police got involved. We got a look at the place today. I'm telling you this because, technically, you are still considered a witness, Paul, but anything I tell you is strictly off the record. I have a selfish reason, and I'll get to that in a minute. Do you follow?"

Paul nodded. "Shoot. I'll be as honest with you as you are with me."

"I think we've zeroed in on the place where Jane Doe lived, but we haven't got clear proof yet, and we still don't have a full identity."

"You think the information *Tante* gave brought you there?"

"Yes. It's a pair of loft apartments in a building down near

137

the water. We have reason to believe the woman worked and lived there. One end of the loft was set up like a workshop. Pliers, cutters, files and gemological instruments were neatly arranged on a long bench. The state police lieutenant lifted fingerprints from some of the tools and gauges, but nowhere did we find gemstones or silver or anything that might have been crafted there. No belts like the one found on the body, either. Nothing but tools of the trade. We didn't find one piece of evidence that identified her or the tenant that leased the building. All we have so far is her initials on a painting and a possible first name."

"And *Tante* Margaret gave you the name?"

"Yes. It fit the dead woman. It was a Cherokee name."

"Man, this is weird. Did you say there were two lofts? Was anyone in the other one?"

"Nope. One guy leased the whole building, but the other loft was empty, as far as we know. Didn't get in there. There's nothing down below, either. Just vast empty space with stairs up to the lofts. The occupied loft was as far as we got today."

"I have no idea how my opinion can be of help to you, Sarge."

Remi looked away, unsure of how to go on. "Your opinion has more to do with Clare than anything I've told you so far. Clare thinks Margaret may have been hurt because of what she did for the investigation. She feels guilty for influencing her mom to get involved in the first place. In a way, I think Clare takes more of the blame than me. She wouldn't allow me to notify BPD that night, but I had to report it later for reasons she wouldn't understand. Now she refuses to talk to me about it. She didn't even tell me she'd brought her mom home from the hospital."

Remi's eyes darkened with intensity. "I'm kind of messed up over Clare. She's important to me, and I'm unsure how to get back on track with her."

"Hell, I've known CeCe as a straight shooter all her life. I can't see her acting like this unless . . ." Paul placed a hand on Remi's shoulder. "Unless maybe she's messed up about you, too."

Remi shook his head, unable to chase away his doubts. "It sure doesn't seem like it."

"I've learned that with women, Remi, nothing is as it seems. Just when you perceive something is done, it becomes undone. Let me talk to Maddy about it. If anybody can tap into Clare's psyche, my sister can."

CHAPTER FIFTEEN

"I was dozing when the doorbell startled me, *chèrie*. I could barely hear the voice through the front window, but I guessed who it was . . . Sergeant Windspirit, eh? You sent him away. Why, Clare? Why did you do it?"

Clare had helped *Tante* shower and get into her nightgown. She set her up nice and comfy on the sofa with her prayer books and her rosary. Clare was bone tired and not ready to fudge answers. Especially answers for the Barbara Walters's shoo-in, *Tante* Margaret.

"I don't know, Mom. I'm just tired, I guess, and I didn't think you'd want to talk to Remi just now."

"Well, I know I don't look so good, but I don't think Sergeant Remi minds that. He's an officer of the law, for goodness sake. Maybe he wants to talk about what I told him about the belt, eh? You think so, Clare?"

Crap! How does she manage to zero in on what I'm trying to avoid? Clare raised her eyebrows and shrugged. "Could be, but I don't think you're ready for that, Mom."

"Me, not ready? *Non, mon petite.* It is you who is not ready. I think your heart is mixed up with your head. Remember, Clare, what my Jean used to say: 'Have a heart that never hardens and a touch that never hurts.' "

Clare was saved from trying to respond to that zinger by the ringing of her cell phone. She pulled it from her pocket and checked caller ID. "Hi, babe," she said, turning to gesture to her room. "It's Maddy, Mom." She strolled out of the living room, down the hall to her old bedroom, kicked off her slippers and flopped on the bed.

She tried to keep her voice low. "I'm here, babe, but frankly, I feel like I'm stranded in the desert with Al Quaeda on my tail."

"Paul said you only had a short nap while he was there. You're probably not caught up on the sleep you missed last night."

"I think it's more mental fatigue than physical. *Tante* is one tough tiger. Here I am trying to keep her comfortable, quiet and resting, and she just balled me out royally for not letting Remi come in the house to talk to her."

"You didn't let him in? Clare! This is the guy you said was living in your head. You learned all about clairvoyance to convince *Tante* to help Remi. What's going on?"

"You just said it. I convinced her to help with the investigation because of my feelings for Remi. Maddy, I think my mom was deliberately silenced. There's no other reasonable explanation. Somebody got to her so she couldn't do any more psychic readings. She wasn't robbed or molested, and she certainly didn't get that injury from falling in the foyer."

"What about the medics or the ER staff? Wouldn't they have called in the police with that kind of a suspicious injury?"

"They probably would have, but they all know me and know she's my surrogate mom. Luckily, because of you, I got to the ER in time for them to honor my wishes. I don't want her subjected to police questioning. I don't even want to think about it, for her sake."

"Oh, Clare. Not knowing who did this, or why, will be awful."

"I can't do anything about it yet, Mad. I just can't until *Tante* gets her memory back. When that happens, I'll let her call the shots. She has to make that decision based on what she remembers. I'm damned sure not letting this investigation come before her safety. That's why I can't talk to Remi."

"But what about him? He must be hurting."

Clare closed her eyes and swallowed a sob. "It's so hard, babe. I wanted him to hold me and make everything go away. He's so gentle and sweet. It's tearing me up not being able to pour my heart out to him. I've never felt like this with anyone before."

Maddy was silent for a moment, and in the silence Clare could hear *Tante's* voice in the other room, sounding like she was praying the rosary aloud, in French. "Hold on, Mad, I want to check something." She slipped off the bed and listened at the hall door. Prayer-like mumbling continued from the living room.

"I have to go check on Mom. I think she's praying out loud. She's been antsy and a little testy since your brother came over with my clothes, so this prayer thing is a twist. Call me after school tomorrow, or I'll call Patrick at the shop if it's something that can't wait. Love ya to bits, babe. Bye."

The Jensen Construction office was locked up tight, and the phone answered with a recorded message: "Will Jensen here. I'm in Boston on a construction bid and will return calls after September first. In case of emergency, call Billy."

Remi drove down Harbor Road looking for the address Billy Jensen had given him. Early morning fog rolled in, but he had no problem spotting the small cottage, number 408. It was not much bigger than the shop where Jensen Senior was interviewed and looked to be of the same vintage as the construction shop.

An old man was mowing a small patch of lawn in front of the cottage. He cut the motor as soon as the truck pulled up and Remi stepped out. It happened all the time. People froze when they saw the uniform, especially when they saw the tall, broad-shouldered man who wore it.

"I'm looking for Billy Jensen. He live here?"

142

The old man gave a stiff nod. He peered at Remi through rheumy eyes. "Ayuh. He lives here, but I ain't seen him."

"Is this your property, sir?"

"Nope. I worked for Missus Jensen before she passed. I take care of things for the family, ya see. Mowin' lawns in the summah and plowin' in the wintah time."

Remi strode past him to the door of the cottage. "Well, we'll just see if Billy Junior is home."

Front windows were shuttered, but Remi could hear what sounded like a high-powered fan whirring somewhere inside. No one answered his knock. He pounded a second time with his fist. "Marine Patrol. Open up." No sound.

Remi eyed the old man, still standing, watching. "Is there a back door?"

"Ayuh." He pointed to a side path bordered by beds of hydrangea and hosta. Remi walked the path to the back of the cottage, pushed open a screen door and stepped into a mud room. Through another unlocked door, he entered a small kitchen.

The stench of garbage, cigarettes and beer hung in the musty air. Dirty dishes overflowed the sink, and empty take-out food boxes and beer bottles littered a table. The contents of a broken bottle pooled on the floor amidst shards of glass and an overturned chair.

Remi walked cautiously around it to an arched alcove. A small living room was straight ahead. He could see the whole room from where he stood. It was dark and unoccupied. Walking left, he passed an empty bathroom next to a bedroom at the end of the short hall. There was no missing the sole occupant of the bedroom.

A double bed took up most of the room. Billy Jensen lay on his back across the width of it, knees bent over the edge, feet dangling to the floor. A floor fan whirred next to the bed, making little impact on the stench in the room.

Billy reeked of beer, sweat and vomit, the last dried on the front of his t-shirt. "Damn," Remi said, checking Billy's wrist for a pulse. It was weak and slow, his breathing shallow. His left eye was bruised purple and swollen shut. Blood had crusted in the hair at the side of his head and dried on the quilt beneath him.

Unhooking his cell phone from his belt, Remi dialed 911. After giving directions to EMS he leaned in close, checked the pulse at his neck. "Billy, can you hear me?" No response.

He looked around the bedroom. A single oak dresser held the usual clutter of keys, baseball cap, lottery tickets. Nothing seemed disturbed, yet he sensed violence here in this small space.

Walking back through the hall to the living room archway, he eyed the floor, then back-tracked to the bedroom again. The edge of a braided rug he hadn't noticed before stuck out from under the bed where Billy lay. He bent to examine it with his key light. Blood stains. Visually, it looked as though Billy might have been dragged into the bedroom on the rug and thrown across the bed.

Sirens sounded in the early morning air. Remi moved quickly to the living room, unlocked the front door, propped it open so the gurney could come through and stepped outside.

The old man still stood like a sentinel, leaning on his mower at the side path. He nodded, a quick jerk of his head, and Remi nodded back as an emergency vehicle screeched to a stop on the road.

Opening his truck door, Remi radioed the state police. "Marine Patrol Sergeant Windspirit calling Lieutenant Meloche. Man down at 408 Harbor Road. Holding on EMS dispatch to the medical center."

Within minutes of Remi's leading the EMS team to Billy,

they were hustling Billy out on a gurney to their van. Remi sent a short salute to the old guy with the mower, hopped in his truck and followed the emergency vehicle.

Clare greeted Jacques Fontaine at her mother's door. "What a nice morning wake-up, Papa Jacques. *Tante* will be happy to see you. Come in the kitchen and have some breakfast with us."

"Thank you, Clare. That sounds good to me. I have theses from summer classes to grade, but they can wait." Jacques leaned close to her ear. "Any change?"

Clare shook her head. "Not much, but maybe your talking with her will help."

"That's what I'm hoping for."

Margaret's face lit up when they walked into the kitchen. "*Bonjour,* Jacques," she said.

"Ah, Margaret," he said, bending to kiss her forehead. "*Bonjour, mon ami.* You're looking better this morning. How are you feeling?"

"Much better now that my Clare is here with me."

"Breakfast order, please, Professor," Clare asked. "What will it be, an omelet or sweet rolls and fruit with your coffee?"

Jacques smiled as he sat next to Margaret at the table. "Just something light. A sweet roll will be fine."

"That's easy." Clare bustled around, pouring coffee and adding rolls to a plate of orange and grapefruit sections. "I've just finished my breakfast, so if you think you will be here for a while, would you mind if I run out to do a little shopping?"

"Of course not, my dear. I'm in good hands with your mom."

"That goes both ways, Papa Jacques. I know she's glad you're here. I'll just grab my purse and be off. You two have a good visit."

"Take your time, my darling, and don't forget to stop at the

145

deli and the bakery," *Tante* said.

Clare picked up bread and cookies at the bakery, ordered cold cuts and cheese at the Café and sipped coffee latte while she dialed Patrick's shop.

"Hi, Patrick. This is CeCe. I'm just around the corner in Pepperell Square. Do you have a minute to talk with me if I stop by?"

"Sure thing. How's your mom? Not more problems, I hope."

"No, no. Not with Mom. I'm here at the Blue Elephant Deli shopping for her. I'm picking up some great corned beef and Swiss cheese. Can I bring you some?"

"No thanks, I have a bag lunch today, and we promised to go to my mom's for an early supper as soon as Maddy gets home this afternoon. But hey, come on over."

"Okay, see you in five."

Clare's mind was churning on the short drive to Patrick's shop. Hearing Maddy's opinion increased her guilty feelings about Remi. *Maybe talking to Patrick will help. He ought to be able to give an objective opinion because he isn't directly involved with the investigation, . . . he has a strong sense of loyalty and fairness, and besides, I need a man's point of view.*

The bell jangled over the shop door as Clare stepped inside. She was heading for the back room when Patrick appeared.

"Come on back, Cec, I'm hand rubbing a finish on a table, so we can talk while I work. That is, if you don't mind the smell of linseed oil and terp—short for turpentine."

"That's fine with me." Clare perched on a stool. "I had a chance to get away for errands while Maddy's dad is over to the house, trying to talk with my mom. They were jabbering away in French when I left."

"In French?"

"Yeah. That could be a good sign. Mom and Jacques are both

146

very comfortable with the language, unlike Paul and babe and me. We don't use it enough to remember. She may open up to him, you know?" Clare shrugged. "It's worth a try."

Patrick studied Clare's unusually serious face and sensed tension. "It must be hellish for you, not knowing how the injury happened. Has Remi got any leads on it yet?"

Clare drew in a deep breath. She stared at the gleaming maple table Patrick was polishing as though its shiny top could mirror her thoughts. *God, help me here.*

"Remi came to *Tante*'s to tell us something yesterday, but I didn't let him in."

Patrick shot her a questioning look. "I don't understand. Why not?"

"It's hard for me to explain. I know Remi's not to blame for my mom getting hurt, but I let my feelings for him get in the way. I practically forced *Tante* into helping with the evidence, and she got hurt as a result."

"So you think she was hurt by someone connected to the investigation?"

Clare closed her eyes and nodded. "And I don't want *Tante* involved with the police until she can remember what happened. I don't think she should be interrogated unless she is really lucid and agrees to it."

"Did you tell Remi that?"

"No. Not in so many words." She pushed up her bottom lip and sent him a sheepish look.

Patrick put his rubbing cloth aside and pulled his stool up close to Clare. "In my opinion, you have to trust Remi. What happened with your mom could have been random chance. On the other hand, it could have been connected to the evidence. Somebody may want to silence her."

Clare shuddered. "I know, but if her memory comes back, she could probably identify the attacker."

"CeCe, Remi is basically a cop. He's not going to stop investigating until his case is wrapped up. If he has agreed to wait on you for a go-ahead, then that shows he has more than a casual interest in you." Patrick shook his head. "That's not something to be disregarded. God, CeCe. Just the way he looks at you tells me that. You mentioned you had feelings for him before all this happened, right?"

Clare could feel heat creeping up her neck. She nodded. "Yes."

"Then if you really care about him, I think you should let him talk to your mom. And to you."

CHAPTER SIXTEEN

Images of Remi swept before her eyes on the drive back to *Tante*'s house. Clare couldn't get him out of her mind. He is incomparable to other guys she dated . . . they were too short, too shy, too macho, too intellectual. Remi defied all comparisons. *He's both gentle and strong. In fact, something about him radiates strength—strength that I need, yet I've been pushing him away. Neither Maddy nor Patrick think I'm being fair to him.*

Jacques Fontaine watched from the window for Clare to drive up. He greeted her at the door, put a finger to his lips and took the shopping bags from her arms. Setting them just inside the foyer, he took Clare's arm and walked with her away from the house through the small front yard to his car.

"She's fallen asleep. I was reading Psalms to her, and when I looked up after a particularly long passage, she was sound asleep." He chuckled and shook his head. "But there is more to tell, Clare, and I hope it will sound like good news to you."

"I hope so, too, because my mind is turning to mush right about now."

"Your *tante* and I were chatting away in French about the medical center and the ER where you work. She was talking about the care she received for her head when suddenly she stopped talking and laughed. She complained that no one at the hospital understood her French. I laughed with her, and then an amazing thing happened. Your *tante* suddenly stiffened, sat up straight on the sofa and gingerly touched the gash on her head. She pointed at the foyer and her voice quieted to a whisper.

" 'The man!' she said. 'The man at my door understood me. He spoke French. He asked to use my phone, and the next thing I knew I was at the hospital, mumbling in French about my head. My head hurt so badly I couldn't see or think straight.' "

"OhmyGod!" Clare said, grabbing Jacques's hand. "*Tante* remembered someone coming to her door? Did she tell you who it was?"

Jacques sent her a beseeching look. "Your *tante* was agitated, my dear, so I simply asked her if she knew the man. She said no, that he was a stranger who had a problem with his car. Margaret looked frightened, so I didn't think it wise to probe any further. I didn't want to cause her more stress, so I changed the subject and asked if she would like to hear some Psalms read."

Clare put her arms around Jacques's neck and hugged him. "Oh, Papa Jacques. You worked the miracle I've been praying for."

The corners of his mouth lifted in a sad smile. "A miracle maker I'm not. Your mother and I conversed in the language we grew up with, one that we've been comfortable with over the years. I believe that she was able to make a connection about the man at her door because her memory is coming back. Give praise where it is due and thank the good Lord for that, Clare."

"I will, for sure," Clare said as she walked with Jacques to his car. "Will you tell Paul about her, please? I'm sure he'll be relieved to hear what my mom said."

Jacques bent to kiss her cheek. "I will. Paul is in Portland helping to set up the new gallery today, but I'll be sure to tell him. Have faith, my dear, and God will sort things out."

Remi was pacing the ER waiting room, the confines of which

were getting to be all too familiar. He wished Meloche were with him. He waved a hand at the triage nurse when his cell phone rang, pointed to it and quickly exited the room.

"Remi, are you somewhere we can talk? It's Clare."

"Not comfortably, no. I'm standing outside the ER door at the medical center."

Clare stared at her phone to be sure she heard him correctly, then placed it back to her ear. "Oh, geez, I should have realized you're working, huh? I mean, it isn't anything personal, your being at the hospital, is it?"

He didn't want to get into details about why he was here, but he didn't want to push her away either. "No, but I should have time to get back to you, hopefully, within an hour. Will you be at your mother's?"

"Yes . . . please do come over, Remi. I'm sorry about yesterday."

Clare tiptoed around the house trying to tidy things before *Tante* woke up. In her mind she could picture Remi everywhere. She even reminisced about him folding her in his arms in his truck when the thunderstorm struck. She fantasized about other things he could do besides rub her back. *Don't go there, Clare . . . he may have nudged his way into your heart, but dreaming those dreams might just cost you your soul.*

She heard *Tante* stirring in the living room, trying to wake up. Clare called to her from the kitchen. "It's a little cooler today, Mom, and I'm making a pot of tea. Would you like a cup?"

Margaret sat up on the sofa, rubbing her eyes. "*Mais oui.* Is Jacques having some?"

"No. Jacques left while you were sleeping. He and I had a little talk before he left. You had a nice visit, he said."

"*Mon Dieu!* The last thing I remember, he was reading to me. I must have fallen asleep."

"So he said. He also told me you remembered something

about the day you got hurt. The day Maddy and Patrick came to pick you up for Paul's celebration."

Tante's brow furrowed as she pushed her tousled hair back, trying to tuck it into the bun at the back of her head. Her fingers grazed over the gash on her head. "Ouch. Will these stitches dissolve, Clare?"

She's deliberately avoiding the memory. "They will, yes, but the important thing is to keep the wound clean and your hands away from it. Didn't they tell you that at the hospital?"

"I don't know. You were there, *chèrie*. Maybe you told me and I forgot?"

Clare shook her head. "I didn't get there until after you arrived in the ambulance." She set a teapot and cups on the coffee table and deliberately met *Tante*'s gaze. "It was Maddy and Patrick who found you, Mom, and sent you off in an ambulance. I was at the concert with Remi, remember?" Clare poured their tea.

Tante held her cup, staring into space, deep in the web of her thoughts. When she finally took a sip of tea, there were tears in her eyes. "I tried to help him, Clare Margaret."

Oh, God. Whenever she calls me by my full name, something very serious is going down.

"When the man came to my door, I thought he was one of us . . . French, you know. He spoke French when he asked to use my phone, and he had the looks of a fisherman, like my Jean, big and brawny—" Her words stopped, and a sob erupted from *Tante*'s mouth. Tears rolled down her cheeks.

"Oh, Mom. Of course you tried to help." Clare took the cup from her and set it down. "You always help those who need it. You couldn't know he was not who he seemed—"

Now it was Clare who couldn't go on. She mirrored Margaret's crestfallen face and drew her close, pressing *Tante*'s cheek to her own. Their tears mingled. Clare groped for words.

152

The doorbell buzzed, and they both started at the sound. "Drink your tea, Mom," she told her, brushing tears from *Tante's* face. "I'll go."

Remi's intense eyes stared down at her from the doorway. A frown puckered his brow when he ran a forefinger down her wet cheek. "Tears? Are you all right?"

"I'm okay, really," she said, wiping her face with both hands.

"Maybe I should come back later."

"No, no. Please come in." Clare took his arm, urging him into the living room. "We were just having tea. Come say hello to *Tante* while I get a cup for you." She disappeared into the kitchen, relieved to tremble out of sight.

Hearing Remi's voice, Margaret attempted to regain her composure. She wiped her eyes with a handkerchief and managed a smile as he came toward the sofa.

"Sergeant Windspirit, it is good to see you. I'm afraid I'm not looking my best, but I'm better than yesterday." She patted the sofa cushion next to her. "Please come sit down."

She called to the kitchen. "Clare. Bring something besides a tea cup for our guest, please. I think some ginger cookies, okay?"

"Tea will be fine, Mrs. Chamberlaine. I only stopped to see how you two are doing. I can't tell you how sorry I was when I heard you were hurt."

"*Merci,*" *Tante* said. She looked away, seemingly threading her way through the fog of her memory, trying hard to fit things together. "Clare must have told you what happened, hmm? It was after I surprised you at her apartment on that rainy day . . ." She looked beseechingly into his eyes. "You brought your evidence to my Clare's. Right, Sergeant Windspirit?"

As she arranged cookies on a plate, Clare heard *Tante's* question. She drew in a breath and hurried into the room, drawing Margaret's attention. "Here we go," she said, giving Remi a meaningful look. *Go slow—let her take the lead.*

153

"You're right, Mom," she answered for him. "You looked at the evidence bag that day." Clare poured tea into Remi's cup and set a plate of cookies on the table.

Tante nodded. "*Oui*. I remember the belt and *grandmère*'s energy. Did it help, Sergeant?—What I told you about the dead woman?"

"Yes, ma'am. We found the place where the woman lived. You were right about that. It is near the ocean, and we're pretty sure Awinita is her given name, but I'm still waiting on a positive ID. She's not from the area, you see."

Remi drank his tea, staring at Clare over the rim of the cup. If eyes could speak, they were saying *cut me some slack; say something.*

Clare's face brightened. "It's amazing, Mom, that you found things out about a dead person by holding her belt in your hands. Remi probably needs to keep that information confidential. Isn't that right, Sarge?"

"It's partially true, yes, but every piece to the puzzle needs to be investigated. When I found out the deceased woman lived outside of town, that meant the state police got involved."

Margaret placed her fingers to her mouth, drew in a sharp breath. "Do they need to see me about that?" she asked.

"No, ma'am. Not yet. But your getting hurt right after giving evidence . . . that's suspicious. It could be related to the investigation. I don't want to frighten you, but it is a possibility. I think the local police may want to question you. No one wants you in harm's way, Mrs. Chamberlaine." His tender smile spoke words for him.

CHAPTER SEVENTEEN

Remi hated to leave. He really wanted to break the news about Billy without frightening Clare any more than she already was, but that couldn't happen with Margaret present. The session with her mom was pretty tense as it was, but there was a caveat. Clare wanted him to come back, no matter how late, so they could talk. It was a sure thing that he'd be on call late tonight, following up on Meloche's lead, but for now, it was important to get back to the medical center, pronto.

One of Jensen Construction Company's workers had found the place in Boston where Will Jensen was bidding on a job. The state police investigative team tracked down the Jensens and notified them about their son. Remi wanted to be there before they arrived at the hospital. Things didn't look good for Billy Jensen. He had not regained consciousness.

"Blunt trauma to the head sometimes results in brain injury." The doctor was talking to Billy's parents. "We've done skull and neck X-rays and a CT scan to determine the extent of your son's injury. The scan indicates contusions and swelling, but no hemorrhaging. That's good, but intracranial pressure is being monitored. We've given him medication to reduce the swelling."

Billy's mother gulped back a sob as tears streamed down her cheeks. Will Jensen looked from the doctor to Remi. "We were out of town when we got the call. When was he brought here?"

"He was brought in by an emergency team at eight-ten this morning."

155

"Can we see him now?" Mrs. Jensen asked.

The doctor nodded, then cautioned, "He's in our intensive care unit. Your son is still unresponsive, Mrs. Jensen."

Will turned steel-blue, fierce eyes on Remi. "We need to talk," he said, before leading his wife toward the elevator.

When Lieutenant Meloche arrived minutes later, Remi blew out a relieved breath. "You're in time, Frank," Remi said. "There hasn't been a chance to tell the Jensens what happened to Billy, and Will wants answers."

"Well, we're closer to an answer. Where is he?"

"You just missed him. He and Mrs. Jensen went up to ICU. What do you mean, closer?"

"The bartender at the Yardarm described a guy that was drinking with Billy the night before. Said he was a stranger, looked like he came off the docks. A big, beefy guy. Seemed friendly enough. The office is sending someone to the tavern to do a profile from his description."

"Did Billy come into the bar alone?"

"Yep. Then the stranger came in, bought him a beer and they moved to a table. He kept lining 'em up, the barkeep said. Billy tied on a good one before he shut him off."

"What about the stranger?"

"The stranger wasn't drunk, just talkative. The barkeep said you couldn't miss hearin' him 'cause he spoke like a Frenchy, you know. Heavy accent, used his hands a lot. He heard him on a cell phone at one point, confirming a pizza delivery to 408 Harbor Road. The Yardarm knew that was Billy's place, so he was glad to see the guy haul Jensen to his feet and drag him out of there."

It all began to fit together like puzzle pieces. Two people with head injuries right after they came forward in the investigation. A man who spoke French. Remi was about to comment on the similarities when Will Jensen came out of the elevator door, alone. Will flashed an angry look their way.

"They only let you stay a few minutes at a time up there, and my wife won't leave the waiting room until it's time to go back in." Will choked up a little, closed his eyes, fighting to gain control. He let out an oath and grabbed Frank's arm. "What the hell happened?"

Lieutenant Meloche extended a hand, palm out toward Remi, and gave a quick nod. Remi took the cue. "Our investigation into the death of a drowning victim has taken some twists, Mr. Jensen. After Billy showed us the loft and talked about the young woman who lived there, a witness led us to reinvestigate your loft. She gave a partial ID of the dead woman. When you were unavailable, I went to your son's cottage to question him about the person who leased the lofts. I found Billy unconscious on his bed. His injuries were suspect—not the results of a drunken brawl."

Meloche calmly described the scene at Billy's cottage, just as Remi found it. "Prints were lifted, and all suspected evidence was logged in and is being analyzed. The bartender at the Yardarm gave us a pretty good description of the guy who was with your son. A profile will go out on an APB, but we've got more to do here, Will. Billy was the second person of interest in this case to sustain an injury to the head right after coming forward to help with evidence in the drowning case."

Remi looked straight into Will's eyes, silently willing him to make the connection.

"God Almighty." Will Jensen scowled, puzzled, and turned to the lieutenant.

Frank Meloche nodded. "Same MO, Will. It's no longer a simple identity case of a dead Jane Doe. Something's rotten in the barrel."

Her faith in him mattered. Clare knew she wasn't going to be able to stay away from him any longer. She was always loyal to those she loved. She looked up, smiling, when she let Remi in. "I'm glad you came back," she said.

He walked slowly beside her into the living room. "I almost didn't come back. It's close to midnight, and I was afraid I'd wake your mom."

"Not to worry. She's sleeping soundly."

Remi sat beside Clare on the sofa. He brushed her cheek with his thumb. "No more tears, I hope. Did I cause them?"

She shook her head. "No. They were tears for *Tante* because she finally remembered what happened to her and felt so badly about it. I was waiting for her to get her memory back before I let you see her . . ." She looked down. "Or me." Clare raised her head to look into his eyes. "I was wrong to do that. I should have had more faith in you."

"Faith and doubt often exist together, Clare. I have something to tell you that proves that. Something I should have told you when we first met." The smile left his eyes. "But first, you need to hear about the investigation."

"Does it have to do with Mom and the police department?"

Remi nodded. "Place, motive and circumstance are all big factors in any investigation. Your mom confirmed the place, a big building that the state police and I were already suspicious of."

"The place by the sea?"

He nodded again. "It's an unbelievable structure. A huge building restored by the owner, Jensen Construction. It's called Mariner's Lofts. The owner's son, Billy, worked on the place. He showed us one loft and gave us information about the occupant and the guy who leased the building from his father. Billy said the leaser brought our Jane Doe to live there.

"To follow-up that lead, I went to Billy Jensen's house this morning and found him beaten and unconscious." Remi took

Clare's hand, held it tightly. "Jensen had a head injury, a severe one. He's at the medical center."

Clare shuddered. "This is unreal. Why would someone go around trying to kill people over a suicide victim? There has to be more to it."

"There is. Someone is trying to silence people. It's the motivation and circumstances we're working on, trying to flesh out a theory. It's almost out of Marine Patrol hands at this point, but I . . . uh . . . I have a personal interest that I don't want to let go of." Remi searched her face for understanding.

She felt a surge of warmth spread from her chest to her cheeks. She wanted to throw her arms around him and say, "Me too." Instead she nodded. "I understand that feeling, but what is it that you should have told me before?"

In the pause before he spoke, Clare saw a flash of sadness in his eyes.

"Something that's been under the surface since we first met. When I came to interview you about the drowning victim, you said you recognized me. You said you thought I became a big hockey star."

Clare nodded, obviously puzzled. "Yeah. That was after I remembered you were captain on the BHS all star hockey team. I checked you out in my yearbook, and that's how I knew who you were."

"Well, I denied what really happened to me after graduation, Clare. I left out a year of my life that I've worked hard to forget."

Clare eased herself back on the sofa to listen.

"I signed on with a Canadian hockey league right after graduation, and I was on a glory trip for six sweet weeks. I was the macho hockey star with a winning streak that was hard to believe." He paused, seeming to search for words. "Until my best friend and team mate was fatally injured in a game. He was a half-breed, like me. A hell of a nice guy. We had become good buddies. His death affected my performance so badly, I finally gave up, quit the team and came home. I couldn't get over it, couldn't let it go. For a long time I crawled into a shell. I was pitiful. A weakling, with no interest in anyone or anything."

"Remi, that's hard to believe. You are the exact opposite of that. You are a caring person. Everything about you is a dichotomy when I think about the job you hold."

He nodded. "You could say that now. My mom was responsible for most of the change. She has such faith, you know? She sees the good in everyone." He shook his head and shifted uneasily to face her.

"My parents expected a lot from me because they believed in me, and love was never absent from their expectations. I hadn't been home long when Mom insisted I go into therapy. My dad agreed, and the short of it is, after three months of counseling I applied and was accepted into the Police Academy. Marine Patrol was my first job, right out of the Academy." He shrugged and shot Clare a sheepish grin. "I guess you could say the change was a good one."

Clare reached her arms around his neck. Her luminous gray eyes held his gaze. "Definitely a good one. So, Sarge, tell me more about the personal interest in this case that you don't want to let go of."

Remi brought his mouth down to cover hers. The kiss was slow, soft and sweet.

A moan burst from his throat before it ended. He whispered in her ear. "I don't want to let go of you, Clare." He gently pulled her arms from him, holding her hands in his. "It's nothing against your aunt or this house, but I'd feel much more comfortable out of here, and out of uniform. We need some private time, and I don't know where or when that will happen."

Clare could see tenderness and worry in his eyes. She nodded. "Patrick's mom is coming over to be with *Tante* when I start the day shift tomorrow." She reached up to touch his cheek. "I promise to find that private time."

CHAPTER EIGHTEEN

Mary Windspirit gazed at Remi, stretched out, feet dangling off the end of the day bed, sound asleep. She hesitated to wake him. She heard him come in long after midnight, but Jamie said it couldn't wait, that it was important for him to know this first thing this morning. She shook his shoulder gently.

"Sorry, love, but you have to wake up. Your dad left a message for you."

Remi opened one eye and groaned. "Can't it wait? It's hardly light yet, and I only crawled in here a few hours ago."

"I know, son, but your father is down at the docks already, and I know you'll be wanting to join him when you hear what I have to tell you."

Remi pushed himself up, swiping his hands over his face. "What is it?"

"Captain Eddie says they can ID the guy who was with the Jensen boy at the Yardarm. One of Eddie's crew recognized him from a profile the sheriff put out. The new crewman is down from Portland, filling in for Lefty. Your father's gone down to talk to him."

"Geez, when did Dad leave?"

"Five o'clock. I've a thermos of coffee for you to take. Breakfast will be ready when you come back."

Heavy fog slowed the drive to the docks, giving Remi time to think about Jamie's message. Lefty was Captain Eddy's oldest worker. He was a crusty old Frenchman. Years of hauling traps had left him with an arthritic back, relegated to the job of banding the catch. As he eased his truck in line on the wharf, Remi could see Lefty waving his arms and moving his fingers in front of a younger man.

The tall figure of Jamie Windspirit was silhouetted by first light creeping over the water. Jamie's height dwarfed the two men.

Playing it cool might gain me an edge, was the first thought that ran through his mind. Remi pocketed his keys in his jeans, glad he was not wearing a uniform. He strolled casually toward the men. "Hey, Dad. Mom said I'd find you here. What's up?"

"Just tryin' to get a handle on things, Remi. Not sure if the boat is goin' out this morning. The wind is whipping up pretty fierce, and Cap may be waiting it out a bit. Eddie isn't here yet, but Lefty's here." Jamie clamped a hand on the old salt's shoulder. "You remember Lefty from the old fishing crew?" Jamie pointed a thumb at a young man standing beside him. "Well this is his nephew, Louie. Louie, this is my son, Remi."

Remi shook Lefty's hand and reached a hand out to his nephew, but Louie shrank back. He looked warily at Remi. "Hey," he said in a guttural voice.

"You working the lines with Eddie today?" Remi asked.

Jamie cleared his throat. "Louie knows you're with the MMP, son. Lefty just told him in sign language that he had to come forward and make a statement to the police."

Remi pulled his cap off, rubbed the back of his head and put the cap back on. "Maybe I can take care of some of this here and now, Louie," he said, speaking slowly and directly to him. "If you can give me a name, I'll take it uptown and see if we come up with a match. I'm sure your uncle will guarantee your appearance later today, right?" Remi said, raising an eyebrow at Lefty.

"*Oui.* You betcha," Lefty said, clamping a beefy hand on his nephew's arm. "If he's earnin' money takin' my place on the boat, I'm makin' sure he comes in to the police station." He signed while he talked. "Eh, Louie?"

Louie glared at his uncle, nodding silently.

"Were you in the Yardarm two nights ago while Billy Jensen was there?" Remi asked, while Lefty signed and spoke his reply.

"He was there, but he don't know no Billy Jensen. He seen that guy in the drawing, though. Plenty of times. He's in and out of the harbor bars. Keeps a boat in Portland's Old Harbor."

"That where you're from, Louie?"

Louie nodded.

"Do you know his name?"

This time Louie's words came out muffled and throaty. "I hear guys call 'im T-bone."

Lefty shook his head and grunted. "Louie reads lips, but he don't hear squat, Remi. Born deaf, but he don't forget a face."

"Tell us what you saw when you came into the bar," Remi asked.

Louie shuffled his feet. His eyes shifted to his uncle, and he signed rapidly to Lefty. "If what Captain Eddy says is true and this guy is a hit man, I don't want to be the one putting the finger on him." Lefty repeated it to Remi.

Remi looked steadily at Louie. "Anything you say will remain confidential, until such time as a suspect is brought in. If you ID him and he's arrested, then you can be under police protection until the case is resolved."

Louie looked again at his uncle, and Lefty nodded. "Believe him. I'd trust this big guy here with my life," Lefty said, looking up at Jamie. "The fruit doesn't fall far from the tree, eh, my friend?"

Jamie's dark eyes sparked at the praise. "Thanks, Lefty. Remi's a well trained law enforcement officer. His word is good, and he will respect yours, Louie, as long as you're honest with him."

Louie's testimony was half spoken, half signed: "I walked in and sat at the bar. People at the bar were turning to look at a guy talking at the nearest table. When I turned around to look, I saw this Frenchy. It was T-bone all right. I knew his face. He was pulling a blond-headed drunk guy out of a chair. Finally, he dragged the guy out of the place, and that's all I saw."

"Okay, Louie, that's a good start. I'll get back with you in a few hours. If I need to, Dad, will I have any trouble finding Captain Eddy's boat?"

"No. You go do what you have to do, and Lefty and I will hang here for a while. Eddie should be here any time now. It looks like it's gonna storm, but if the boat goes out . . ." He shrugged. "We'll see . . . Tell the queen not to wait on me. She's not to worry, either."

Remi was halfway to his truck when Jamie called to him. "You better eat a good breakfast—make up for me."

We'll see, Remi thought as he climbed into his truck. *I've been hearing "we'll see" since I was a kid. Always when they didn't want to answer or didn't know how to answer. I have to be thankful Dad gave me this lead just when I needed one, but geez! A deaf guy and a suspect named, T-Bone? I'll have to move those letters around and see if anything French comes up. What I need is some of Mom's faith.*

Mary Windspirit was taking blueberry muffins out of the oven when Remi came into the kitchen. "Mmm, they smell good." Remi said, hanging his cap on the back of a chair and sitting down at the table. "I hope they're not just for the guests."

"No, love. No guest breakfast today. These are for our table," she said, smiling. "The rooms are emptied out."

"All the rooms? Does that mean I get my apartment back today?"

"Yes." There was a distinct pause as she put the plate of muffins on the table. "The guest in your apartment turns out to be the biggest puzzle. Up until yesterday I thought that he was content to browse around the shore towns. All week he kept to himself, always left the Inn right after breakfast and didn't talk much to anyone. Yesterday, that changed. He was quite chatty at breakfast. He even asked questions about you, Remi."

"About me?" Remi's head snapped up. "Why would he ask about me?"

"I really don't know, unless your father might have been bragging to him about you. Jamie talked to him for quite a while in the driveway after breakfast. Said he asked directions for the quickest route to Portland airport. It was a total surprise when Mrs. Boudreau came in from her morning rounds with your linen and the apartment key in an envelope. He left her a ten-dollar tip and was gone before noon."

Remi tilted back on the chair, scowled and shook his head. Something niggled at the back of his mind. Something about that guest that he should have checked out a week ago. "That's weird. I mean to ask Dad what this guy talked about, for sure. Meantime, Dad says not to wait breakfast on him. He'll be back later. I have to eat real quick and get into uniform. I have to see the state police investigator, pronto."

Mary set a plate of sausages and eggs in front of Remi. "Does that mean that Captain Eddy's tip panned out?"

"Yes. Actually, the tip came from the new boatman working in Lefty's place."

"Lefty's still around? Good heavens! He was ancient when your father first went to work for Eddy."

"One and the same man, and lucky he was there. The new guy is Lefty's nephew. He's deaf and a reluctant witness. He might have taken off if Lefty wasn't with him."

His cell phone rang just as Remi took his first bite of sausage. He checked his watch as he looked at caller ID. State police.

"Remi here." He closed his eyes, listening. "Oh, God." He looked at his mother, stood up and pushed away from the table. His mouth tightened in a thin line as he drew in a deep breath, then blew it out. "I'm on my way."

"What is it, love?"

Remi clicked his phone shut. "Billy Jensen just died."

CHAPTER NINETEEN

A nurse who worked intensive care stopped at Clare's ER station on her way off duty. Clare often joked with this nurse and had dubbed her facetiously Nurse Not Ratchett because she was usually upbeat and positive. Today, the woman's theatrics took Clare by surprise.

Resting her elbows on the station, the woman swiped her hands over her face, then stretched them out in front of her, palms upward. "Christ on a cross! Why did I ever think I should be a nurse. Life just ain't fair, Cec."

Puzzled, Clare cocked her head and stared. "That doesn't sound like the Nurse Not Ratchett that I know. What happened to you?"

"Billy happened. He didn't make it, Cec. Never came out of a coma. He died at six-o-five, barely nineteen years old." She closed her eyes, shaking her head. "He was beat up bad, but when I closed his eyes, I wasn't seeing his battered head. All I could see was the cute blond-haired kid he used to be when he played with my kid brother. To make matters worse, Billy's mother collapsed on me when he passed, and I nearly lost it. I'm a mom too, you know."

"Oh God, oh God!" Clare whispered. "Are you talking about Billy Jensen?"

The nurse nodded. "I've got to get out of here," she said. "Maybe the wind that's blowin' out there will clear my head."

Stunned beyond words, Clare walked to the window and

watched her friend struggling against the wind to open her car door. The sun was buried under thick, heavy clouds, and a cold wind was blowing. It called to mind a scene almost a year ago when a hurricane blew in off the coast when a head injury sent her friend Maddy back in time.

Tante's head injury pressed on her mind. If only she had second sight like *Tante*. If only she could see into people's minds and know what made a drowning woman trigger such terrible happenings. *Tante* could have ended up dead, like Billy Jensen. Clare shuddered and went back to the desk. Thankfully, no one was waiting in triage. The ER had been strangely quiet since her shift began.

The examining rooms were still empty a half hour later when Remi came through the corridor from the elevators. A man wearing a sheriff's uniform walked beside him. Remi paused at the desk, speaking in a voice just above a whisper.

"If you tell me what time you get off, I'll meet you at your apartment—later." A muscle in his cheek twitched. He shot a look toward the officer standing waiting at the door.

Clare whispered, "Three o'clock."

"It might be later than that, but I'll call your cell phone, okay?"

She nodded. "Okay."

Mrs. Donovan had not only been a great companion for *Tante* while Clare worked, she had invited her home for dinner. Relieved but nervous, Clare went straight to her apartment, showered and changed into comfortable jeans and a cotton pullover. The stormy day didn't help her mood. She turned away from a window filled with storm clouds and closed her eyes to the rain. Talking about Billy Jensen's death was not going to be easy. She was determined to let Remi take the lead on that subject.

Her cell phone rang at five o'clock. "I'm calling from a block away, Clare. If you don't mind a wet and tired visitor, I can be there in two minutes," he said.

Clare didn't mind one bit. She'd been dancing around the clock, watching the rain slash at the windows, waiting for the phone to ring.

She lit one of her scented candles, sat in her most comfortable chair and held her hands out in supplication. Her voice was a soft chant: "Angel, Adnakiel, empower me with light and love."

The doorbell rang in answer, and her smile as she went to the door turned into a laugh at herself, at the weirdness of what she just did. *But, that's what my new little book about angels said to do . . . Call on Sagittarius's angel. God knows I need his power!*

Remi stood at the door, the peak of his baseball cap dripping water on a large pizza box in his hands. He took off his hat and extended the box toward her. "I didn't have time for lunch today. Care to share?"

Clare ushered him into the kitchen. "Actually, pizza is perfect on a rainy day." She took the box from him, noticing how wet his sweatshirt was. "You were wearing that shirt when I saw you early this morning. No uniform today, Sarge?"

"You're very observant, Miss Chamberlaine. I've had no time to change clothes—or eat. It's been a long day."

"Well, let's see what we can do about that. She opened the pizza box, put slices on a paper plate in the microwave and motioned Remi to a chair. "Sit here for a minute. Take the pizza out when the bell rings, and I'll be right back."

She returned with an oversized flannel shirt, faded and soft from many washings. "This belonged to my dad. I wear it around the house on days when I need his comfort. As long as we're sharing food, you can share his comfort." She put the shirt on the table. "Give me your wet shirt and put this on

170

while I throw yours in the dryer."

Twisting his mouth sideways and cocking his head as though he was trying to decide, Remi hesitated. Finally he stood and raised an eyebrow. "Sounds like a good deal," he said, smiling and pulling his wet shirt over his head.

Clare wasn't prepared for the sight.

Shoulder muscles rippled. Lots of black hair curled and glistened across his broad chest, beading a line down into his jeans. She drew in a breath, grabbed his wet shirt and exited the kitchen, fast.

When she returned, Remi was eating a second slice of pizza. "Sorry, but I'm starving." He pointed at his chest and the half-buttoned shirt. "A little snug, but it feels good. Thanks, Clare."

Clare bit her lip and tried one of *Tante* Margaret's zingers. "*Tante* would say, 'If it keeps you from getting a chill, then God has sent tender mercies when they were needed.' "

She sat down next to him and stared at the pizza, wondering what to say next. She would rather not bring up Billy Jensen. It scared her to even think about it. *What if the killer thinks I know what Tante knew? I could be next!*

"So what's kept you busy today, Remi?"

"Good things and bad. I'll start with the bad, cuz you probably heard it at the hospital, anyway." Clare looked up to meet his gaze. "Billy Jensen died today."

With those big brown eyes fixed on her, she couldn't lie. She pursed her lips and toyed with the pizza plate. "I know. I found out at the hospital, but the knowing made it too scary to tell *Tante*." She raised her eyes to his. "Is that why you wanted to talk here at my place?"

"Partly, yes. I wanted you to know and understand what happened earlier this morning, before I got the word about Billy." Remi reached to brush his thumb along her cheek. "The knowing might ease your mind, okay?"

171

Clare clenched her hands under the table. "Are you going to tell me that *Tante* has to come forward to the police?"

"Maybe, maybe not. Hear me out first. Early this morning I got a lead. Someone related to a guy in Dad's old fishing crew recognized the profile of the man who was with Billy the night before he died. He gave us a name. Actually, it wasn't the right name, but state police ran several configurations through the system and came up with a match to the profile. He's from Portland."

"That's it? Nothing else about him?"

Remi paused and reached for Clare's hand. "Yeah. He's had prior arrests for drugs, and he's French. That's what you can tell your mom after we find him."

Clare's palms were sweaty. She squeezed Remi's fingers. "Do you really think you'll find him?"

"This morning's witness ID'd him from a mug shot, so unless the guy left the country, we'll find him."

"Then what happens?"

"We start working on motive. The police suspect he may be a hired hit man, and if that's the case, then he's probably holed up somewhere nearby. In my gut, I believe someone and something else is involved here. It could get messy, Clare."

Clare slumped in her chair, shook her head. "This has become a lot more complicated than a drowning-suicide, Remi. I'm beginning to wish I never saw that dead body floating on Paul's marker."

Remi pushed back from the table, reached for her arms and tugged her out of her chair, onto his lap. "Then I would never have met you, would I?"

He pressed her head against his chest and buried his chin in her hair. "This is the personal time I need, Clare. I wanted you to know about the case for your mom's protection, but I had other motives for being here. I need to be alone with you for

172

other reasons."

She could feel his heart thudding under the mat of silky chest hair. They seemed to breathe in rhythm. His bare skin felt like fire against her cheek. She could smell soap and sweat on his skin.

Remi turned her face up to his with one finger under her chin, his dark eyes blazing.

"Something terrible happened that brought us together, but something good was the result. I care about you, Clare, and I don't want us to end." He threaded his fingers through the short curls around her face and lowered his mouth to hers.

His kiss thrilled her. She clung to him, wanting more. He heard her whimper, and he pulled back, his hands still cupping her cheeks. "Did I do something wrong?"

"No, no. You didn't. I wanted you to kiss me . . . I've wanted you to for quite a while."

He blew out a sigh of relief. "My head says I shouldn't let my personal life interfere with my job, but it has, Clare. I can't get you out of my mind."

Clare stared steadily into his eyes. She saw her own longing reflected there. Pointing to her head, she closed her eyes. "You're living up here too, but I'm so overwhelmed with all that's happened, I'm afraid now to let my feelings take over."

She pressed her cheek against his shoulder. Remi stroked her head and rubbed his strong fingers in a soothing pattern over her back.

"Afraid to let love in, Clare?"

She reached for his hand and held it tightly. "It's strange that you ask that because I said something similar today. I did something I've never done before. I asked my celestial angel to do what you just asked . . . to empower me and let light and love into my life."

He swallowed to squelch a chuckle. "Celestial angel? Do you

mean your guardian angel?"

"No. My Sagittarius ruler angel. A celestial angel named Adnakiel. His energy and wisdom is supposed to bring clarity to your dreams, lift them skyward to a more fulfilling future." Clare lifted sparkling eyes to his. "That's what my book on angels says."

Remi's eyes were wide, his lips curled in a smile. He tucked his fingers under her chin. "I'm not laughing at you, Clare. I'm amazed at you. You are the most honest, forthright person I've ever known." He kissed the tip of her nose. "And the most lovable, too. I think your angel is on my side."

CHAPTER TWENTY

"I owe you, Dad. Big time. State police are searching for the guy who Louie ID'd. Did I tell you his name turned out to be Tibeault, not, T-bone?"

"Tibeault!" Jamie shook his head, laughing. "I'll bet Lefty got a rise out of that one. For all his rough, tough shell, that old guy is a cream puff. I know he tries his best with Louie."

Remi swung a duffle over his shoulder, shoved his toiletry kit under his arm and picked up his laptop. "Got to move it, Dad. Would you grab those clothes on the hangers? It'll save me a trip."

Jamie nodded, following his son out the back door of the Inn and across the drive.

"Man, I'll be glad to get back to my own bed." Remi said as he climbed the stairs.

"What! We don't treat you right in the big house?" Jamie laughed. "Only kidding. I do know what you mean about wanting to be in your own bed."

Remi shifted the laptop under his arm and opened the apartment door with his key. Both men looked around. "Everything looks okay in here," Jamie said, as he hung the clothes in the closet. "The guy must have been pretty neat."

Remi laid his computer atop the small desk. He turned the key in the file drawer and checked his manuals. "Nothing's been disturbed," he said. "No signs of tampering with the locked drawers."

Hands on his hips, Jamie scowled. "Tell me why a guest would do something like that?"

"You tell me. Mom says you talked with him for quite a while the day he left. What did he have to say?"

Jamie scratched the back of his neck and shrugged. "He asked if I did anything else besides run the Inn, and I told him I used to fish for a living. He asked if you fished with me, and I told him no."

"What else did you tell him?"

His father smiled that winsome smile that was definitely a Windspirit charmer. "Well, I told him how proud we are of your work on MMP. Not much else. He said he didn't know anything about Marine Patrol or what they did. He only knew about Coast Guard. Why so curious?"

"Mom said he asked her about me, too. It doesn't seem to me that his questions were idle curiosity, that's all."

Jamie shook his head, seemingly mulling over Remi's suspicions. "The man was kind of odd, come to think about it. Most of our guests like to sit around and talk in the evening. They're pretty sociable you know, but this guy never said anything until his last day. Then he took off without telling us he was leaving."

The thought plagued Remi. "How did he sign the register? Do you know?"

"No. I don't get into that. The queen takes care of the books."

"I'll check it out—later. Got big business downtown."

Clare took deep breaths of the crisp air drifting in her car window. It was a welcome change from the heat wave that broke after a storm closed out the first week of September. She pulled to a stop at the wine shop. The Donovans had invited them for dinner, and Clare volunteered to bring wine. "Roll up your window, *Tante,* and lock your door. I should only be a few minutes."

Tante clicked her tongue and mumbled something that Clare didn't hear. "*Mon Dieu.* She worries things to a frazzle lately."

True to her word, Clare was back in a jiffy, putting her purchase on the back seat. "I bought three bottles of a good Chardonnay 'cause something tells me we're going to eat lobster, what d'ya think?"

"It's a good guess. Everything will taste good, eh? I will be spoiled, having dinner out two nights in a row. Patrick's mama had an Irish stew last night that was *délicieux. Si bon,* Clare."

"I'm not sure about Maddy's kitchen skills, but I know Mrs. Donovan is a good cook, like you, Mom."

"We have other things in common," Margaret said, raising a brow with a sideways glance at Clare.

"Like what?"

"Like, we have daughters who worry over us all the time."

"Now, *Tante.* You know we have to be cautious while this investigation is still going on." *If she knew about Billy Jensen, she'd appreciate my being cautious. If Maddy knows, I'm gonna have to alert her not to say anything.*

Clare parked outside the restored Mill Complex apartments. "Okay, out of the car, *Tante.* We're right on time."

Clare rang the bell but walked right in. Maddy and Patrick met them in the long hallway. Patrick wrapped *Tante*'s arm over his. "Right this way into our kitchen, Mrs. Chamberlaine. I need your advice."

Clare walked arm in arm with Maddy to the great room, whispering to her. "I'm really glad we're here, babe. Things are getting tricky with her nibs."

"I'm glad you are here, too." She peeked into the bag Clare carried. "Your wine choice is perfect, CeCe. Patrick's cooking lobster, and Paul will be especially happy. We're trying to make

177

up for his failed celebration, you know."

"I was sure that's what this was about." Clare moved close to Maddy's ear. "Has Paul said anything about the latest in the drowning investigation?"

"No, and since school started, I haven't had time to even think about it. Why? Has something happened?"

"Well, please don't bring it up in front of *Tante*. There's been another attack on a person of interest in the case, and this one resulted in death. *Tante* doesn't know."

Maddy raised her eyebrows and opened her mouth, but Clare's words were punctuated by the doorbell. "Oh, Lord, Cec," she whispered, "I can't wait to hear—" But there was no more time. Maddy grabbed Clare's hand and pulled her with her, to the door.

"Hi, Papa and Kathleen," Maddy said, greeting the first two through the door. "And . . . who is this behind a bouquet of flowers? A-ha. My illustrious brother!"

"Hi, babe." Paul handed Maddy the bouquet and kissed her cheek. "It's amazing what a few posies will do. I don't think I deserve that greeting, but I'll take it, and I'll take a kiss from my favorite sailing partner, too. Hey, Cec, it's been a while." Paul's lips brushed her cheek with a noisy smack.

Clare laughed. "Yeah, it has been a while. I'm glad, though, that I finally get to congratulate you on the exhibit, Paul. It isn't every day I get kissed by a featured *artiste*."

Clare took Jacques's arm and walked with him and Kathleen into the living room. "My *tante* is in the kitchen with Patrick," she said. "I know she'll be glad to see you, Papa Jacques." She leaned close to whisper in his ear. "Her memory is back, and she's doing pretty well."

He nodded. "Madelaine told me when she called about dinner. Thank God for that, Clare."

They were about to sit when Maddy and *Tante* came from

the kitchen, carrying covered dishes to the buffet. She motioned *Tante* to a chair at the table and called for everyone's attention. "We're going to divert a little from the usual this evening."

"I'm dispensing with a cocktail hour," Maddy said as she poured the wine. "Patrick says the lobster is ready sooner than expected, and Clare brought this nice wine, so, please, everyone, come to the table and we'll raise a glass to Paul and his new beginnings."

"How lovely," Kathleen said. "New beginnings. It was just last year when we toasted new beginnings for you and Patrick, Madelaine." She smiled up at Jacques. "Remember, darling?"

Jacques's face glowed. "Of course. Their announcement made me a happy father of the bride" He winked at Maddy. "And now, hopefully, I'll be a grandfather and you'll be an uncle, Paul." He moved close to Paul and whispered, "Your mother would be very proud of you." Jacques's eyes filled with tears and Patrick quickly raised a glass.

"Here's to a bright future for Paul. We're proud of you, Buddy. *Slainte*, everyone." Glasses clinked together around the table.

Tante cleared her throat. "I wish you the best, *mon chérie*. Just remember the deck under your feet is preferable, eh."

Paul threw his head back and laughed. "I won't forget, Auntie Mame." He reached across the table to click his glass with *Tante's*. "Here's to both of us staying out of harm's way."

Clare rolled her eyes.

Maddy caught her breath and tapped her glass with a spoon. "Chef Patrick, take your station in the kitchen, please, and if everyone will sit, I'm going to pass the potatoes and corn, family style. As soon as you take your veggies, you can carry your plate to the kitchen and pick up your lobster. *Bon appetite*, everybody."

With a little help from *Tante*, Patrick turned out to be masterful in the kitchen. The lobster was succulent and sweet, and the homemade desert got many compliments, especially from *Tante*.

Lively conversation centered on the paintings Paul would be exhibiting. Tension between Paul and his father seemed to have disappeared, and Paul glowed with all the attention.

Kathleen and Jacques were the first to leave. *Tante* was in the kitchen, helping with the clean up, when Clare cornered Paul. "I need to tell you something, Paul. I don't mean to spoil the festivities, but you really need to hear this."

"Okay, CeCe, shoot."

"Worse things than my *Tante*'s injury have gone down since last week. You wouldn't know about this unless you're in the habit of reading the daily obituary column. A guy named Billy Jensen was attacked right after my mom. The police have kept the circumstances about it quiet, but Billy was a person of interest in the case. He gave information about the dead woman, just like *Tante* did." Clare closed her eyes momentarily, taking a steadying breath. "Billy Jensen died from his injuries, Paul, and it's scared me half to death."

Paul's eyes widened. "Jesus. I don't wonder." He glanced toward the kitchen and leaned in close. "Does *Tante* know?"

"No and I'm not telling her—not yet."

"Do they have a line on who's doing this?"

"Well, yeah. A state police detective stepped in, and Remi got a tip. There's an all points bulletin out, plus a BOLO."

"Geez, CeCe, you're beginning to sound like a cop. What the hell is a BOLO?"

"Yeah, well Remi explained that. It means 'be on the lookout.' "

"You got all this from Remi?"

Clare nodded, her cheeks coloring. "We've become pretty close."

Paul clutched her arm. "Listen. This is your big brother talking now, Cec," he said sternly, ruffling his fingers through her hair. Then he gentled his voice. "So I want you to take a little brotherly advice, okay? I guessed your feelings for Sarge a while back. A blind man couldn't miss that connection, but the turnaround in this supposed suicide—now a homicide—has become way too dangerous. I think you should cool it with Remi."

Clare closed her eyes and shook her head. "Dangerous? Uh-uh. Remi would never let me be in danger."

"He is a law enforcement officer, isn't he? Did you ever stop to think your involvement with him could bring you under suspicion? After all, you did discover the woman's body! Disasters, like dominoes, followed your discovery. It has become too dangerous, Cec. Not just for *Tante*'s sake, but your own. You could be the next victim!"

Luckily, the kitchen crew came into the room at that moment. Clare was feeling as though she'd been backed into a corner—a corner she couldn't easily get out of. *Tante* solved the dilemma.

"Time to go home, *ma chérie*. Are you ready?"

Lieutenant Meloche sipped his coffee. He scanned the place from a back booth. Annie's Coffee Park was a fishermen's favorite, but it was eight A.M. and the restaurant had almost emptied out. Still the two men kept their voices low and checked the traffic coming in and out.

"I got the word on Jensen's funeral arrangements. It's next Monday at Good Shepherd Lutheran."

Remi stared at him, wishing he hadn't heard him. His jaw clenched at a sudden flashback of his friend on the hockey team, dead in the prime of his life. In his mind's eye he was watching a cocky Billy Jensen, standing in the rain by his red truck outside Mariner's Lofts.

I was just checkin' out something for a friend. Billy's words echoed in his mind.

"My wife heard Mrs. Jensen is taking it real bad. Will Senior got the skinny on the profile the sketch artist put out, and he's putting pressure on BPD. Will doesn't believe the death was the result of a mindless act. He wants the FBI called in. 'Course that will be standard procedure in a homicide, but Will wouldn't know that."

Remi shook his head. "Can't be the results of a mindless act. I didn't buy that from the beginning, Frank, and you didn't either." Remi stroked the stubble on his chin. "It's hard to believe my initial investigation into a suicide drowning has careened into a probable homicide. I've been involved with search and rescue, lobster theft and complicated fishery disputes, but this is a first for me, Frank. If the feds come in, MMP probably won't get in the mix, will they?"

"You could be in the barrel if a task force is established. Our CID unit would be chief investigators with the feds. Depends on what's involved. I was talking to a crime tech guy about the evidence pulled from Billy's place. It's possible that DNA evidence transferred during a struggle between the perp and Billy. Analysis isn't conclusive yet."

Lieutenant Meloche finished his coffee and eased his big frame out of the booth. He clamped a hand on Remi's shoulder. "Well, Sarge. Let's go see if they've got anything this morning."

Before they opened the doors of the patrol car, they heard a call coming in over the wire: Boat owners at Charley's Marina reporting gunfire on the docks after midnight last night.

"Geez, that's home territory for me." Remi said. "I keep my boat at Charley's."

"I thought you drove the patrol boat that's in the harbor."

"I do, on assignment, like when we retrieved the body from Wood Island waters, but the boat at Charley's Marina is my own. That baby is just for pleasure."

Remi checked with the only boat owner he found at the marina, an old fisherman living out his years on a dilapidated houseboat which looked as old as he was. He said he was awakened by what he thought was an explosion. By the time he got up on deck there was a second noise, definitely a gun shot. He saw the tail lights of a small speed boat racing off toward Saco River.

One thing Remi learned from his Dad: fishermen are a clannish lot. They're loyal and they protect their own. This old salt was no exception. "Couldn't see much," he said. "A few young fellers moor their fishin' boats down this end of the docks. I think it was those young bucks fightin' over God knows what and raisin' hell with guns. Couldn't tell which boat the shots came from, and didn't see nothin' but a small boat gunnin' the engine, churnin' water, and takin' off."

Involved as this case had become, Remi admitted to himself that his investigation of Jane Doe had moved to the end of the road for Marine Patrol. He spent the rest of the day traveling to Boothbay regional headquarters. He documented all procedures and evidence with the captain. Everything from retrieval of the body to Margaret Chamberlaine's testimony, her injury and the death of witness Billy Jensen. The captain agreed that pursuit of the Jane Doe drowning would probably be in the hands of the Criminal Investigation Division of Maine State Police. Any further involvement for MMP was a moot question.

Remi climbed out of his truck at the Inn parking lot and headed for his apartment. It was a little after four o'clock, and he was determined that nothing he'd learned today would spoil this weekend. Marine Patrol men were always on immediate recall, no matter their shift, *except* when on vacation, and day one of vacation was about to begin.

He checked his E-mail. The only message was from Paul Fontaine, in very few words. "Hey Remi, give me a call, please." Later, Paul . . . much later.

CHAPTER TWENTY-ONE

Clare faced the truth. She knew she wanted Remi Windspirit—in all the ways a woman wants the man she loves. Despite all the bad that had happened, she was determined "to let love into her heart." Nothing stopped her thinking about him, the longing for his tender-hearted caring, his gentleness. Not her worries about *Tante,* not the horrible consequences of the investigation and certainly not Paul's warning. She knew Paul had her interest at heart, but she had come to a conscious decision.

She accepted a phone invitation to spend some of that "private time" that Remi was looking for. "Very private time," he said. "A moonlight boat ride." His mom had packed a picnic supper for two, and he would pick her up at five o'clock. She was going to tell Remi how she felt.

Clare rented a movie for *Tante* to watch, made sure there was supper to eat and prompted *Tante* to agree not to wait up for her. Back in her own apartment, Clare soaked away her frustrations in the tub. She had to get dressed here, in her own place, paying meticulous care to every detail.

At the last minute, she decided to add the topaz necklace she wore when Remi first took her to lunch at Ocean Park. It seemed to bring her luck. *After all,* she thought, *it is the star stone of Sagittarians.*

The necklace glowed in the v neck of her favorite sailing shirt, a black and white pullover with little anchors on a wide

185

sailor collar. She pulled it down over hip tight jeans and went searching for a windbreaker. It might be chilly on the water at night. She crossed her fingers that she would have comforting arms to warm her.

When the door bell rang promptly at five, she took her time answering it. She touched the smooth topaz of her necklace. *Keep him waiting just a bit.*

Clare's stomach fluttered as Remi's gaze traveled from her head to her toes. She blinked at him.

"Am I okay for the boat?"

"You're better than okay. 'Course it's not a fancy sailboat like Fontaines', but fact is, you'll grace my little cruiser and make it look like a yacht." Remi took her arm and escorted her to his truck.

She was determined not to talk about anything except their destination and the surprise picnic his mother had made. But Remi's mention of the Fontaines' boat prompted Paul's niggling warning that still rankled. The warning festered like a sliver. "Did you happen to speak to Paul Fontaine before you called me?"

"No. He did send me an E-mail, asking me to call him, but I didn't because there were more important things to do." Remi grinned, raised his eyebrow and shot her an inquisitive sideways glance. "I don't need his permission to take you out, do I, Miss Chamberlaine?"

His grin was infectious. Clare chuckled. "No, Sarge," she managed, relieved to brush Paul's warning aside. "I'm looking forward to the boat ride. I hope it wasn't trouble for your mom to make a picnic for us."

Remi swung his truck into the marina parking lot and turned his full attention to Clare. "That would never be trouble for my mother. She loves to cook, and she loves to please. She said she would like to meet you, Clare, under kinder circumstances than that night at the concert."

Remi didn't wait for a response. He reached across to push the passenger door open, resting his hand on her shoulder. "I love to please, too." His lips grazed her cheek and electric current spiraled down her neck.

Remi grabbed the picnic basket and a duffle from the back. "Let's go," he said. "The boat is three docks down."

Clare looked out to sea. A few sail boats dotted the lead-colored water in the bay. The last rays of sunlight glistened on the western curve of the shore. She was glad that the sea was calm. A choppy sea wouldn't make for a romantic ride. Boats bobbed against their fenders as water churned against the docks at high tide.

A large yacht backed slowly out of its mooring, and Clare paused to watch it go.

"My boat won't look like that. Look down to the end of the third dock, next to the catamaran. She's blue and white. I named her *Cherokee,* but my mom dubbed her *High Hopes,* so I had both names put on her hull."

"*High Hopes?* For you?"

"I guess." He shrugged, smiling awkwardly. "I bought the boat just after I had been hired on the Patrol, and my folks had a lot of confidence in me. That was then, and this is now, Clare. Are you ready?"

Clare followed Remi's long legs down and across three docks, taking two steps for every one of his. One glance at the boat and she could tell that he must have come to the docks earlier. There was no cover on the boat. The deck looked scrubbed clean and the rails and windshield were gleaming. Two deck chairs were positioned facing the stern rail, and a big cooler sat by the leeward locker.

She smiled at Remi and unhooked the fore rope from the

dock cleat. "I'm ready," she said, stepping smoothly down into the boat.

Remi cocked his head and stared. "Well, now." He handed her the picnic basket and tossed the duffle down. "Guess Paul's sailing lessons paid off. Looks like you won't need any instructions from me."

A wily expression crossed her face. "Oh, but I will. *Julie's Dream* is a sailboat," she said. "Some things are the same, but really, Sarge, this kind of boat is a first for me."

"I'll have to make it first and best, then." Remi took Clare's hand and pulled her to a cockpit seat opposite the wheel. "You can be my navigator. Once I back out, if I get too close to the markers, give a holler. It's a short ride to Channel Island, but I might need help if it's busy out there."

He stowed the ropes, put the picnic basket inside the large cooler and took his seat at the wheel.

It wasn't busy. Most of the traffic was heading into the harbor; fishermen coming in with a day's catch.

"Ever been to the island?"

"Nope. We sailed past it, though, on *Julie's Dream*." *Stop it, idiot,* she told herself. *That's not where I want to go.*

"It's nice. Mostly wooded, with cleared groves at each end. If folks have beat us to it, we'll anchor out a ways and eat on the boat."

"Sounds good to me."

The *Cherokee* plied the water at a leisurely five knots. Clare leaned back to let the wind blow through her hair. A pale moon was visible, low in a cloudless sky. She closed her eyes, remembering the night she first met Remi, out of uniform . . . listening to jazz music and watching Sagittarius in a star bejeweled sky. She had wished then that she was sharing his blanket at the concert in the park. Her wishes had come full circle.

Remi nudged her. "Hey, no sleeping allowed. Channel

Island's coming up."

Clare's head jerked up. She stared at a tree-studded island dead ahead. Waves beat against its rocky edges.

"There are shoals at the north end, but just enough sand bar at this end for a safe approach." Remi stood, maneuvering the boat to drop anchor in an inlet with a ragged shingle of beach. A rocky path led up the steep side of the island to a clearing, but no one was in sight.

"Looks kind of deserted. Is it usually?"

"Pretty much. We'll sit here a while, watch and see. Maybe we won't have any company at this end of the island."

Remi pulled a corked bottle of wine from the cooler, handing plastic wine cups to Clare. He grabbed the hamper, pointing the bottle aft. "There're holders on the deck chairs. Shall we?"

Her mind was tap dancing through the details. Picnic supper, calm water, deserted island . . . "You surprise me, Sarge. Such a polished host."

He smiled, reached for her hand and sipped his wine. She stared at their entwined hands, his thumb kneading her fingers.

"There's been no time for us, Clare, and I told you that I've wished for it."

A light breeze rippled the waves. A shiver traveled down her spine, but it wasn't from the cool breeze.

"I want to know you, Clare. All about you. Your favorite things, your gripes, your dreams, and your demons." He faced her. "Your desires?"

She gulped. "You may not like what you hear."

"No chance of that," he said, raising the bottle to pour more wine into her glass. The boat rolled with sudden swells and the bottled tipped. "Whoops!" Remi swung out of his chair, wine splashing on their feet and the deck. He glared at two boats racing past, headed to the far end of the island, leaving double wakes.

"So much for quiet island and polished hosts." He rummaged through the locker for a sponge and paper towels to wipe up the spills. Clare held her sneaker-clad feet in the air as he mopped up.

He cast a sideways glance at her, a disgusted expression on his face. "I'm botching this miserably. I planned to start this conversation after we had our picnic. Now it's getting dark, and we haven't eaten. Are you hungry, Clare?"

"I'm always hungry. Especially when somebody else's cooking is in the offering."

"Sit tight, then." He dragged the cooler over to use as a table, lined up paper plates and napkins, and lifted a foil covered dish out of the picnic hamper.

Clare peeked inside. "Lobster rolls! I love them."

Remi put the rolls on their plates and continued digging in the hamper. "I knew it was in here. Mom's special potato salad." He spooned a big helping on her plate.

"Relax, Remi." Clare took a big bite of her lobster roll. "Mmm. This is delicious."

Remi ate silently, watching the last of daylight barely visible beyond the horizon. He leaned forward over the picnic hamper.

Clare's eyes traveled from his broad back to his narrow waist and trim butt. She swallowed and drew in a breath. *He seems nervous. Truth is I needed this supper to calm my own nerves. Anything but talk about myself. What can I tell him? Truth is, I want to know you, too, Remi Windspirit—more than you know!*

Remi was digging in the hamper. "I knew she put cookies in here," he said, coming up with a plate in one hand, munching on a cookie. "But I didn't know about this." He handed Clare the plate and held up a candle in the other hand. It was a scented candle set in a small pot of sand.

Clare raised her eyebrows. "Could it be your mother's a romantic?"

Remi laughed, seeming to relax with Clare's question. "She's that, all right. She'd have to be a romantic to keep up with my Dad. She calls him her Casanova," he said, grinning.

He dragged the cooler aside and pulled boat cushions from the locker. Giving Clare a foxy look, he lowered his tall frame down to the deck and stretched out. Head in hand, and one elbow on a cushion, he patted the cushion next to him, gazing up at Clare.

"Is Remi taking after his dad?" Clare asked.

In one swift movement he pulled her from the chair and eased her down beside him, cradling her head under his arm. "Could be . . . Mmm. You smell like oranges or something sweet and wonderful."

"It's jasmine. Like it?"

"Mmm." He nodded, settling his mouth over hers. It was a long and intimate kiss, tender and disturbing at the same time.

Her heart raced. He tasted like cookies and wine. Scrumptious cookies and heady wine.

Heads together on the cushions, bodies side by side, they held hands and looked up at the darkening sky. A full moon shone, threading the sky with silver. It bathed the boat in soft light, shimmering on the water, flicking silver tips on rippling waves.

"Look at the water, Remi. It's moonglade." Clare said.

"What?" he asked, turning her face toward him and tracing one finger down to the tip of her nose. "What's moonglade?"

"It was an enchanted, magical place in ancient time. A glade. Druids believed in it and reveled in it. The contemporary definition would be a bright reflection of moonlight on an expanse of water. Beautiful, isn't it?"

"Uh-huh." He toyed with the topaz necklace that rested between her breasts. "Beautiful, like you, Clare."

Suddenly, he pulled her into his arms and pressed her close.

She felt his need, his hardness against her belly. *He's everything I want in a man, but, OhmyGod, am I ready for this?*

Clare blinked and met his gaze. Moonlight and hope shimmered in his eyes. She pushed her body away a little and hid her face in his shoulder, fighting a battle against impulse.

"Clare. I don't want to push you into anything." He stroked her hair and kissed the tender spot below her ear. He pushed up her chin, forcing her to look at him. "I think I'm in love with you, and I'm going crazy with the knowledge of it. I need to know if you feel the same way."

Swallowing her surprise, she struggled to catch her breath. She breathed in his masculine scent, felt his heat building and wanted to wrap herself in it. At last, she looked into his eyes and nodded her head slowly. "I do. I feel the same. I'm smiling inside and out whenever I see you, Remi. You're the best thing that's ever happened to me." Her eyes brimmed with tears. Surprised at her own emotion, she pressed her fingers against her lips. Remi opened his mouth to speak, but she quickly covered his lips with her fingers.

"Wait," she whispered. She took a deep breath. "Let me get this all out. My world was turned upside down after I met you. I've dreamed about this, but as much as I truly want to, I can't act on my desires. Not now . . . not yet."

Remi cupped her cheek in his hand. "It's okay, Clare. I understand—"

"I'm not sure you do. It's not you; it's this investigation. It has me terrified. There's so much at stake for *Tante* and for me. I even feel guilty leaving her tonight." She wiped tears from her eyes.

Remi's tender smile spoke words for him. He pushed up from the deck and pulled her to her feet, holding her tenderly in his arms, rocking back and forth for several seconds. "I really do understand, and we can wait, Clare, but you have to promise to stop worrying about the case."

He broke the embrace momentarily to hold Clare's face in his hands, kissed her forehead, and smiled. "I think that celestial angel of yours needs to work overtime. We're gonna find another moonglade, soon, okay?"

His optimism was just what she needed. "I'd like that," she said.

Remi took her hand, guiding her back to the cockpit chair. He put the running lights on and started the engine. "I'd better get you home."

The ride back to Charley's Marina seemed too fast to Clare. She shivered in the cold night air, longed for the warmth of Remi's arms, relived the feel of his lips seeking hers. Water pounded against the bow, drowning out sounds as they approached the marina, but there was no mistaking the lights on the wharf. BPD cars, state police cars, and an EMS van were lined up, headlights glaring.

Remi whirled in his chair, his body tensing. He cast an anxious glance at Clare. There was both silk and steel in his voice. "There's something going down here, Clare, and I want you to stay calm. We're going to take it nice and easy coming in. I'm going straight in to my dock space. I'll cover *Cherokee* up, tie her in, same as always. Just stay calm, okay?"

Clare bit down on her lower lip, determined to keep her cool. Remi did just as he said. Clare sensed the urgency and helped, but when everything was done and they got to his truck, he almost pushed her inside quickly. The police scanner was crackling.

"Damn. I turned my beeper off on the boat, but I forgot this was still on call. Close your eyes and ears, Clare. I'm going to try and pull out of here and get you home."

CHAPTER TWENTY-TWO

Clare heard the wiffle of snoring as she tiptoed to *Tante's* bedroom door. She peeked in, then closed the door softly, relieved to find her mom asleep and safe. One worry down, but the other more terrifying one could only be answered by Remi.

Too keyed up to sleep, she desperately needed to talk to someone. Maddy. *God, I miss our late night chats.* She piled pillows behind her, stretched out on the bed and keyed in the programmed number. Patrick answered on the fourth ring.

"Hey, CeCe, what's up?"

"Am I calling too late? Maddy isn't asleep is she?"

"Oh, no." she could hear the laughter in his voice. "She's just out of the shower. Hold on."

"Hi, Cec. Is everything okay?"

"Yes and no. I'm so strung out I hardly know where to begin. You've always been my best sounding board, babe. Do you have time to listen?"

"Of course. Is it about *Tante?*"

"No, but it has a lot to do with her. First, though, answer a question for me. After dinner the other night, did Paul mention to you that he warned me to avoid Remi?"

"Yes, he did. He mentioned it after you guys left. Knowing what I know about you and Remi, I don't suppose you took his advice?"

"I couldn't. You were right, babe. It's much more than a physical attraction between Remi and me, and tonight, I was determined to tell him how I felt."

"And?"

"It was a picture-perfect setting. A moonlit night, wine and supper on his boat out by Channel Island."

"Sounds great."

"Well, yeah, it was. It all led up to him telling me he thinks he's in love with me before I had a chance to say anything!"

"That's fabulous, Cec! What more could you ask for?"

"Uh . . . that's just it. There was more for the taking, if you know what I mean. It was sooo tempting, Maddy. He wants me, and I nixed it! Mister Right finally comes along and God help me, I couldn't do it. Couldn't take that next step. It really tore me up."

"Oh, Clare!"

"Part of it is this damned investigation and *Tante* and me tangled up in it. Mostly *Tante*. I'm so worried about her, Mad. Remi understood. He was really sweet about it, and the evening did end with hope."

"Then what's got you so riled?"

"Something happened back at the marina that threw me into chaos. Oh, God, Mad, maybe Paul is right."

"What happened?"

"When we came back, the wharf was loaded with police cars and emergency vehicles, headlights flashing and sirens blaring. It was a crime scene! Some cop that Remi knew waved us through. And Remi was able to skirt around the scene and bring me home. He told me to stay put, but he had to go back to the marina. Last thing he said was whatever happened at the marina had something to do with Billy Jensen's killer. He promised to call when he knows more."

There was dead silence for a second. "I don't think you should be alone, Clare. Shall I send Patrick over?"

"No, no. *Tante*'s sound asleep. She doesn't know any of this,

195

and the quieter it is here, the better, for now. It helped just having you to talk to, like old times—" Clare's voice cracked as her breath hitched on a sigh. Tears burned her eyes. "Love you to bits, babe. Call you later."

Emotion and fear caught up with her. She clicked her phone shut, and this time, tears fell relentlessly. She sobbed into her pillow so *Tante* would not hear.

Remi pulled into his parking space, grabbed the picnic hamper and headed for the Inn. He hoped his Dad was still up, but it was Mary he found, sitting at the kitchen table, poring over her guest book and ledgers. He set the picnic basket down on the counter. "Hey, Mom. Kind of late to be doing book work, isn't it?"

"It's all relative, Remi. Tomorrow's banking day. If I don't balance last week's income with the guest register before I turn the page for a new week, then I'm in trouble. It's time to balance expenses against profit and hopefully, give me a net gain for the period."

"You had a pretty good week, full house and all, huh?"

"Yes, love, things are really good right now. How about you? Did the picnic go well?"

"Oh, Mom." He rapped his fist on the top of the basket. "I should have told you first thing. Clare asked me to be sure and thank you. The supper was great." He looked away, unsure of what else to tell her.

She smiled, pointing her pencil at him. "How about you? It was a beautiful moonlit night, but you don't sound very happy."

Remi shrugged. "It's just that the evening ended a bummer."

Mary put her pencil down, frowned, and reached out to touch his arm. "With Clare? What do you mean?"

"Nothing to do with Clare. Something was happening at the

marina when we got back. They were roping it off as a crime scene."

"But you didn't stop there with her, I hope."

"No. I wouldn't do that. Officer Meloche from the state police barracks waved me through so I could bring Clare home. By the time I got back to the marina, the ambulance had taken a gunshot victim to the medical center and Meloche had brought a suspect in. I haven't followed up yet, Mom, because there's something I have to do here first."

Mary raised her eyebrows. "At Lord's Castle Inn? What could that be?"

"I was going to explain it later, but what I need is right in front of me." He pointed at her guest register. "It's a hunch I should have followed up last week but didn't." Remi slid the guest register in front of him and flipped the pages back. He traced his finger down and stared at a line. "Your Miami mystery man signed in as A. Smith? Humph."

Mary shrugged her shoulders.

"Not very original, was he? No license number?"

Mary glanced at the page. "Sometimes guests can't remember their tag number, and then, you know, I'm forgetful, love, and I don't ask for it again."

"The queen's forgetful?" Remi teased.

She laughed, the lines around her eyes crinkling. "Yes, but there again, some of life is just as well forgotten, and eventually I do remember the important things."

"How about remembering the day A. Smith checked out."

Mary turned the page, tapping her finger on a line. "August thirtieth. Your father spoke to him that morning. Mrs. Boudreau brought your apartment key to me in an envelope with a big tip for her. That's how we knew he was gone. Of course he paid cash in advance, so there was nothing to settle."

"Didn't he say anything to Mrs. Boudreau?"

197

"If he did, she didn't tell us. She was so surprised about the money that was all she talked about. Why all the questions, Remi?"

"I don't think your guest was A. Smith—or any Smith, for that matter. I think he may be a person of interest in my investigation. Dad said he asked about the distance to the airport, so now I have the date and I need to chase down whether he flew out of the Portland airport."

He rose from the table. Mary's face reflected her surprise. She looked at the kitchen clock. "Surely, not now, darling. It's almost eleven-thirty."

"Just making a phone call, Mom. Since this case is a possible homicide, Marine Patrol probably won't have much more direct involvement. State police and BPD share assistance, you know. I didn't tell you, but I've taken this coming week as vacation time so I can do some independent stuff." He bent down to kiss her cheek. "This is a hunch of mine, Mom. Nobody knows about it, and I'd like to keep it that way. Until I'm sure. I don't want the Inn involved if I can help it, but that's why all the questions about A. Smith."

"You do what you have to do, love. Just remember your father and I are here whenever you need us."

At his desk, Remi searched the net for airlines with flights from Portland to Miami, afternoon of August thirty. No direct flights. All flights had a connection, in either La Guardia or Philadelphia. The shortest time was a US Air flight with a connection in La Guardia. Five hours, forty-six minutes, total. He dialed reservations.

"Sergeant Windspirit, Maine Marine Patrol, requesting a check on the manifest of flight thirty-seven sixty-three, Portland to Miami, connecting in La Guardia, August thirtieth. Subject I'm looking for is a male Caucasian. Travels as A. Smith."

"It may take time, sir, if it's not a tangible manifest. Can you leave us a contact number?"

Remi gave the number, kicked off his shoes and stretched out on his bed to wait. His gaze traveled from the desk to the club chair and reading lamp, to the open bathroom door and the clothes closet. *I should have acted on impulse when he left. There could have been DNA testing on everything he touched in here—if he is who I think he is.*

He closed his eyes, tried to focus on anything but the "should haves, could haves." Clare's gray eyes glistening with tears, her chin trembling before she hid her face in his chest. The cell phone startled him.

"US Airways. Is this Sergeant Windspirit?"

"Yes, Ma'am."

"There is no A. Smith on the manifest for flight thirty-seven sixty-three. One female passenger listed as Smithington, Alice, but no males under the name Smith. I suggest you come to the airport and check the manifest for variances, or have a look at other flights dated thirty August."

CHAPTER TWENTY-THREE

Tante Margaret hung the wall phone on its hook as Clare shuffled into the kitchen. Clare rubbed her eyes and stared, as though she was seeing a vision. "What are you doing up so early, all dressed? It's only six-fifteen."

"Doing what I usually do in the morning, fixing a little breakfast."

"But you were on the phone."

"*Oui.* I was making arrangements with Paul Fontaine to bring my car here so I can go to Star of the Sea Center."

Clare sat at the table and held her head in her hands. "Whoa, *Tante.* Back up. You haven't had your stitches out, and last night your head was still hurting. How can you think about going out to Biddeford Pool in your car?"

Tante put her hands on her hips, cocking her head at Clare. "Plain and simple, Clare Margaret. Because Sister Agatha invited me. I'm not driving. Jacques Paul is taking me to the Retreat Center. You are working today, so I made my own plans, eh, like usual." *Tante* sat down with her coffee.

Clare sensed her agitation and tried to diffuse it. "I'm just surprised, I guess. I slept like a rock until my alarm went off, and I didn't hear a thing out here."

"Well, the plans were made last night. Sister Agatha called me. She thinks it would be good for me to be at the Center for a weekend retreat. It starts today, and Jacques Paul agreed to get me there by eight-thirty this morning. I want him to continue using my car for a while. I really don't need it, and if I do need transportation, you can come get me or take me where I need to go. Now you can go back to your apartment, and everything will work okay. You'll see."

Clare sighed with relief. It did sound like a good solution. She reached out to give *Tante* a hug. "Sorry, Mom, if I'm sounding like Nurse Clare. It's because I worry about you."

"Too much, you worry! *Laisse béton.* I have been independent for too long, *chérie.*" She kissed Clare's cheek and pushed a sweet roll in front of her. "Now, tell me quickly, how was your boat ride?"

Clare swallowed hard and turned to pour her coffee. "It was fine. Remi has a neat boat, and his mom made us a picnic supper."

"She sounds like a nice lady. Maybe I'll meet her someday, eh?"

Clare caught the gleam in *Tante*'s eye. She nodded, slowly. *Don't go there . . . change the subject or you'll be in deep doo-doo.* "Maybe. I do think a weekend retreat is a great idea for you, Mom. Sorry I'll miss Paul, but I have to eat and run or I'll be late for work. You're sure he's coming?"

"*Mon Dieu.* Yes!" *Tante* rolled her eyes upward. "You are worse than your papa Jean, God rest his soul."

Clare made it to the medical center with five minutes to spare. She argued with herself driving in, then sat in her car staring at her cell phone for two long minutes. *Ring, dammit. You know my schedule and you said you would call.* She checked her watch, threw her cell phone in her purse and got out of the car.

Pushing through the ER door, the first person she saw was her friend Mary swishing past the desk, pushing an IV stand into an examining room. *I can easily find out for myself who was brought in on an emergency last night. Might even end up knowing more than I want to.*

Unusual that Remi was still in bed after sunrise. His day ordinarily started at six A.M., but this wasn't an ordinary MMP day. It was day one of seven that Remi had pinned his hopes on. He was dreaming a wonderful dream. He couldn't possibly leave this beautiful, tropical island. There was only one other person on the sun sparkled beach. Clare.

He groaned at the sound of someone knocking, then a voice calling outside his door.

"If you're in the world yet, Remi, I'm here to tell you you've got a visitor."

His eyes flew open. "Mom?" He sat up in bed, blinking at sunlight streaming through the half open blinds. "Mom? What are you saying?"

Mary let herself in. "Like I said, love, there's a man to see you at the Inn. After our talk last night, I hesitated to send a stranger up here, so I set him up in the breakfast room until I could fetch you. He doesn't look very dangerous, but looks are often deceiving."

Remi swiped a hand over his face. "A stranger? Did you get a name?"

"He said just to tell you Paul is here."

Remi groaned and lay back on his pillow. "Paul's a friend, Mom. But I can't believe he'd come here at this hour."

"It's nine o'clock, Remi. You must have needed the rest to sleep this late. Shall I tell your friend you'll be down shortly?"

He nodded. "Don't feed him, Mom. He might decide to stay."

Reluctantly, Remi dragged out of bed. Searching for something to wear, he stared at a clean uniform hanging in the closet. Memory clicked. The airport! It has to be first priority this morning. He didn't like getting into uniform, not on the first

202

day of vacation, but he knew how important it would be to look the part when he approached the US Airways counter.

Remi rushed through bathroom routine and was in the Inn's kitchen in twenty minutes.

"Your friend is a charmer," Mary said. "I gave him a tour of the Inn, told him a little about the history of Ocean Park and fed him blueberry scones. He gave me this." She waved an engraved announcement in front of Remi's eyes. "Pretty impressive, huh? You didn't tell me he's an artist. He has an exhibit at the opening of a new gallery next month. I'm going to post this at the desk. Our guests like to go to these kinds of things."

"I know he's an artist, but I didn't know about this," Remi said, giving the announcement a quick read. Remi carried it with him into the breakfast room.

"Morning, Paul. Looks like congratulations are in order." Remi laid the announcement on the table.

Paul stood and shook Remi's outstretched hand. "Sorry for the surprise visit, Sarge." He pointed to the announcement. "This was an afterthought because your mom was so nice to me. This wasn't my reason for stopping by this morning. Did you get my E-mail?"

"Yeah, I did. I just haven't had a chance to call you."

Paul pointed to the insignia on Remi's uniform shirt. "I didn't think you'd be working this morning. I was hoping we could take a drive and have a little talk."

"Do you have a problem, Paul?"

"Not me, necessarily, but I, uh . . . have some concerns, and I thought maybe we could talk about them."

Remi guessed what those concerns might be. The last thing he wanted was for the queen to hear any conversation about Clare. "Sorry to put you off, but I'm on my way to the jetport, Paul. I have business there this morning that can't wait. If it's important to talk now, can we walk outside. I have a little time before I leave."

"It is important to me."

Remi led the way out the front door and took a path through the pine grove that bordered the Inn.

"I'll get to right to the point," Paul said. "I'm worried about CeCe, Remi. I'm not her keeper, but maybe you don't realize that our families have been friends for a long time. I wonder if she's in danger after this latest death in your investigation. Danger because of a close connection to you."

Remi could feel a tightening in his chest. He stopped on the path and stared at Paul. "God Almighty, Paul, what do you mean? I would never put Clare in danger."

"I'm thinking maybe someone might connect the dots, you know? CeCe is the one who found the body of an Indian woman. You are Native American, and now you two are involved. If Clare's a person of interest in this investigation, couldn't your romantic involvement make it tough on her? Maybe suspect?"

"Romantic involvement!" Remi fought for control, but the edge in his voice gave him away. "No way! Yes, I care about Clare and worry about her, too. No way would she be in danger because of me. In the first place, she's not a person of interest. Secondly, no one knows about our relationship except you and your sister."

"CeCe knew about Jensen's attack when it wasn't even in the press, and you still don't think she's in danger?"

"No, I don't. Clare was at the hospital when Jensen died, so that's how she was privy to that news. We talked about it afterward because it's police policy to keep victims apprised of progress in any investigation. Clare is not a victim, but her mother is, and you know that scenario. Everybody is trying to protect Margaret."

"I hear you, Remi. I just took *Tante* Margaret to a retreat house at Biddeford Pool. I'm sure CeCe is relieved to have her there. Cec seemed so scared the last time I talked with her that my suspicions immediately jumped to you. Your situation is getting clearer, but your investigation is getting more complicated."

"Tell me about it." *A homicide investigation could involve the Inn, if my hunches pay off.* "It has taken a radical swing, and as a Patrol officer, I'm not likely to stay involved with a homicide." Remi put his hands flat out in a stop position. "There's more to it than meets the eye, Paul, and I can't comment on it any more than that."

They had walked full circle around the Inn to the parking lot. Remi checked his watch. "I take your concerns seriously, and I'll let Clare know we talked about it, but remember this. I'm not going to let her be in harm's way, ever. I really have to leave."

The reservationist looked him up and down when he presented his ID and made his request. She picked up an envelope and walked with him to an empty ticketing booth. "There you go, Officer. Let me know if I can be of help." She handed him the copies of the printed manifests for flights starting at noon, August thirtieth.

Top of the pile was flight 3763. He scrolled down. Smithington, Alice, just as they told him last night. Next was Stuart, John; then Suarez, Arturo; and Swenson, Olga. He hesitated, finger twitching, before he turned to the next flight. No names there could be construed to be A. Smith. On the next page there were only two surnames beginning with S. Neither was male. No other names on that flight fit, either.

He couldn't imagine Mister Miami taking later flights that were eight or more hours long. He went back to flight 3763, traced his finger down the list and paused at Suarez, Arturo. Suarez, Arturo. Arturo Suarez . . . A. S., seat 3B, first class.

Remi underlined Suarez and folded the list into his notebook.

He returned the other documents, thanked the reservationist and hurried outside to call state police barracks from his truck. "Sergeant Windspirit calling Lieutenant Meloche."

A clipped voice barked over the speaker "Lieutenant Meloche is briefing a CID unit and isn't available. I'll give him the message you called."

Well, that tells me something, he thought. *CID is responsible for major investigations.*

Remi drove back to his apartment and changed into casual clothes. He unclipped his cell phone from his uniform belt and stared at it. His conscience nagged that he hadn't called Clare since he brought her home from the marina. Lieutenant Meloche's words were running interference in his head. "Don't let your personal life interfere with your judgment."

"Damn," he muttered. "My judgment isn't being called for now. I'm on vacation." He flicked open his phone and punched her number.

Clare's cell was on vibration, but she knew it was Remi before she glimpsed the readout. She raised her eyebrows to Mary, who stood beside her at the desk. "Go out," Mary said, pointing toward the door. "Go."

"Hold on, Remi," Clare spoke into the phone. "I'm taking this outside."

"I'm sorry. I know you're working, but my intent was to leave you a message if you couldn't take this call. There wasn't anything conclusive for me to call you about last night."

"I may have one-upped you, then, Remi, because I got some info through the grapevine about the guy who was brought in last night."

"Tell me."

"There's been a police guard outside his room since he came out of surgery. The duty nurse says detectives and police were in and out like flies until the surgeon stopped them."

"Anything about his condition, age or race?"

"Geez, Sarge, are you taking notes?"

Remi laughed. "I can't turn off my training, I guess. Seriously, though, this is off the record anyway, Clare. I'm not on duty this weekend, and I won't be for the whole week starting tomorrow. I'm taking a week of my vacation time."

"Lucky you. So, off the record, I can tell you that it was a shoulder wound. They extracted a bullet, and he sustained no damage to vital organs. The guy had lost a lot of blood until EMS got him here, but he's not in any danger, now. All I know is he's Hispanic and young. I have to get back inside, Remi. Mary is covering for me and it's damned chilly out here."

"Thanks, Clare. I'll expect an up-front, in-person talk later today. Can you manage that?"

"Yes," she murmured softly on a sigh. "I'll be at my place after three. *Tante* is off on retreat for the whole weekend."

CHAPTER TWENTY-FOUR

Remi headed for the state police barracks. The conversations with Paul and Clare ran like a double feature in his mind. The talk with Paul ended amicably, but it still dogged him. Maybe finding out how the whole marina thing went down would push everything else away.

The dispatcher informed him that Lieutenant Meloche had gone to the harbor. "He left word for you to meet him at noon at Annie's Coffee Park."

Remi drove into the parking lot at five minutes before noon. Frank Meloche sat in a patrol car in front of Annie's. He pushed open the passenger door and motioned for Remi to get in. "Sarge," he said giving Remi the once over. "Not in uniform today?"

When Remi explained that he was off duty and starting the beginning of a vacation, Frank whistled softly through his teeth. "You may miss the grand finale, Remi. We're almost there. BCI caught the perpetrator. His boat was in a hideaway up Saco River, and your witness, Louie, picked him out of a lineup this morning. Narcisse Tibeault. Got a rap long as a six-inch ruler. He wouldn't talk about Jensen, but they nailed him on drug charges."

"Drug charges? That means the feds are in?"

"Yep. A big stash of cocaine in Tibeault's boat. Looked like it may have been a late night drop. The box was waterproof sealed."

"What about the gunshot victim?"

"That's how we got the boat's description and location. The victim claimed Tibeault shot him. Sounds like a drug ring gone sour, and it could be the tip of the iceberg."

Remi worked this around in his mind for a few seconds. He stared at his knees, ran his hands up and down his jeans. "I've got something that may or may not be relevant, Frank." He looked Meloche straight in the eye. "It's a hunch that I haven't spoken about—been trying to work it out on my own. Right now I could use a little help."

"I'm listening."

"If I give you a name and a Miami location, would you check it out, no questions asked?"

"You betcha. You gave us the witness that counted, Remi. I owe ya."

A gorgeous vase of flowers was delivered to Clare's apartment not long after she got home from work. A dozen peach and white roses combined with baby's breath in a crystal vase perfumed the air. The card read, *Waiting for your celestial angel to get back to work . . . Love, Remi.*

The realization that this was a first occasion brought tears to her eyes. She placed the vase on the coffee table and sat in front of it, silently reveling in its beauty. When the doorbell rang, she knew it was Remi. Arms opened wide, Clare hugged him fiercely to her.

"Whoa! All this for flowers?" Remi chuckled, hugging her back.

"Come see," she said, grabbing his hand and leading him into the living room. "No one ever sent me flowers before."

"We'll have to change that, then, won't we?"

"They're so beautiful, Remi. They make me feel special."

Still holding her hand, Remi sat with her on the sofa. "You

are special, Clare. I hoped the flowers would tell you that." He enfolded her hand in both of his, fixing his eyes on her. "I have other things to tell you about. I had a conversation today with your friend, Paul."

Clare fought the urge to look away from the intensity in his eyes.

"Things ended on a friendly note, but some things were said that didn't sit well. I need to hear from you if there's something between you two . . . I mean . . ." Remi shrugged nervously. "Have you and Paul—"

"No." She frowned, shaking her head. "I'm surprised you would think that."

"You sailed with him. You were at the concert in the park with him. He was at your apartment after your mom got hurt."

"There's an explanation for all of that. Paul lost his job and was back at his father's having a pity party—depressed and drinking too much. There were bad vibes at Francois's Fancy between Kathleen, Paul, and his dad, and I'm not going into that, Remi. It's a long story."

"Does it have to do with the boat?"

"In a way. We go way back, Paul's family and me. Maddy asked me to fill in, sailing on the boat because Patrick really didn't have time for it. The sailing lessons were planned to keep Paul's focus on something he loved more than alcohol—that boat and the sea. I took Patrick's place and the plan was working. The concert was more of the same, just trying to boost Paul's ego and keep him out of trouble. I'd try most anything for Maddy's sake. Paul . . ." Clare shrugged and shook her head. "It was not what you think."

"I didn't want to think that, but Paul acted so protective about you that he got me all fired up. He thinks our relationship—you and me—puts you in danger." Remi's eyes blazed, then softened as he drew in a breath. "Of course that's not true, but it made me suspicious . . . maybe he has a hidden agenda. Maybe he really wants you for himself."

Clare closed her eyes, shaking her head, again. "I thought that once, too, but that's not so. He's just trying to be a big brother." She put her hands on Remi's shoulders. "Not to worry, Sarge. There's nothing between Paul Fontaine and me, and there never was."

Remi pulled her close. "I needed to hear that." He brushed his lips across her mouth. "I have other news to tell you, but I want to hold you first. Just for a minute, Clare."

You can hold me for a lifetime.

Silent moments passed and Remi reluctantly drew back, speaking softly. "This is about the investigation, but for once it's good news for your mom. I may not be involved much for a while—with the investigation, I mean. The police caught the guy who killed Billy Jensen, and that turns the case into a homicide. Your mom will not have to make an ID."

Clare sat back, clasping her hands and raising her eyes upward "OhmyGod! Prayers do work. I've prayed so hard that *Tante* would not be in danger anymore." Eyes closed, she reached up and kissed him. Seconds later her eyes flew open. "But what about the corpse we found? Is that investigation over?"

Remi pulled her to him to nestle her head against his chest. "No. It isn't over as far as I'm concerned. I have a hunch I'm working on, on the QT."

"Tell me."

"I'll try to make it short. About the time I was investigating the drowning, a guy called the Inn. He was a single guy with a little different request than most B and B guests. He asked for a suite, and my mom put him in my apartment. He drove a new, silver Mercedes, signed the register A. Smith, but he didn't look like a guy named Smith. He didn't socialize like most guests do

211

at breakfast or at Mary's wine and cheese hour."

Out of the corner of his eye, Remi could see the puzzled look on Clare's face, but she was quiet. "Twice that week, a silver car came close to my truck. Once at Mariner's Lofts and once when I returned from your apartment. I think he was tailing me." He heard her quick intake of breath.

"I never got his plate number, but I had an uneasy feeling about him. Foolishly, I didn't follow it up. He paid the Inn cash in advance for a week, left a huge tip for mom's helper, then left without using his days and without giving notice." Remi paused. "He left town on the day Billy Jensen died."

Clare wrapped her arms around his neck, holding tight. "Oh, Remi. Don't leave here now. Please don't leave me."

Remi woke with a jerk, as though something had intruded into the quiet. His left arm was numb as he slid it from underneath Clare's head. Pushing back against the sofa, he tried to push himself up without waking her. Clare moaned. He lay still for seconds and then pushed with his heels, scooting down to ease his long legs off the sofa. His cell phone was vibrating. He reached across the coffee table, breathing in the scent of the roses.

Lieutenant Meloche was on the readout. One glance at Clare, still sound asleep, and Remi cat-walked barefoot toward the kitchen, whispering into the phone, "Hold a minute, Frank. Any luck, lieutenant?"

"Better than luck, Remi. Your hunch doubled the score, man. You better come down to the station ASAP."

"I'm on my way."

It wouldn't be easy convincing Clare that he wasn't in any danger, that things were going to be okay. A note would have to do. Remi tore a sheet from a kitchen "to do" pad, scribbled a message and propped it against the vase of flowers. He grabbed his shoes and left the apartment.

Lieutenant Frank Meloche showed him the sheet that came from an MDEA task force office in Portland. A positive match from the State Bureau of Identification in Florida for Arturo Suarez, alias Arthur Sanchez, alias A. Smith.

"DEA Undercover in Miami has been watching this guy's operation for months. He's an elusive bastard. Big-time drug lord, he sets up elaborate bases along the Atlantic seaboard, hires his runners and disappears until it's time to cash in. This time, his plan for a female decoy in an elaborate warehouse went bad."

Remi scowled. "You mean Jane Doe at Mariner's Lofts was a decoy?"

"Yep. Your Native Indian artist and the loft were a front for his drug base. The plan to set her up in a legitimate jewelry business was a lot of crap. When it didn't happen, she found out what was really going on. She threatened to expose Suarez. He got desperate and hired a sloppy hit man. The woman became victim number one."

"Tibeault?"

"You got it. Tibeault got orders to row her out in the harbor at night on a pretense to meet the boss on his yacht."

Remi shuddered. *The guy was watching me. I led him to* Tante, *then to Billy Jensen.* "Oh God, Frank. Do you think Will Jensen Senior knew what was going on in that building?"

"No, I don't. Will Senior couldn't forget Billy's shenanigans with a high school girl a couple years ago. That one ended in court. Will thought this Indian girl was going to be more of the same, and he ignored Billy's suspicions. Didn't have a clue what was going on, but Billy did. Now we know that Billy wasn't the only one attracted to your Jane Doe."

"I'm not following."

"The marina gunshot victim, Esposito. He and Tibeault were

Suarez's runners, moving drugs by boat to the Mariner building. Like Billy, Esposito felt sorry for the girl. He leaked the plan to her and tried to convince her to leave before Tibeault got to her."

"So Tibeault turned on the runner?"

Frank nodded. "Snitches get taken out. If Tibeault hadn't been a drunk and a lousy shooter, Esposito would have been victim number three at Charley's Marina. Everything clicked like tumblers in a lock when your lead came through on Arturo Suarez. Esposito only knew his boss as 'Art.' No last name was ever given to runners. When you gave me the name, I sent it to DEA. The DEA agent in Portland confirmed the connection. You wrapped it up for us, Sarge."

Remi stared at the badge on Meloche's shirt. He grimaced and drew in his lower lip. "Thanks, Lieutenant. It's been a ride I wouldn't choose a second time, but there are those who need to know how it all came down."

CHAPTER TWENTY-FIVE

Moonlight flooded the darkened room and the scent of roses filled the air. Remi held her close. "No more tears, Clare, please? It's over. It's all over."

She nodded her head against his chest. "I know. Stories always end when they catch the bad guys, but for me, it just doesn't take the worry away."

He held her at arm's length. "Still worried about your mom? You told me she's on a retreat. You know what I think? I think Margaret's going to believe that her prayers were answered at the retreat center."

"You're probably right, but I'm not worrying about *Tante.*" Clare looked into his eyes. "I'm thinking about you and me and your job, and whether my prayers will be answered. This roller coaster we've been on, Remi . . . will it always be like this?"

"No, no. My job has never been this complicated before." He cupped her cheek in his hand. "I will make time for you, Clare. This week will be the start." His mouth settled on hers for a long, tender kiss. "We're going to put that celestial angel of yours to the test."

Margaret stared into her teacup. Worry played across her face.

Clare watched *Tante's* mouth work, her head waggle. She waited for her to break the silence.

Tante's eyes followed the pattern of tea leaves in the bottom of her cup. "If I read these tea leaves, I would say that this shows broken hearts. I'm thinking of the parents of that poor Jensen boy. It's so sad that nothing could have saved him."

"I feel the guilt of not telling you about him, Mom. I wanted to tell you, but I didn't have the heart to. You were in danger before Billy Jensen was killed. I was worried half out of my wits."

Tante reached to cover Clare's hand with her own. "I know. But something good came from all of it, eh, *ma petite?*"

Clare sipped her tea, puzzling what that meant. She gazed at *Tante* over the rim of her cup. "You mean Remi?"

"*Oui.*" Margaret's big brown eyes sparkled. "I think Sergeant Remi caught more than a criminal, eh, Clare? I think he caught you."

"How you manage to read my heart, Mom, I'll never know, but you're right again. I really do care for Remi, and the feeling is mutual. The thing is, his job is so demanding and the ER keeps me in shift work, so it's hard for us to get together, you know?"

Tante closed her eyes, her hands clutched under the table. Her brow furrowed while silence hung in the air.

She's got to be scheming . . . shouldn't have told her . . . Clare sat back, cocked an eyebrow and spoke to *Tante's* closed eyes.

"I've got it, Mom. You could have another séance! This time, just for me." Clare smirked, playing with the handle of her teacup. "You could work with Hetty, huh? Let those seer powers take a little look see into the future?"

Margaret was deadly quiet until suddenly her eyes shot open. For several seconds, she stared silently into space as though in a haze.

Clare touched her arm. "Mom I didn't mean that. I was teas-ing—"

With a knowing look, *Tante* wagged a finger at Clare. "Not to worry, *ma petite*. There is no need for Hetty this time. I sent up a prayer, and this time God, in his wisdom, has given me an answer for you. I heard a fluttering like bird's wings, and suddenly, a voice, true and clear. 'If God has joined your hearts, He will bring you together.' It's blessed assurance for you, my *chérie!*"

AFTERWORD

Summer had its last stand. Fog and cold rain had blanketed the shore for a week. Today, early morning whiskers of frost painted the rooftops along cobblestoned Commercial Street. Paul unlocked the wide oak door and entered the old brick building under an elegant brass-plated sign over the lintel: CORNER-STONE GALLERY.

Paul's experience with the museum gallery in New York saved hours in the restoration and planning of the physical space of this old building. Even so, he was fortunate that Patrick volunteered countless hours partitioning space and creating recessed niches and backdrops to showcase his paintings. The gallery director had insisted on a state of the art security system and temperature control monitoring for the studio. Everything was ready.

He threw a switch, drew in a breath, and let it out slowly. An engraved announcement rested on an easel just inside the door. *Maine Shore Artist, Jacques Paul Fontaine.* Focus lighting was in place. His eyes traveled the walls, stopping on the west wall. It was his smallest, but most ethereal, painting—the last to be finished, and the only one that would not be for sale. The gallery director was positive and confident it would be a successful show. Paul wasn't so sure.

The day mellowed into crisp autumn sunshine. It cheered the hearts of visitors eager to see Cornerstone Gallery without dodging raindrops. Paul need not have worried about attendance. People swarmed the gallery.

Patrick and Maddy brought Patrick's sister, Rosie. Her shy presence, seriously studying each painting, touched Paul's heart. Jacques and Kathleen gathered with university colleagues and garden club friends. One of the group was Paul's art history professor. He purchased "Sunrise at the Wildlife Refuge," the show's first sale.

The bar tender and waitress from the Yardarm surprised Paul. He led them to the hospitality table and raised a glass with them. Two visitors from Lord's Castle Inn came, bringing greetings from Mary Windspirit. Paul personally brought them to painting number one, "The Wood Island Harbor Lighthouse." He was explaining the lighthouse history when *Tante* Margaret arrived on Clare and Remi's arms. The trio paused at the entrance easel.

"Voila!" Tante said, pointing to the sign. "I knew he could do it." She bent to Clare's ear. "He has good genes, eh, Clare?" Margaret left them standing there, smiling at each other.

She hurried forward to find Paul. Opening her arms wide, she exclaimed "Ah, Jacques Paul. I prayed for this day. You made it to the top, *mon ami.*"

Paul laughed, pointing to the floor. "And my feet are firm on the deck, Auntie Mame." He kissed Margaret's forehead. Over her head, he watched Remi and Clare stroll toward the small painting centered on the west wall. "Excuse me a minute, please." He nodded to the Lord's Castle Inn guests and nudged Margaret forward. "These guests could use some of your local knowledge about the lighthouse. I'll be right back."

Remi and Clare stood hand in hand, staring at an exquisite seascape. Moonlight shimmered silver on the sea, bathing ghost-like boats in soft light. A voice from behind them spoke softly. "Notice it is not numbered. It's not for sale." They turned as

Paul placed his hands on their shoulders.
"It's promised to two very special people."

ABOUT THE AUTHOR

Mary Fremont Schoenecker took early retirement from teaching at State University of New York to live with husband, Tom, in Southwest Florida. Mother of four grown children, Mary's debut historical novel, *Four Summers Waiting*, depicted true ancestors of her children in an epic story of the Civil War. Her second book published by Five Star, *Finding Fiona* was Book One in the contemporary series, Maine Shore Chronicles. *Moonglade* is Book Two of the Chronicles series. The final book in the trilogy is a work in progress. Read more about Mary on her Web site www.maryschoenecker.com.